THE CADWALADR QUESTS

The Unique 11+ and SATs Vocabulary Novel—
a book with a built-in dictionary on every page

THE CADWALADR QUESTS

1

TANGLED TIME

S. L. AGER

Developmental editor: Anna Bowles
Copyeditor and proofreader: Leonora Bulbeck
Cover design and interior formatting: Mark Thomas / Coverness.com

ISBN 978-1-9993018-0-4 (paperback)
ISBN 978-1-9993018-1-1 (ebook)

Need *The Cadwaladr Quests* in US English? Please visit your local Amazon site for the US version!

www.slager.co.uk

For all children, regardless of difficult exams

Table of Contents

Preface

I wrote this book whilst helping my children pass the 11+ exam. My aim was to try to make learning difficult vocabulary easier by including and defining it on the pages of an original and exciting book of fiction.

My daughter was an avid reader, so vocabulary came more naturally to her. My son was the opposite, a reluctant reader. For him, learning vocabulary was dull (especially if it was set within classic texts).

Many of the words included and defined in this book come from the practice materials we covered and amassed during the time working towards the 11+ exams and SATs in primary school, as well as Key Stage 3. We worked with both GL and CEM materials.

Of course, no published aids can guarantee that their material will appear on any exam paper, and neither can I. However, considering *The Cadwaladr Quests: Tangled Time* contains almost three thousand word definitions and hundreds of corresponding synonyms and antonyms (in a fun story for girls and boys), what does any parent or young reader have to lose?

My children have been my beta readers and a constant encouragement to finish the book. Without their approval, I wouldn't have published it.

A final note of endorsement for the concept also came from my son's friend on the way home from sitting a mock exam. He didn't know I was writing this book and said to his mum, 'Mum, why isn't there a book that I can read that includes lots of these words, rather than learning them from lists and exercises. It's so boring.'

My son, who knew I was writing the book, smiled at me but said nothing.

His friend's mum replied, 'Well, I can't write a book overnight, so we'll just have to continue as is.'

That conversation gave me the final push to finish this book.

As a child, I had the privilege of living on the beautiful Isle of Anglesey, the setting for part of this book. The legend of Beddgelert, which also features, is a story I told my little brother when he could not sleep at night.

I hope you enjoy Claire and Ben's gripping journey in the first book of *The Cadwaladr Quests*, but moreover, I hope it helps you and your children with any challenging vocabulary exams they are facing.

Get A Free Comprehension Exercise

Some *Cadwaladr Quests* novels have accompanying workbooks.

To receive your free, 45-question comprehension (with answers) based on *Tangled Time* (this comprehension does not appear in the workbooks), please leave a review for *Tangled Time* on Amazon and email a screenshot to: **freebies@slager.co.uk**

I will add you to my mailing list[1] and send you the comprehension by return.

---

1 You can unsubscribe from the mailing list at any time. Further details will be emailed to you, as soon as you are added.

How to Use This Book

This story has been specially written to help young readers prepare for their 11+, SATs and entrance exams, as well as Key Stage 3. It includes difficult vocabulary embedded in a fun narrative that provides context for the new words and makes them easier to learn and understand.

On every page, key words are in bold, and each has a correlating footnote with a concise definition. The words are defined using the context in which they appear in the text, and definitions are as child-friendly as possible. Chosen key words are defined only *once*, when they first appear in the story.

Synonyms and antonyms are also provided, although some words do not have antonyms if they do not exist. The vocabulary becomes more complex as the story progresses.

This book does not aim to replace a dictionary or purport to be one, but dictionaries have been used to check the credibility of each definition.

PS: There are a few Welsh words in the story. To learn how to pronounce them, please visit **slager.co.uk/welsh-words.**

Top Tips

- You may find it beneficial to read this book for the first time with an adult, but you and your parents can decide.
- The definitions are included for convenience and to guide the learning, not as a definitive 'must learn' list.
- Chosen key words are defined only *once*, when they first appear in the story.
- To make learning difficult words easier, try to associate the words with the relevant scene in the book and to picture their meanings.
- Chapter lengths vary, so do not necessarily aim to finish a chapter in each sitting.
- Some pages have more definitions than others to fit in with the storytelling.
- The definitions decrease in the final chapters, enabling the reader to enjoy the ending with minimal interruption to the story.
- Read the book as often as is needed, and continue to use its vast resource of definitions, synonyms and antonyms to reinforce learning.
- The best way to learn new words is to read as widely and with as much variety as possible. Every book is a world of adventure waiting for you to turn to the first page. I hope my book helps in this journey of discovery and learning.

Key to Abbreviations of Word Type

(v) verb

(n) noun

(adj) adjective

(adv) adverb

(prep) preposition

(con) conjunction

(int) interjection

(s) synonym

(ant) antonym

Claire

*Today, Claire Cadwallader **suspects**[1] her **surname**[2] is the only **memorable**[3] thing about her. She thinks she's an ordinary girl whose life is normal. Tonight, she won't do her homework or enjoy her **ritual**[4] read. Her sneaked snack will go uneaten. She'll fall asleep early, her book flopped on her chest, her lamp glowing. She's neither tired nor ill. Today is an ordinary day. From tomorrow, Claire will never be the same again.*

---

1. **suspect** *(v)* believe in the existence or truth of something without proof. *(s)* assume, think, suppose. *(ant)* know.

2. **surname** *(n)* a person's name that is in common with other family members. *(s)* last name. *(ant)* first name.

3. **memorable** *(adj)* worthy of remembrance or noting. *(s)* unforgettable, noteworthy, notable. *(ant)* ordinary.

4. **ritual** *(adj)* coming from practice or habit. *(s)* usual, normal, habitual, customary, predictable. *(ant)* unusual.

THURSDAY

1. A Normal Day

'Oh no, not you!' Claire stiffened, staring at the carpet.

'Wallace! No! No! No!' She thudded down onto **bare**[1] knees. 'Wallace, what is it? What have I done to you?' she cried as the unfortunate scene **unfurled**[2].

She **shuffled**[3] along on all fours, creeping closer, afraid of what lay on the floor. **Dithering**[4] and uncertain, she **gingerly**[5] lifted him to avoid more damage. As she realised it was worse than she'd thought, she almost dropped him. **Cradling**[6] him, she tried and tried, but it was too late. Her old friend was beyond repair.

As Claire gazed down at his broken body, her **earnest**[7] face wore a mixture of love and **sorrow**[8]. Tears glazed her eyes as **fond**[9] childhood memories unfolded before her. Was this repairable? How could she fix this accident? She held him in her hand.

'I wonder if I could glue you,' she said, holding Gromit in the other hand. 'I'm such a clumsy **klutz**[10]!'

A regretful smile separated the three friends. She tried to push him back together, but on

---

1   **bare** *(adj)* (of body parts) unclothed. *(s)* exposed, naked, nude, unclad. *(ant)* clothed, covered.

2   **unfurl** *(v)* (of a situation) develop or show. *(s)* open out, unfold, expand, unroll. *(ant)* furl, fold up.

3   **shuffle** *(v)* move the feet along the ground without lifting them. *(s)* shamble, limp, scuffle. *(ant)* stride, strut.

4   **dither** *(v)* act indecisively or waver between. *(s)* hesitate, dally, dawdle, teeter, vacillate, fluctuate. *(ant)* decide.

5   **gingerly** *(adv)* in a careful manner. *(s)* cautiously, delicately, tentatively, warily, gently. *(ant)* boldly, rashly.

6   **cradle** *(v)* hold gently and protectively. *(s)* support, embrace, clasp, nestle, lull, tend, rock. *(ant)* drop, abandon.

7   **earnest** *(adj)* serious and sincere. *(s)* solemn, deep, heartfelt, devoted. *(ant)* insincere, superficial.

8   **sorrow** *(n)* a feeling of grief or sadness. *(s)* anguish, regret, agony, remorse, heartbreak, distress. *(ant)* joy, cheer.

9   **fond** *(adj)* affectionate or loving. *(s)* tender, warm, sentimental, caring, doting, mushy. *(ant)* unfeeling, uncaring.

10   **klutz** *(n)* a clumsy, awkward person. *(s)* bungler, butterfingers, lummox, clod, oaf, lump. *(ant)* sharp cookie.

closer **inspection**[1], she feared poor Wallace may well have been silenced forever.

Claire Cadwallader lived in Chorlton, Manchester, England. She enjoyed simple things, like her now-broken Wallace and Gromit alarm clock.

She **considered**[2] books to be friends, living in her bedroom on dusty shelves. Not a massive fan of pop stars and fashion, she found even school **appealed**[3].

'I will try to mend you. Don't you worry, Wallace,' Claire said, forcing a cheery tone.

As if handling the Crown Jewels, she gathered up the broken pieces. Her dad had gifted the talking clock to her brother, Peter, on his fourth birthday. It belonged to her now, and she **cherished**[4] it like a family **heirloom**[5].

Then, bang on time, as if an alarm had sounded, the shrieking **commenced**[6]. Once Dee surfaced, so did the **commotion**[7]. They lived in a shouty house.

'Here we go again.' Claire rolled her eyes and snatched at a pile of creased clothes.

'Peter, you're getting the wet flannel treatment! Come on now! Right this minute, I mean it! I'm not kidding this morning!'

On weekdays, **chaos**[8] ruled. 'The wet flannel treatment' was the threat Dee, Claire's mum, gave Pete, Claire's older brother, every single schoolday yet never carried out.

'If you don't get up right now, I'm going to wet this flannel with freezing water, and it will head straight for you,' Dee **threatened**[9] again.

'Yeah, right, Mum, course you are,' grumbled Claire, **barging**[10] past Rebecca, her sister.

With a swift move to the right, a couple of smart steps to the left, she ducked through the bathroom door and locked it. 'First in this morning, ha!' she **gloated**[11] out loud.

---

1   **inspection** (n) careful examination or scrutiny. (s) evaluation, assessment, review, analysis. (ant) neglect.

2   **consider** (v) think about or look at carefully. (s) acknowledge, regard, believe, judge, deem. (ant) disregard.

3   **appeal** (v) attract or interest. (s) engage, draw, please, grab, allure, invite. (ant) discourage, repel, bore.

4   **cherish** (v) hold dear and protect. (s) prize, treasure, adore, appreciate, value, revere, relish. (ant) neglect.

5   **heirloom** (n) something inherited from ancestors. (s) inheritance, bequest, heritage, legacy.

6   **commence** (v) begin. (s) start, arise, launch, embark, kick off. (ant) cease, stop, conclude, end, terminate.

7   **commotion** (n) a noisy disturbance and confusion. (s) pandemonium, uproar, tumult, hubbub. (ant) calm, peace.

8   **chaos** (n) total disorder and confusion. (s) mayhem, bedlam, pandemonium, disarray. (ant) order, tranquillity.

9   **threaten** (v) state one's intention to take hostile action. (s) warn, menace, intimidate. (ant) protect, reassure.

10   **barge** (v) move forcefully or roughly. (s) rush, charge, burst, surge, push, shove, jostle, elbow. (ant) pull, glide.

11   **gloat** (v) dwell on one's own success with smug pleasure. (s) revel, glory, smirk, crow. (ant) commiserate.

'Hurry up, Choccy **Eclair**[1],' Pete **whinged**[2], hammering on the door.

Most of her family called her 'Eclair'. She pretended it didn't bother her, but it did. She **tended**[3] to be weak around chocolate.

To **irritate**[4] her brother, Claire took ages cleaning her teeth. Struggling to see her blurred reflection through the **streaks**[5] of splattered toothpaste, she **grimaced**[6] and pulled funny faces at the **grimy**[7] mirror. She sucked in her chubby cheeks for the mirror, posing. She lowered her eyelids and **pouted**[8], flicking her wavy hair with a **flamboyant**[9] **flourish**[10]. Claire would never be a model. Still, acting like one was fun. Crossing her eyes and poking out her tongue, she thought of her dad and Jayne coming to visit at the weekend.

Her parents had recently separated. She missed her dad every day but hid her guilty relief. They had argued badly towards the end, and home had improved without it. Yet things weren't so bad. Claire liked her dad's new girlfriend, Jayne, although her mum and sister **despised**[11] her. Dee insisted that Jayne had been the reason her dad had left, yet Jayne's kindness hadn't **wavered**[12] since she had met her, so Claire judged as she found.

'Will you hurry up?' Pete yelled, banging on the door again.

'I'm coming now,' she fibbed, thinking of the weekend.

Rebecca no longer spoke to her dad, and Pete didn't care either way, so Jayne had **reserved**[13] **theatre**[14] tickets in town, just for the three of them. Claire hadn't seen a live performance before,

---

1   **eclair** *(n)* an oblong choux pastry filled with cream and topped with icing. *(s)* cake, bun.

2   **whinge** *(v)* complain or whine in an irritating way. *(s)* moan, gripe, bellyache, bleat. *(ant)* accept, agree.

3   **tend** *(v)* regularly or frequently behave in a certain way. *(s)* be prone, be inclined, favour. *(ant)* shun, dislike.

4   **irritate** *(v)* make annoyed or slightly angry. *(s)* aggravate, bother, vex, exasperate. *(ant)* soothe, pacify, appease.

5   **streak** *(n)* a thin line or mark on something. *(s)* band, strip, smudge, smear, stroke, stripe.

6   **grimace** *(v)* make an ugly, twisted expression on one's face. *(s)* scowl, frown, smirk, pout. *(ant)* smile, grin.

7   **grimy** *(adj)* covered with or characterised by grime. *(s)* dirty, grubby, encrusted, caked, soiled. *(ant)* clean, neat.

8   **pout** *(v)* thrust out or protrude the lips. *(s)* purse, pucker. *(ant)* smile, grin.

9   **flamboyant** *(adj)* attracting attention by being lively and confident. *(s)* showy, extravagant, glitzy. *(ant)* simple.

10   **flourish** *(n)* a bold or extravagant gesture or action. *(s)* display, wave, shake, gesture, brandish.

11   **despise** *(v)* look down upon, view with contempt. *(s)* hate, detest, loathe, spurn, deride. *(ant)* love, admire.

12   **waver** *(v)* become weaker or falter. *(s)* fluctuate, change, hesitate, dither, shake, vary. *(ant)* continue, persist.

13   **reserve** *(v)* arrange something to be kept for use. *(s)* book, secure, prearrange, retain.

14   **theatre** *(n)* a building or outdoor area in which dramatic performances are given. *(s)* playhouse, auditorium.

and she was so excited she'd spent the week **reverting**[1] to toddler behaviour, counting the sleeps. They'd booked an **expensive**[2] restaurant too; she might even be reduced to **scrounging**[3] clothes from Rebecca. Claire's wardrobe consisted of jeans, hoodies and trainers.

'Can't work out what Princess Jayne sees in your dad,' her mum would **snipe**[4]. 'She's too **grand**[5] for him. She's **snared**[6] him, and why? What's he got to offer her? Doesn't add up.'

Claire put the **former**[7] down to her dad's **charming**[8] good looks, and the **latter**[9] – her mum's **peevishness**[10] – to jealousy. And why shouldn't her mum be jealous? She'd lost her husband to a **sophisticated**[11] beauty with a high-powered job, no nuisance kids and a gorgeous home. No wonder Dee **loathed**[12] her.

Claire loved her mum, though she didn't always like her. Same with her sister. Both were so different from her. Peas in a pod. Hair, make-up, fashion. Often, in Claire's **humble**[13] opinion, not the most tasteful. Recently her mum reminded her of an over-iced cupcake.

Her brother's **persistent**[14] hammering and football-style **chants**[15] of 'Come on, Eclair! Come on, Eclair!' **jolted**[16] Claire back to her toothbrush. Slimy, foamed toothpaste dribbled down her hand and onto the sleeve of her navy school jumper, leaving a white trail in its **wake**[17].

'Doh!' she muttered, rubbing at the stain, smearing it into a smudgy blob. Giving up, she

---

1   **revert** *(v)* return to (a previous state, practice, topic). *(s)* regress, lapse, revisit. *(ant)* develop, grow.

2   **expensive** *(adj)* costing a lot of money. *(s)* dear, costly, pricey, steep. *(ant)* inexpensive, cheap.

3   **scrounge** *(v)* live at the expense of others. *(s)* sponge, beg, cadge, borrow, bum, solicit. *(ant)* offer, give.

4   **snipe** *(v)* make a sly or petty verbal attack. *(s)* criticise, scoff, taunt, ridicule, jeer, dig. *(ant)* praise, applaud.

5   **grand** *(adj)* of high rank or behaving in a proud or dignified way. *(s)* impressive, striking. *(ant)* unimpressive.

6   **snare** *(v)* entangle or entrap. *(s)* trap, net, bag, land, lure, catch, capture, tempt, seduce. *(ant)* free, disenchant.

7   **former** *(n)* the first mentioned of two people or things. *(s)* previous, preceding, earlier. *(ant)* latter.

8   **charming** *(adj)* very pleasant or attractive. *(s)* appealing, charismatic, delightful, pleasing. *(ant)* unattractive.

9   **latter** *(n)* the second mentioned of two people or things. *(s)* last. *(ant)* former.

10   **peevishness** *(n)* spiteful or obstinate behaviour. *(s)* irritability, pettiness. *(ant)* pleasantness.

11   **sophisticated** *(adj)* having experience of life, fashion and culture. *(s)* classy, refined. *(ant)* unrefined, naive.

12   **loathe** *(v)* feel intense dislike or disgust for. *(s)* hate, despise, abhor, detest, disdain, scorn. *(ant)* adore, love.

13   **humble** *(adj)* having a low estimate of one's importance. *(s)* modest, respectful. *(ant)* proud, arrogant.

14   **persistent** *(adj)* continuing firmly or over a prolonged period. *(s)* tireless, unrelenting. *(ant)* irresolute, fleeting.

15   **chant** *(n)* a repeated rhythmic phrase. *(s)* song, mantra, tune, shout, slogan, chorus.

16   **jolt** *(v)* give a surprise or shock to initiate (cause) a change or act. *(s)* jar, nudge, push, jerk.

17   **wake** *(n)* disturbed air or water following behind something. *(s)* aftermath, trail, path, track, furrow, wash, train.

turned to the **racket**[1] coming from the door. It bulged in **rhythm**[2] as Pete barged and banged. **Smirking**[3], she sneaked closer and **squared**[4] her shoulder against it. Patiently she listened, waiting for Pete's **impatience**[5] to reach its **crescendo**[6], then climb to its peak, then *WHOOSH!* With **impeccable**[7] timing, she **yanked**[8] at the door. Pete, mid-shove and **unwitting**[9], sailed in through the air, landing with the **grace**[10] of a hippopotamus, face down and feet up in the bath. **Triumphant**[11], Claire fled down the stairs, squealing with delight.

'Ha ha, my big brother, thou art **vanquished**[12]', she shouted, remembering a **quote**[13] she'd read somewhere. **Despite**[14] his dumb actions, Claire adored her brother, and it was **mutual**[15]. They had an understanding, a **pact**[16]: so long as Claire didn't make Pete look uncool in front of his mates, then that was cool with him.

Looking **defeated**[17], Pete followed her downstairs, **swaggering**[18] his best **nonchalant**[19] northern walk. **Outmanoeuvred**[20] this time, he gave her a **magnanimous**[21] nod, pursed his lips and muttered, 'Nice one, our kid.'

---

1   **racket** *(n)* a loud, unpleasant noise. *(s)* row, din, rumpus, clamour, commotion, uproar. *(ant)* silence, peace.

2   **rhythm** *(n)* a regular pattern of movement or sound. *(s)* beat, cadence, flow, pace.

3   **smirk** *(v)* smile, but in a smug, conceited or silly way. *(s)* grin, sneer, leer, simper.

4   **square** *(v)* bring (shoulders) into position for a difficult task. *(s)* adjust, align, prepare, brace.

5   **impatience** *(n)* the tendency to be impatient. *(s)* annoyance, irritation, exasperation. *(ant)* patience.

6   **crescendo** *(n)* the loudest point reached in a gradually increasing sound. *(s)* peak, pinnacle. *(ant)* diminuendo.

7   **impeccable** *(adj)* having the highest standards. *(s)* faultless, flawless, precise, accurate, exact. *(ant)* flawed.

8   **yank** *(v)* pull with a sudden, hard movement. *(s)* tug, jerk, wrench, heave, haul. *(ant)* push, shove.

9   **unwitting** *(adj)* not aware. *(s)* unknowing, unconscious, oblivious, ignorant. *(ant)* knowing, conscious.

10   **grace** *(n)* smoothness and elegance of movement. *(s)* poise, finesse, agility, refinement. *(ant)* awkwardness.

11   **triumphant** *(adj)* showing great jubilation (joy) after a victory. *(s)* celebratory, gleeful, elated, delighted. *(ant)* defeated.

12   **vanquish** *(v)* defeat thoroughly. *(s)* conquer, crush, trounce, annihilate, beat. *(ant)* lose, surrender.

13   **quote** *(n)* a quotation (line) from a text or speech. *(s)* extract, citation, reference, repetition, excerpt.

14   **despite** *(prep)* in spite of, regardless of. *(s)* even though, even with, undeterred by. *(ant)* because of.

15   **mutual** *(adj)* having or experiencing the same thing as another. *(s)* reciprocal, joint, shared. *(ant)* unshared.

16   **pact** *(n)* a formal agreement. *(s)* deal, understanding, bond, alliance, bargain. *(ant)* disagreement.

17   **defeated** *(adj)* beaten in a conflict. *(s)* conquered, vanquished, pulverised, overpowered. *(ant)* victorious.

18   **swagger** *(v)* walk or behave in a confident and arrogant (self-important) way. *(s)* strut, parade, sway. *(ant)* creep.

19   **nonchalant** *(adj)* casual and relaxed. *(s)* cool, calm, untroubled, unruffled, blasé. *(ant)* nervous, concerned.

20   **outmanoeuvre** *(v)* evade (avoid) an opponent using speed or agility. *(s)* outwit, overcome, outdo.

21   **magnanimous** *(adj)* generous or forgiving. *(s)* benevolent, indulgent, ungrudging. *(ant)* mean, petty, selfish.

With a **fleeting**[1] grin, he joined her to find some breakfast, and in their kitchen, *find* meant **literally**[2] that. More **akin**[3] to a ship's tight **galley**[4], it **resembled**[5] a corridor littered with a **disarray**[6] of **miscellaneous**[7] clutter and mess. An **abundance**[8] of crusty dishes, lipstick-stained mugs, make-up and hairbrushes lay **strewn**[9] across the worktops. Without her dad around to keep them in check, tidiness had slipped, and Claire had to admit she was as guilty as the rest of them.

Her mum perched in her usual **pampering**[10] place, surrounded by cosmetic **debris**[11]. Nobody risked sitting there in the mornings; they'd named her stool at the breakfast bar 'the Throne'. **Habitually**[12] the kids didn't dare murmur a word to their mother until she'd downed a **minimum**[13] of three cups of coffee. Coffee so strong it rivalled steaming **treacle**[14].

Dee had never been an earth mother. She didn't cook, not in the true sense. She defrosted frozen pizza in the microwave, blasted it on full power and served it with chips done the same way. Her food **warranted**[15] a **government**[16] health warning. If she worked late, she'd leave a **scrawled**[17] note saying 'Kids, your tea's on the side.' 'Tea' being three Pot Noodles left next to the empty kettle. Their dad had been the cook of the family.

Claire's stomach groaned.

'Morning, Mum' was all Claire dared to say.

---

1   **fleeting** *(adj)* lasting for a very short time. *(s)* brief, momentary, sudden, transitory. *(ant)* lasting, permanent.

2   **literally** *(adv)* in a literal manner or sense. *(s)* exactly, precisely, really, truly. *(ant)* figuratively, indirectly.

3   **akin** *(adj)* of the same character. *(s)* similar, like, analogous, comparable. *(ant)* unlike, different, dissimilar.

4   **galley** *(n)* the kitchen in a ship or aircraft. *(s)* kitchen, scullery, cook-room.

5   **resemble** *(v)* have a similar appearance to or qualities in common with. *(s)* approximate, echo. *(ant)* differ.

6   **disarray** *(n)* a state of disorganisation or untidiness. *(s)* mess, disorder, shambles. *(ant)* order, organisation.

7   **miscellaneous** *(adj)* of a group composed of different things. *(s)* various, assorted, varied. *(ant)* same, identical.

8   **abundance** *(n)* a large quantity of something. *(s)* plenty, myriad, plethora. *(ant)* lack, dearth, few, deficiency.

9   **strew** *(v)* scatter or spread things untidily. *(s)* throw, cast, distribute, toss, litter. *(ant)* gather, assemble.

10   **pampering** *(n)* indulgence. *(s)* spoiling, coddling, cosseting, gratification. *(ant)* abstinence.

11   **debris** *(n)* the remains of anything broken down or destroyed. *(s)* waste, rubbish, detritus.

12   **habitually** *(adv)* by way of habit. *(s)* usually, routinely, normally, customarily. *(ant)* seldom, rarely, unusually.

13   **minimum** *(n)* the least or smallest amount possible. *(s)* lowest, minimal, fewest. *(ant)* maximum.

14   **treacle** *(n)* a thick, sticky dark syrup made from partly refined sugar. *(s)* molasses, syrup, compound.

15   **warrant** *(v)* justify or necessitate (allow) a course of action. *(s)* deserve, merit, demand.

16   **government** *(n)* the system by which a state is governed. *(s)* administration, authority, regime. *(ant)* anarchy.

17   **scrawled** *(adj)* written in a hurried, careless way. *(s)* dashed off, scribbled, doodled, squiggled, sketched.

Dee didn't look up. 'Morning,' she eventually replied when she took the mascara wand away from her eye.

Barely[1] able to clear a path through the **discarded**[2] shoes covering the kitchen floor, Claire took an **almighty**[3] swing with her left foot. Pete's trainers skated **blithely**[4] across the room, smacking into the wall opposite. No one noticed. She enjoyed kicking a football around with the boys at school.

Navigating[5] the untidiness, she walked over to the **cereal**[6] cupboard and rattled a **suspiciously**[7] light box. The only other **gaped**[8] open, its inner **translucent**[9] plastic revealing **limp**[10] shapes and dust.

'There's no cereal, Mum,' Claire sighed. 'None that's **edible**[11], anyway.'

'What?' mumbled Dee, glancing between her mirror and her phone whilst she hummed along to Take That on the radio.

Pushing a stack of dog-eared magazines to one side, Claire tried the bread bin. One **shrivelled**[12] doughnut sat amongst **stale**[13] crumbs, **morphing**[14] into a sugary rock. With an **indignant**[15] bang, she slammed the metal lid closed.

'God! What's that awful racket?' complained her sister, Rebecca, **tottering**[16] into the kitchen, balancing on heels way too high for school. She was glued to her phone, and her long, varnished

---

1   **barely** *(adv)* only just, almost not. *(s)* hardly, narrowly, scarcely. *(ant)* easily, amply, fully, profusely.

2   **discarded** *(adj)* thrown aside, as no longer useful or desirable. *(s)* abandoned, dumped, ditched. *(ant)* retained.

3   **almighty** *(adj)* great or enormous. *(s)* massive, supreme, mighty. *(ant)* weak, insignificant, feeble.

4   **blithely** *(adv)* in a blithe (carefree) manner. *(s)* casually, carelessly, unthinkingly. *(ant)* anxiously, warily.

5   **navigate** *(v)* find the way, guide or steer. *(s)* cross, traverse, direct, journey.

6   **cereal** *(n)* a breakfast food typically eaten with milk. *(s)* grain, oats, corn.

7   **suspiciously** *(adv)* in a way that arouses suspicion or distrust. *(s)* questionably, doubtingly.

8   **gape** *(v)* be or become wide open. *(s)* part, split, separate, divide, yawn. *(ant)* close, shut.

9   **translucent** *(adj)* (of a substance) allowing light to pass through. *(s)* clear, transparent, lucent. *(ant)* opaque.

10   **limp** *(adj)* lacking internal strength or structure, not stiff or firm. *(s)* bendy, droopy, floppy. *(ant)* stiff, rigid.

11   **edible** *(adj)* fit to be eaten. *(s)* eatable, appetising, palatable, comestible. *(ant)* inedible, unpalatable, poisonous.

12   **shrivelled** *(adj)* contracted, wrinkled or curled up. *(s)* dehydrated, shrunk, withered. *(ant)* expanded, grown.

13   **stale** *(adj)* no longer fresh and pleasant to eat. *(s)* decayed, dry, hard, old, spoiled, rank. *(ant)* fresh, edible.

14   **morph** *(v)* undergo a gradual process of transformation. *(s)* convert, modify, transform. *(ant)* preserve, sustain.

15   **indignant** *(adj)* angry or annoyed at what is perceived as unfair. *(s)* offended, disgruntled, irate. *(ant)* content.

16   **totter** *(v)* move in a feeble or unsteady way. *(s)* falter, wobble, stagger, teeter, dodder. *(ant)* balance, stabilise.

nails tapped an **incessant**[1] and irritating rap on the screen.

Wide-eyed, Claire stared at her sister's false eyelashes. She giggled. They waved like two leggy spiders stuck to her eyelids. *Spiders wearing way too much mascara*, she thought, **stifling**[2] a full-on laugh but wondering why Rebecca was so overdone. Becca was so naturally pretty she didn't need it, and school would have something to say for sure.

'What you gawping at, Choccy Eclair?' **sniggered**[3] Rebecca, her spiders **fluttering**[4].

Claire **toyed**[5] with flinging the **fossilised**[6] doughnut at her, but knowing her mother would probably side with Becca, she pulled herself up short. She'd learned from **bitter**[7] experience not to fuss, particularly in the mornings, when Dee was at her **absolute**[8] worst. Besides, a quick **reckoning**[9] **flagged**[10] she was only on coffee number one.

'Do you good not to have breakfast, anyway, Pie Face,' sniped Rebecca, **craftily**[11] out of her mother's **earshot**[12]. Claire called on every **ounce**[13] of **self-restraint**[14] to **clamp**[15] her mouth shut, shooting her sister a death **glare**[16] instead.

'Morning, love. Your hair's **fabulous**[17]' **cooed**[18] Dee.

---

1   **incessant** *(adj)* continuing without pause or interruption. *(s)* non-stop, ceaseless, constant. *(ant)* ceasing.

2   **stifle** *(v)* restrain a reaction or stop oneself acting on an emotion. *(s)* suppress, repress, curb. *(ant)* encourage.

3   **snigger** *(v)* laugh in a half-suppressed, typically scornful way. *(s)* snicker, sneer, smirk. *(ant)* admire, applaud.

4   **flutter** *(v)* move with a light, irregular or trembling motion. *(s)* beat, flap, wave, tremble, flicker.

5   **toy** *(v)* consider an idea or proposal casually or indecisively. *(s)* contemplate, ponder, muse. *(ant)* decide.

6   **fossilised** *(adj)* preserved so that it becomes a fossil. *(s)* calcified, petrified, ossified.

7   **bitter** *(adj)* painful or unpleasant to accept or contemplate. *(s)* acrimonious, harsh, upsetting. *(ant)* agreeable.

8   **absolute** *(adj)* complete, total. *(s)* utter, outright, entire, pure, sheer, downright. *(ant)* partial, uncertain.

9   **reckoning** *(n)* the act of calculating or estimating something. *(s)* calculation, total, count, estimation, guess.

10   **flag** *(v)* draw attention to. *(s)* indicate, highlight, signpost, signal, identify. *(ant)* ignore, conceal.

11   **craftily** *(adv)* in an indirect or deceitful way. *(s)* shrewdly, cunningly, slyly. *(ant)* sincerely.

12   **earshot** *(n)* the distance within which one can hear or be heard. *(s)* close range, hearing range.

13   **ounce** *(n)* a small amount. *(s)* scrap, grain, jot, smidgen, iota, speck, bit, particle.

14   **self-restraint** *(n)* self-control. *(s)* discipline, willpower, moderation, restraint. *(ant)* impulse, abandon.

15   **clamp** *(v)* fasten firmly together. *(s)* clasp, brace, press, lock, hold, secure. *(ant)* open, release, unclamp.

16   **glare** *(n)* an angry or fierce stare. *(s)* scowl, glower, frown. *(ant)* grin, smile.

17   **fabulous** *(adj)* very good. *(s)* wonderful, tremendous, magnificent, extraordinary. *(ant)* ordinary, normal, poor.

18   **coo** *(v)* make soft murmuring sounds. *(s)* fuss, cluck, murmur.

Dee worked as a hairdresser, and she'd recently **chemically**[1] straightened Rebecca's **wayward**[2] curls, which now obeyed all her teenage **whims**[3] and commands. All three **siblings**[4] had **inherited**[5] their dad's curly hair, so Dee had **eradicated**[6] any signs of a bend and **transformed**[7] Rebecca's **locks**[8] from Shirley Temple to Pocahontas.

Unnoticed[9] and **exasperated**[10], Claire grabbed her bag and coat, and left for school, hoping she might get something to eat at Ben's.

∗

Ben Lee Brady lived a short stretch from Claire, but in the big houses. Chorltonville was an **oasis**[11] of leafy green **tranquillity**[12] with **affluent**[13] homes **camouflaged**[14] by Victorian and **modern**[15] **dwellings**[16]. 'The Ville' had become a peaceful but **pricey**[17] **respite**[18] from urban traffic. Dee **referred**[19] to it **sarcastically**[20] as 'Pleasantville', but Claire knew her mum would secretly love to live there.

---

1   **chemically** *(adv)* done with chemicals. *(s)* synthetically. *(ant)* naturally.

2   **wayward** *(adj)* difficult to control. *(s)* unruly, disobedient, rebellious, wilful, defiant. *(ant)* obedient, compliant.

3   **whim** *(n)* a quick or impulsive decision or change of mind. *(s)* impulse, urge, inclination, desire, fancy, notion. *(ant)* plan.

4   **sibling** *(n)* a brother or sister.

5   **inherit** *(v)* receive a genetic trait from a parent or ancestor. *(s)* acquire, derive, obtain.

6   **eradicate** *(v)* destroy or completely put an end to. *(s)* eliminate, remove, abolish, expunge. *(ant)* preserve.

7   **transform** *(v)* markedly change something. *(s)* alter, modify, convert, remodel, revamp. *(ant)* preserve, sustain.

8   **lock** *(n)* a strand of hair. *(s)* strand, tress, curl, wisp, tendril.

9   **unnoticed** *(adj)* unseen. *(s)* ignored, overlooked, disregarded, unobserved. *(ant)* seen, noticed.

10   **exasperated** *(adj)* irritated greatly. *(s)* agitated, frustrated, annoyed, infuriated, incensed. *(ant)* pleased.

11   **oasis** *(n)* a peaceful area or period amidst a difficulty. *(s)* shelter, refuge, retreat, haven, sanctuary.

12   **tranquillity** *(n)* the quality or state of being tranquil. *(s)* calm, serenity, peacefulness, lull. *(ant)* turmoil, agitation.

13   **affluent** *(adj)* having a great deal of money. *(s)* wealthy, rich, prosperous, comfortable. *(ant)* poor, destitute.

14   **camouflage** *(v)* hide or disguise by means of camouflage. *(s)* conceal, mask. *(ant)* reveal, show.

15   **modern** *(adj)* the most up to date and in fashion. *(s)* current, contemporary, new. *(ant)* dated, outmoded.

16   **dwelling** *(n)* a house, flat or other place of residence. *(s)* home, accommodation, abode, habitat, lodgings.

17   **pricey** *(adj)* expensive. *(s)* costly, dear, steep, exorbitant, overpriced. *(ant)* cheap, inexpensive, economical.

18   **respite** *(n)* a period of rest or relief from something difficult. *(s)* break, interval, delay. *(ant)* continuation.

19   **refer** *(v)* describe or denote something as. *(s)* signify, mean, indicate, allude, imply, state.

20   **sarcastically** *(adv)* in a sarcastic (mocking) way. *(s)* ironically, cynically, derisively.

Ben was an only child, loved **unconditionally**[1] yet not **spoiled**[2]. A **studious**[3], well-mannered boy, with his mop of shaggy hair, smooth caramel skin and **lithe**[4], athletic build, he'd be equally at home riding the surf on Bondi Beach. He and Claire had been **inseparable**[5] since playschool and were still best buddies; their friendship had stood the test of time. He **exuded**[6] the **epitome**[7] of cool; if she was asked to rewrite the **dictionary**[8] **definition**[9], it would say 'Ben Lee Brady'.

By the time she'd reached Ben's, her stomach was growling. She patted it. 'Quiet, boy!' she laughed. *Am I fat?* she asked herself, sucking in her tummy, turning bright pink.

Rebecca was always saying she had 'chicken drumstick legs'. At least her mum softened it to the **euphemism**[10] of 'twiggy **calves**[11] and meaty thighs'. Claire couldn't decide which sounded worse.

'I'm not that bad, am I?' she asked, looking down and **tilting**[12] her head to inspect herself from a **variety**[13] of angles. 'Not really?' she **debated**[14], wishing she preferred exercise to food.

The door opened; Mrs Brady's kind, **vaguely**[15] **amused**[16] face smiled down at her.

'Morning, Claire. Come in,' she **beckoned**[17].

Caught in the act, Claire let out a squeaky **yelp**[18], stepped back and straightened up.

---

1   **unconditionally** *(adv)* in an unconditional (unlimited) way. *(s)* absolutely, utterly. *(ant)* conditionally.

2   **spoil** *(v)* harm by being too soft or giving someone too much. *(s)* ruin, indulge, pamper. *(ant)* neglect, deprive.

3   **studious** *(adj)* spending a lot of time studying or reading. *(s)* academic, bookish, brainy. *(ant)* unscholarly.

4   **lithe** *(adj)* (especially of the body) thin, supple and graceful. *(s)* agile, fit, nimble. *(ant)* dumpy, chubby, stiff.

5   **inseparable** *(adj)* (of people) unwilling to be separated. *(s)* close, devoted, faithful, bosom. *(ant)* separable.

6   **exude** *(v)* display an emotion or quality strongly and openly. *(s)* radiate, convey, ooze, emit. *(ant)* absorb.

7   **epitome** *(n)* a person or thing that is a perfect example of something. *(s)* embodiment, essence. *(ant)* antithesis.

8   **dictionary** *(n)* something that lists words and their meanings. *(s)* lexicon, wordbook, vocabulary.

9   **definition** *(n)* the exact meaning of a word (often in a dictionary). *(s)* explanation, description.

10   **euphemism** *(n)* a nicer word used instead of something harsh or offensive. *(s)* rewording. *(ant)* dysphemism.

11   **calf** *(n)* the fleshy part at the back of a person's leg below the knee (plural: *calves*).

12   **tilt** *(v)* move into a sloping position. *(s)* angle, lean, slope, incline, tip, bend, roll. *(ant)* straighten, level.

13   **variety** *(n)* the quality or state of being different or diverse. *(s)* array, assortment, range. *(ant)* uniformity.

14   **debate** *(v)* consider or discuss something before reaching a decision. *(s)* wonder, ponder, reflect. *(ant)* decide.

15   **vaguely** *(adv)* in a vague (unclear) manner. *(s)* slightly, loosely, indefinitely, ambiguously. *(ant)* clearly, definitely.

16   **amused** *(adj)* finding something funny. *(s)* entertained, pleased, tickled, charmed. *(ant)* bored, displeased.

17   **beckon** *(v)* make a gesture with the hand, arm or head to instruct someone. *(s)* attract, signal, sign.

18   **yelp** *(n)* a short, sharp cry, especially of pain or alarm. *(s)* squeal, squeak, wail, yell.

'Hello, Mrs Brady,' she **blurted**[1], blushing.

Mrs Brady welcomed her in. Red-faced, Claire followed, **squirming**[2], but **grateful**[3] that Mrs Brady seemed too **courteous**[4] and **discreet**[5] to mention what she'd seen.

'Ben's still fiddling around upstairs. Come on through, Claire.'

Entering their kitchen **transported**[6] Claire into another world, one so different from home. **Hotchpotch**[7] and **unregimented**[8], the room had shelves that **bowed**[9] and strained, **crammed**[10] full of colourful cookery books. Copper pans and cooking **utensils**[11] hung from hooks. An **array**[12] of Chinese herbs and spices filled the air with **exotic**[13] and **pungent**[14] smells, **intoxicating**[15] **aromas**[16] all **alien**[17] to her nose. The only thing hanging up in Claire's kitchen was her mum's hair straighteners.

'Fancy a banana, Claire?' asked Mrs Brady, spooning homemade fried rice into Ben's lunchbox. 'You could eat it on the way to school.'

'Oh, yes, please. Thanks, Mrs B,' replied Claire.

Ben's dad had already gone; he often left early. **Originally**[18] from New York, he worked for an

---

1   **blurt** *(v)* say something suddenly and without consideration. *(s)* announce, exclaim, cry, utter.

2   **squirm** *(v)* show or feel embarrassment or shame. *(s)* agonise, cringe, fidget, feel humiliated.

3   **grateful** *(adj)* feeling or showing appreciation for something. *(s)* thankful, glad, appreciative. *(ant)* ungrateful.

4   **courteous** *(adj)* polite or considerate in manner. *(s)* civil, chivalrous, considerate. *(ant)* discourteous, rude.

5   **discreet** *(adj)* careful in one's speech or actions. *(s)* cautious, circumspect, tactful, diplomatic. *(ant)* indiscreet.

6   **transport** *(v)* cause someone to feel that they are in another time or place. *(s)* move, carry. *(ant)* remain, stay.

7   **hotchpotch** *(adj)* mixed confusedly. *(s)* jumbled, miscellaneous, assorted, messed up. *(ant)* ordered, uniform.

8   **unregimented** *(adj)* not subject to strict order or control. *(s)* jumbled, disorganised. *(ant)* regimented, orderly.

9   **bow** *(v)* bend with age or under pressure. *(s)* strain, distort, sag, curve, yield, succumb. *(ant)* straighten, relieve.

10   **cram** *(v)* completely fill to the point of overflowing. *(s)* pack, jam, fill, stuff, ram. *(ant)* remove, relieve, empty.

11   **utensil** *(n)* a tool, container or article used for jobs. *(s)* gadget, aid, device, implement.

12   **array** *(n)* a significant display or range of something. *(s)* selection, arrangement, group. *(ant)* individual, one.

13   **exotic** *(adj)* unusual, reminiscent of, or from a faraway country. *(s)* alien, different. *(ant)* ordinary, plain.

14   **pungent** *(adj)* strong and sharp in taste or smell. *(s)* powerful, pervasive, overpowering. *(ant)* bland, plain.

15   **intoxicating** *(adj)* exciting or exhilarating. *(s)* appealing, delightful, enlivening, thrilling, rousing. *(ant)* boring.

16   **aroma** *(n)* a distinctive, typically pleasant smell. *(s)* bouquet, scent, perfume. *(ant)* stench, stink, reek.

17   **alien** *(adj)* unfamiliar. *(s)* unusual, foreign, incongruous, strange. *(ant)* familiar, usual.

18   **originally** *(adv)* in the first place, at the start. *(s)* previously, initially, firstly. *(ant)* latterly.

American company in town. What he did **flummoxed**[1] her; it sounded too **complicated**[2], but it must be a **respectable**[3] job, as he drove a **flashy**[4] electric car that steered itself if you asked it to. Ben had inherited both his parents' good **features**[5], but especially his dad's. Mr Brady had looks a film star would **envy**[6].

'Hey, Claire,' said Ben in his Mancunian-American twang. 'You ready?'

'Yeah. Coming,' Claire replied through a mouthful of banana.

'Have a good day, you two,' said Mrs Brady as they left the kitchen and headed off.

*

'I wonder what times were like in 1847,' **mused**[7] Ben, reading from a crooked headstone as they cut through the graveyard towards their school.

'Boo!' Claire **jested**[8], giving him a playful push in the back.

'Yikes! You scared me!' he laughed, crossing his hands over his chest in a **makeshift**[9] cross, faking fear. He pushed his skateboard along with the toe of his black school trainer, and as **slick**[10] as a pro, he hopped on and sported an **adroit**[11] little ollie up the kerb. 'Come on, keep up, slowcoach; we'll be late,' he teased.

They exited the church via a **quaint**[12] archway onto the Green, a hidden **quadrant**[13] of **manicured**[14] grass **enclosed**[15] by red-brick terraces and a Tudor-looking pub. It was hard to

---

1   **flummox** (*v*) perplex or bewilder. (*s*) baffle, confound, puzzle, mystify, bemuse. (*ant*) clarify, demystify.

2   **complicated** (*adj*) involving many varied and confusing aspects. (*s*) perplexing, complex. (*ant*) simple.

3   **respectable** (*adj*) of some importance and merit. (*s*) decent, good, reputable, worthy. (*ant*) disreputable, poor.

4   **flashy** (*adj*) attractive and impressive. (*s*) expensive, jazzy, glitzy, ostentatious. (*ant*) understated, drab, plain.

5   **feature** (*n*) a part of the face and its overall appearance. (*s*) looks, trait, characteristics, countenance.

6   **envy** (*v*) desire to have something for oneself. (*s*) covet, crave, begrudge, hanker, dislike. (*ant*) be glad for.

7   **muse** (*v*) ask oneself in a thoughtful manner. (*s*) think, wonder, ponder, consider, contemplate. (*ant*) disregard.

8   **jest** (*v*) speak in a joking manner. (*s*) joke, kid, tease, clown, banter, quip, spoof, josh, quip. (*ant*) be serious.

9   **makeshift** (*adj*) acting as a temporary or make-do measure. (*s*) pretend, improvised, crude. (*ant*) permanent.

10   **slick** (*adj*) done in an impressive and efficient way. (*s*) deft, smooth, skilful, adroit. (*ant*) amateurish, clumsy.

11   **adroit** (*adj*) skilful or clever. (*s*) practised, able, competent, adept, accomplished, agile. (*ant*) clumsy, inept.

12   **quaint** (*adj*) attractive or pleasingly old-fashioned. (*s*) picturesque, appealing, charming. (*ant*) ordinary, modern.

13   **quadrant** (*n*) a quarter of a circle.

14   **manicured** (*adj*) (of a lawn or garden) trimmed and neatly maintained. (*s*) cut, shaped. (*ant*) overgrown.

15   **enclose** (*v*) close off or surround. (*s*) circle, encompass, encircle, ring, append, bound. (*ant*) open, exclude.

believe that two world-famous football grounds and one of England's most **populous**[1] city centres **resided**[2] a few miles down the road.

On the **idyllic**[3] green's edge, **adjacent**[4] to their flat-roofed school, stood a single row of charming Victorian workman's cottages. Every morning, the two friends called in to say hello to the **feisty**[5] **terrier**[6] owned by Gladys Jones, who lived at number twenty-two the Green. Gladys, a **sprightly**[7] and **amiable**[8] **octogenarian**[9], already stood hanging out the day's washing in her tiny front garden. An excited Jack **yapped**[10] by her feet; he'd spotted his friends approaching.

'Morning, Gladys,' they chirped, reaching down to **ruffle**[11] Jack's **bristly**[12] coat. Claire was panting; she could never keep up with Ben on his board. He'd tried to teach her to ride many times, but after her millionth crash, she'd **conceded**[13] defeat.

'Hello, kids,' **croaked**[14] Gladys, her black cat, Thomas, **slinking**[15] out to join them. 'Work hard today at school,' she added in a **broad**[16] Lancashire **accent**[17].

'We will.' Ben kicked his **deck**[18] into place. 'Come on, Claire, the bell's about to go.'

'You'll do yourself a **mischief**[19] on that **contraption**[20] one day,' laughed Gladys. 'Call in on

---

1   **populous** *(adj)* large and densely populated. *(s)* crowded, packed, overcrowded, numerous. *(ant)* uncrowded.

2   **reside** *(v)* permanently have a home in a specific place. *(s)* exist, lie, locate, occupy, inhabit, dwell. *(ant)* visit.

3   **idyllic** *(adj)* extremely happy, peaceful or picturesque. *(s)* blissful, wonderful, heavenly. *(ant)* bad, nightmarish.

4   **adjacent** *(adj)* next to or adjoining. *(s)* beside, neighbouring, alongside, joining. *(ant)* remote from, distant from.

5   **feisty** *(adj)* lively, determined and courageous. *(s)* energetic, spirited, bold. *(ant)* dull, spiritless, cowardly.

6   **terrier** *(n)* a small breed of dog typically used for controlling perceived verminous animals (pests).

7   **sprightly** *(adj)* lively and full of energy. *(s)* energetic, spry, active, vigorous, vivacious. *(ant)* inactive, lethargic.

8   **amiable** *(adj)* friendly and pleasant in manner. *(s)* sociable, affable, amicable, cordial. *(ant)* unfriendly, aloof.

9   **octogenarian** *(n)* someone who is aged between eighty and eighty-nine years old.

10   **yap** *(v)* bark sharply or shrilly. *(s)* yelp, woof, yip, bay.

11   **ruffle** *(v)* mess up something or someone's hair. *(s)* tousle, disarrange, dishevel. *(ant)* smooth, straighten.

12   **bristly** *(adj)* having a stiff and prickly texture. *(s)* coarse, thick, wiry, prickly, spiky, rough. *(ant)* smooth, sleek.

13   **concede** *(v)* admit defeat. *(s)* acknowledge, accept, recognise, allow, capitulate, quit, cede. *(ant)* deny, fight.

14   **croak** *(v)* make a hoarse, rasping sound when speaking. *(s)* rasp, wheeze, gasp, whisper.

15   **slink** *(v)* move smoothly and quietly in a stealthy way. *(s)* glide, snake, slip, steal. *(ant)* stomp, stamp.

16   **broad** *(adj)* (of an accent) noticeable and strong. *(s)* distinctive, heavy, pronounced. *(ant)* slight, unnoticeable.

17   **accent** *(n)* pronouncing of language in a way that is distinctive. *(s)* pronunciation, intonation.

18   **deck** *(n)* the flat part of a skateboard or snowboard. *(s)* base, bottom, surface.

19   **mischief** *(n)* harm caused by someone or something. *(s)* injury, hurt, impairment, damage. *(ant)* benefit.

20   **contraption** *(n)* an unnecessarily complicated, badly made or unsafe thing. *(s)* gadget, device, gubbins.

your way home for a sandwich if you want, kids.' She smiled, waving them off.

*

'Why did you call him Jack?' asked Claire, munching the promised sandwich in Gladys's cosy kitchen after school. Gladys baked fresh bread to **rival**[1] Ben's mum's, none of that spongy white **stodge**[2] in her house, and Gladys used real butter too.

'Because he's a Jack Russell terrier, the cleverest dogs in the **entire**[3] world, aren't you, my Jack?' replied Gladys, patting his head. 'Although he's more of a Parson Russell terrier with those long legs and that bristly coat. At least you don't **moult**[4] much, Jack,' she laughed, rubbing his coat.

Jack didn't blink at the mention of his name. Statue-still, he **drooled**[5], **longing**[6] for a **morsel**[7] of Claire's bread, not moving in case he missed a falling crumb.

'What did you two do today?' asked Gladys.

'Heaps of maths and English; we've got big tests coming up. We'll be glad when they're done,' replied Ben.

'Yeah, far too much maths,' Claire groaned, interrupted by a wet nose prodding her palm. 'Oh, Jack, I'm so sorry. I forgot to save you some. I'll keep a bit for you next time, I promise, Jackster.'

She **fondled**[8] his **silky**[9] ear, the one soft part of him; the rest felt as **coarse**[10] as the **scouring**[11] pads she washed up with at home.

'Don't be feeding him treats – it makes him beg,' Gladys **chided**[12], tickling his other ear. 'You kids best be off before it's dark,' she warned.

---

1   **rival** *(v)* be equal or comparable to. *(s)* compete, emulate, match, challenge.

2   **stodge** *(n)* filling and heavy food, often carbohydrates. *(s)* starch.

3   **entire** *(adj)* whole or complete. *(s)* total, full, all-inclusive. *(ant)* fractional, partial, incomplete.

4   **moult** *(v)* lose feathers, hair or skin to make way for new growth. *(s)* shed, drop.

5   **drool** *(v)* drop and dribble saliva from the mouth. *(s)* salivate, slaver, slobber, drivel.

6   **long** *(v)* have a strong wish or desire. *(s)* crave, yearn, hunger, pine, ache, wish, hanker.

7   **morsel** *(n)* a small piece or amount. *(s)* mouthful, bite, nibble, bit, sample, spoonful. *(ant)* entirety, total.

8   **fondle** *(v)* stroke or caress fondly. *(s)* massage, touch, rub, pat, pet, cuddle, snuggle.

9   **silky** *(adj)* soft and fine, resembling silk. *(s)* smooth, sleek, lustrous, glossy, silken. *(ant)* rough, coarse.

10   **coarse** *(adj)* rough or hard, bristly. *(s)* wiry, scratchy, prickly, hairy, shaggy, abrasive. *(ant)* smooth, sleek, silky.

11   **scouring** *(n)* the act of cleaning a surface by rubbing hard. *(s)* scrubbing, polishing, abrading, brushing.

12   **chide** *(v)* tell off, rebuke or scold. *(s)* chastise, berate, reprimand, reproach, reprove. *(ant)* praise, applaud.

Eternally[1] jovial[2] and upbeat, Gladys seldom[3] lectured[4] them, but they heeded[5] her s̶ tone.

'OK, Gladys. See you tomorrow, then,' chorused[6] the kids. Jack and Thomas trotted out behind them.

'I'm sure that cat thinks he's a dog,' chuckled Gladys.

This was the closest Claire had ever got to a longed-for pet, as Dee had an aversion[7] to animals. Claire adored Jack and Thomas like they were her own.

'Why are you wasting your time talking to that old witch?' Rebecca's spiteful[8] comments cut through the air, spoiling their goodbyes. She was heading home from school, and showing off to impress[9] the boy with her.

'Yeah, what do you bother with her for?' he chimed[10] in.

Josh Drane was a loathsome[11] boy in Claire's eyes. His arrogant[12] behaviour repelled[13] her, yet her gullible[14] sister seemed to have recently fallen for it. And although he was an obviously[15] good-looking boy, whenever Claire clapped eyes on him, she saw a rat in a baseball cap.

'The only people wasting my time are you,' hissed Claire at them both. 'Come on, Ben, I'm not walking anywhere near these two.' She stepped up the pace[16].

---

1   **eternally** *(adv)* eternal (everlasting) in manner. *(s)* always, forever, perpetually, evermore. *(ant)* temporarily.

2   **jovial** *(adj)* happy, friendly and cheerful. *(s)* jolly, genial, amiable, affable, sociable. *(ant)* miserable, surly.

3   **seldom** *(adv)* rarely, not often. *(s)* never, sporadically, occasionally, infrequently, hardly. *(ant)* often, frequently.

4   **lecture** *(v)* talk seriously to or reprimand. *(s)* scold, chide, reproach, advise, instruct. *(ant)* approve, praise.

5   **heed** *(v)* pay attention to and take notice of. *(s)* listen, obey, follow, regard. *(ant)* disregard, ignore.

6   **chorus** *(v)* say or sing the same thing at the same time.

7   **aversion** *(n)* a strong dislike. *(s)* loathing, repugnance, revulsion, distaste, abhorrence. *(ant)* liking, desire.

8   **spiteful** *(adj)* mean and nasty. *(s)* malicious, cruel, vindictive, snide, cutting, venomous. *(ant)* kind, benevolent.

9   **impress** *(v)* make someone feel admiration and respect. *(s)* affect, influence, inspire, excite. *(ant)* disappoint.

10   **chime** *(v)* join in a conversation. *(s)* say, interrupt, comment, contribute, add.

11   **loathsome** *(adj)* causing disgust or hatred. *(s)* detestable, odious, abhorrent, repulsive. *(ant)* lovable, delightful.

12   **arrogant** *(adj)* having an exaggerated sense of one's own importance. *(s)* haughty, conceited. *(ant)* modest.

13   **repel** *(v)* disgust or repulse. *(s)* revolt, offend, sicken, nauseate. *(ant)* appeal to, enchant, delight.

14   **gullible** *(adj)* easily persuaded to believe something. *(s)* trusting, naive, impressionable. *(ant)* cynical, suspicious.

15   **obviously** *(adv)* in an obvious (clear) way. *(s)* visibly, evidently, noticeably. *(ant)* obscurely, inconspicuously.

16   **pace** *(n)* speed in walking or running. *(s)* rapidity, step, swiftness, progress, quickness.

comforted. 'My kung fu master says you **reap**[1] what you **sow**[2] in this world.

getting much back unless she changes a whole bunch.'

Ben, appreciative of his **tact**[3], **sensitivity**[4] and his funny Americanisms.

en hopped off his board, flicking it up under his arm. A **deft**[5] kick with his other foot opened his gate.

'Nah, thanks. We've got that test tomorrow, and I should tidy my room. It's such a dump I can't find my spellings, and my mum will freak even though she's messier!'

'OK, yeah. Sure. See you in the morning, and don't forget your PE kit. It's cross-country tomorrow, your favourite!'

'Nooooo!' groaned Claire, **envisaging**[6] herself limping over the finishing line. She wasn't the sportiest of children, unlike Ben.

'Oh, I forgot, are you still coming to my competition this Saturday?' asked Ben.

'Oh, yeah, I'd love to, so long as it's OK with your mum.' She knew it would be, yet she never took the invitations for **granted**[7].

'Of course. It'll be fine,' he answered. 'We're going snowboarding to the Chill Factore on Sunday too, if you want to come?'

'I can't on Sunday; my dad's coming,' she said, relieved her excuse was **genuine**[8]. Ben was an **avid**[9] snowboarder, but his hobbies were **dear**[10], and she didn't have the money. Besides, the one time she'd tried boarding, she'd bruised her backside so badly she didn't fancy trying it again.

'Thanks for asking though. See you tomorrow,' she said, heading off.

She loved Ben's **tournaments**[11]; they were so exciting. The smell of rubber mats, the **artistic**[12],

---

1   **reap** (v) cut or gather (a harvest or crop). (s) earn, obtain, collect, gain, produce, realise.

2   **sow** (v) plant seeds in the ground. (s) scatter, disperse, spread.

3   **tact** (n) skill in dealing with others or difficulties. (s) sensitivity, discretion, diplomacy. (ant) tactlessness.

4   **sensitivity** (n) the quality of being sensitive to others or situations. (s) awareness, compassion. (ant) insensitivity.

5   **deft** (adj) neatly skilful and quick. (s) agile, lithe, sprightly, dexterous, supple, adroit. (ant) clumsy, lumbering.

6   **envisage** (v) form a mental picture of. (s) imagine, envision, visualise, picture, foresee.

7   **take for granted** (v) assume to be happening or given. (s) suppose, guess, infer. (ant) disbelieve, doubt.

8   **genuine** (adj) real, truthful or sincere. (s) honest, candid, frank, straight. (ant) insincere, false, hypocritical.

9   **avid** (adj) having a keen interest or enthusiasm. (s) eager, ardent, voracious. (ant) indifferent, unenthusiastic.

10   **dear** (adj) costly. (s) expensive, exorbitant, extortionate. (ant) inexpensive, economical, cheap.

11   **tournament** (n) a series of contests with multiple contestants. (s) competition, series, event.

12   **artistic** (adj) having natural creative skill. (s) creative, imaginative, inspired, inventive. (ant) uncreative, unimaginative.

testing moves and amazing high kicks. The twists, turns and **dynamic**[1] spins. A **choreographed**[2] ballet of self-**defence**[3] **accompanied**[4] by a **concerto**[5] of **exertive**[6] grunts. **Captivated**[7], she'd sit with Ben's parents, **marvelling**[8] at the **competitors**[9]. Children of all sizes, some **wiry**[10], some **stocky**[11], all light-footed and so **deceptively**[12] strong as they **practised**[13] and perfected their **martial**[14] art. She'd love to have a go but, always too **self-conscious**[15], never dared.

Claire had used her own key for a while. Leaving her bag in the hall, she supposed one **redeeming**[16] feature of living here was the warmth. Dee felt the cold, so she **cranked**[17] up the heating to **permanent**[18] **Caribbean**[19] temperatures. First home, and despite the jam sandwich at Gladys's, she had a **prowling**[20] hunger, as usual. The fossilised doughnut still sat alone in the bread bin. She prodded it, picturing it bouncing off Becca's head.

I hope Mum's gone shopping, she thought, heading upstairs.

Not long after, she heard the front door slam. Dee had finished early for a Thursday.

'Glad you're tidying up, young lady – it's a right **tip**[21] in there.' Dee's head popped around the door.

---

1   **dynamic** *(adj)* constantly changing and full of energy. *(s)* lively, vital, strong. *(ant)* lethargic, half-hearted.

2   **choreograph** *(v)* compose a sequence of steps and moves. *(s)* arrange, plan, coordinate, devise. *(ant)* improvise.

3   **defence** *(n)* the action of defending or resisting an attack. *(s)* protection, resistance, security. *(ant)* offence, attack.

4   **accompany** *(v)* support with music or sounds. *(s)* support, back, play with.

5   **concerto** *(n)* a musical composition, often for an orchestra. *(s)* arrangement, creation, piece.

6   **exertive** *(adj)* having a tendency to exert or rouse to action. *(s)* vigorous, strained. *(ant)* languid, lazy.

7   **captivated** *(adj)* attracted, charmed and attentive. *(s)* fascinated, absorbed, gripped. *(ant)* repelled, bored.

8   **marvel** *(v)* be filled with amazement and wonder. *(s)* admire, gape, stare, applaud. *(ant)* deride, disregard.

9   **competitor** *(n)* a person taking part in a sporting contest. *(s)* contestant, participant, player. *(ant)* spectator, fan.

10   **wiry** *(adj)* lean and strong. *(s)* tough, agile, athletic, sinewy, muscular, slim, thin. *(ant)* fat, frail, flabby.

11   **stocky** *(adj)* broad and heavily built. *(s)* thickset, stout, chunky, burly, hefty, squat. *(ant)* slight, slender.

12   **deceptively** *(adv)* in a deceptive (misleading) way. *(s)* dishonestly, deceivingly, spuriously. *(ant)* truly, honestly.

13   **practise** *(v)* repeat something to improve. *(s)* rehearse, prepare, hone, exercise.

14   **martial** *(adj)* relating to fighting (or war). *(s)* military, warlike, combative, belligerent. *(ant)* civilian, peaceable.

15   **self-conscious** *(adj)* feeling overly aware of oneself. *(s)* embarrassed, uncomfortable. *(ant)* confident, natural.

16   **redeeming** *(adj)* putting something right or making amends. *(s)* saving, positive, compensatory. *(ant)* degrading.

17   **crank** *(v)* turn or run something. *(s)* activate, move, change, wind, reel.

18   **permanent** *(adj)* lasting or intended to last indefinitely. *(s)* constant, perpetual, persistent. *(ant)* temporary.

19   **Caribbean** *(adj)* relating to the region of the Caribbean sea, its islands and the surrounding coasts.

20   **prowl** *(v)* move about stealthily, often in search of prey. *(s)* lurk, patrol, sneak, skulk, steal, stalk. *(ant)* parade.

21   **tip** *(n)* a rubbish dump, messy or untidiness. *(s)* junkyard, landfill, scrapyard, hovel, slum.

That's rich! thought Claire. "Ave we got any glue, Mum?' she asked.

'Don't drop your *h*'s, young lady; I've told you about that,' Dee snapped, leaving Claire speechless. Dee often forgot hers.

'Sorry, Mother. *Have* we got any glue?' repeated Claire, **emphasising**[1] her *h* as much as she dared get away with.

'What do you need glue for, anyway?' asked Dee, her eyes narrowing suspiciously to **wily**[2] slits.

'I knocked over my clock, and Wallace's head fell off,' replied Claire, getting up to show her mum.

'Oh, is that all? Ask your dad to fix it when he comes with Princess Jayne at the weekend,' responded Dee **tartly**[3], and with that, she swooped off and went downstairs.

*

'Claire!' Dee yelled from downstairs. 'CLAIRE CADWALLADER, GET DOWN THESE STAIRS NOW!'

'Sorry, Mum. I got carried away,' replied Claire, poking her head around her door. The smell of microwaved chips **wafted**[4] towards her.

'Well, get yourself *carried* down these stairs now, young lady, because your tea's ready,' Dee shouted, disappearing back into the kitchen.

Tea was **uninspiring**[5], as usual. Pete complained about the **mushy**[6] pizza, and the chips still being frozen in the middle. He **jabbed**[7] at his food with his fork, squeezed half a bottle of ketchup on it and **wolfed**[8] it all down anyway.

'Mum, I need extra money for dinner on that stupid trip tomorrow,' said Rebecca, pushing

---

1   **emphasise** *(v)* stress a word when speaking. *(s)* highlight, accentuate, intensify. *(ant)* understate.

2   **wily** *(adj)* clever and sharp, sometimes deceitfully so. *(s)* shrewd, astute, sly, crafty, cunning. *(ant)* guileless.

3   **tartly** *(adv)* in a tart (sharp) manner. *(s)* critically, sarcastically, unkindly, cuttingly. *(ant)* sweetly, kindly.

4   **waft** *(v)* pass gently through the air. *(s)* carry, drift, float, fan, arrive, glide.

5   **uninspiring** *(adj)* without excitement or interest. *(s)* dull, unexciting, lacklustre, bland. *(ant)* inspiring, exciting.

6   **mushy** *(adj)* soft and soggy. *(s)* pappy, pulpy, squidgy, sloppy, spongy, squishy. *(ant)* hard, firm.

7   **jab** *(v)* poke roughly or quickly. *(s)* prod, dig, stab, push, nudge.

8   **wolf** *(v)* eat food greedily. *(s)* consume, bolt, guzzle, scoff, devour, gobble, demolish. *(ant)* nibble, pick at.

her chair away, scraping it **excruciatingly**[1] across the **laminate**[2] flooring.

'Don't you mean *lunch*?' Dee corrected, **wincing**[3] but ignoring the noise, and speaking in a **pretentious**[4], **posh**[5] voice.

Claire rolled her eyes.

'It's your turn to wash up tonight, fat face,' Rebecca said, leaving the kitchen.

'I'm not fat!' Claire **retaliated**[6] indignantly. 'Anyway, Mum, why does Pete always dodge doing the pots?'

'Because he's busy,' her mother answered with a **dismissive**[7] wave.

'Yeah, busy on his Xbox,' said Claire, getting up to clear the table as Pete **sloped**[8] off. 'I am *NOT* doing them tomorrow!' she **proclaimed**[9], pointing. 'He is!'

Fuming[10], she washed up, wishing she could go on Rebecca's school trip. They were visiting a museum in Manchester for their history exam. She'd sneaked a **peek**[11] at the letter. It had mentioned '**ancient**[12] **artefacts**[13]'. She'd had to look up the definition of *artefact*. It said, 'Something historical made by a human being.' History and mystery **intrigued**[14] Claire and she envied Rebecca's trip. She couldn't wait to be at secondary school, going on **excursions**[15] with Ben – her tummy flipped at the thought.

'Night, Mum.' Claire dried her hands on a damp towel.

'Why are you going to bed now? It's not even half past six,' Dee said, swiping her finger across

---

1 **excruciatingly** *(adv)* in a way that is excruciating (agonising). *(s)* awfully, searingly, painfully. *(ant)* mildly.

2 **laminate** *(n)* a material made from thin sheets glued together.

3 **wince** *(v)* grimace slightly in reaction to pain or distress. *(s)* flinch, blench, start, shrink. *(ant)* smile.

4 **pretentious** *(adj)* pretending to be important or better. *(s)* affected, exaggerated. *(ant)* down to earth.

5 **posh** *(adj)* elegant or luxurious and stylish. *(s)* superior, snobbish, grand, upmarket. *(ant)* downmarket, common.

6 **retaliate** *(v)* fight back. *(s)* react, reciprocate, repay, revenge, settle. *(ant)* accept, forgive, pardon.

7 **dismissive** *(adj)* showing something is unworthy of consideration. *(s)* indifferent, unconcerned. *(ant)* interested.

8 **slope** *(v)* sneak away quietly, typically to avoid work or duty. *(s)* leave, evade, creep, slink, steal.

9 **proclaim** *(v)* declare something or make oneself heard. *(s)* announce, state, affirm, assert. *(ant)* withhold, hide.

10 **fume** *(v)* feel or show great anger. *(s)* seethe, burn, smoulder, bristle, simmer, boil. *(ant)* beam, glow.

11 **peek** *(v)* look at quickly or secretively. *(s)* peep, glance, glimpse, gander. *(ant)* stare, overlook.

12 **ancient** *(adj)* in existence for a long time. *(s)* early, antique, olden, obsolete, archaic. *(ant)* contemporary, new.

13 **artefact** *(n)* a historical object or article made by a human. *(s)* item, piece, relic.

14 **intrigue** *(v)* arouse curiosity or interest. *(s)* fascinate, captivate, attract, enthral. *(ant)* bore, disenchant.

15 **excursion** *(n)* a trip taken (mostly) for pleasure. *(s)* journey, jaunt, outing, tour, expedition.

her phone. 'You're not ill, are you?' she asked.

'No. I've got a test, and I want to finish my book; it's brilliant. It's about these kids on **daredevil**[1] **quests**[2] who have to navigate really difficult …' Claire didn't bother to go on. Her mother was tapping out a message on her phone.

'Don't forget to do your homework, brainbox,' **taunted**[3] Pete from the sofa. 'With your beauty, you'll need all the brains you can get,' he joked.

Claire threw the wet towel at him and ran upstairs.

Being youngest meant Claire had the box room, but at least she didn't have to share with Becca. She loved her cosy den, now tidied and ordered. **Brimming**[4] with excitement, she pressed the blue **icon**[5] on her mum's tablet, and the familiar **chimes**[6] of Skype rang out. She didn't have her own phone yet, but her mum had **permitted**[7] her this one **luxury**[8], her own Skype account, so she could call her dad, Vince.

'Hi, Claire, darling. How are you? Your dad's not here; he's just popped to the corner shop.' Jayne's broad smile and twinkling **feline**[9] eyes sparkled at her on the screen. Her long blonde hair tumbled in easy, **luscious**[10] waves onto the shoulders of her **emerald**[11]-green blouse. It was easy to see why Dee had **dubbed**[12] her 'Princess'.

'Hi, Jayne. I'm on my mum's tablet, so I can't be long.'

'Are you excited about the **musical**[13] on Sunday?' asked Jayne.

'I can't wait! I can't sleep! I've read until late at night, but I still can't nod off,' she **gushed**[14].

---

1   **daredevil** *(adj)* dangerous and reckless. *(s)* bold, fearless, intrepid, adventurous, audacious, wild. *(ant)* staid.

2   **quest** *(n)* a long or difficult search for something. *(s)* mission, adventure, crusade, expedition, journey.

3   **taunt** *(v)* provoke or challenge someone. *(s)* criticise, mock, tease, goad, jibe, sneer, insult. *(ant)* compliment.

4   **brim** *(v)* be full of a particular feeling or quality. *(s)* burst, abound, overflow, swell, fill, teem. *(ant)* drain, empty.

5   **icon** *(n)* a symbol on a screen. *(s)* image, logo, emblem, representation, sign, badge, motif, insignia, design.

6   **chime** *(n)* a melodious ringing sound. *(s)* ring, clang, peal, ding, noise, tinkle.

7   **permit** *(v)* allow to do something. *(s)* approve, authorise, let, sanction, consent, OK, facilitate. *(ant)* forbid.

8   **luxury** *(n)* comfort, elegance or treat. *(s)* boon, bonus, indulgence, extra, amenity. *(ant)* necessity, austerity.

9   **feline** *(adj)* resembling a cat. *(s)* catlike, subtle, slinky, graceful, elegant, stealthy, sly.

10   **luscious** *(adj)* appealing to look at. *(s)* delectable, distinctive, exquisite, divine, luxurious. *(ant)* poor, awful.

11   **emerald** *(adj)* a rich bright green colour. *(s)* emerald green, pea green.

12   **dub** *(v)* give a nickname to. *(s)* designate, entitle, call, label, name, term, tag, style, knight.

13   **musical** *(n)* a play or film involving singing and dancing. *(s)* show.

14   **gush** *(v)* speak or write quickly and enthusiastically. *(s)* enthuse, effuse, pour, babble, admire. *(ant)* drawl.

'Do you need any help with your homework?' Jayne laughed.

'No, it's OK, thanks. We've got spelling tests tomorrow, so I'm learning for those.'

'See you on Sunday, then, and I'll say hello to your dad from you when he gets back.'

'I can't wait!' **chirped**[1] Claire. 'See you on Sunday.'

Bloop, the unmistakable Skype **jingle**[2] **warbled**[3], and in a puff of colourful **pixels**[4], Jayne vanished.

Claire put the tablet back into her mum's room. She'd clean her teeth later, after her snack. Surrounded by pages of spellings, a pile of books and a packet of **smuggled**[5] cheese-and-onion crisps to munch and **savour**[6], she snuggled into her squidgy quilt. She loved her bed.

'I'll get you fixed when I see my dad,' she **reassured**[7] a headless Wallace.

She set the alarm for 7.15 a.m., hoping it would still work.

Finally, feeling **conscientious**[8], she settled down to some **meaningful**[9] **study**[10]. But it didn't happen. Her crisps **fluttered**[11] from her hand, floating onto the carpet. Her book settled open onto her chest. Her lamp glowed softly as her **shallow**[12] breathing became deeper and deeper.

---

1   **chirp** *(v)* speak cheerfully. *(s)* cheep, squeak, twitter, pipe, sound, tweet. *(ant)* lament, groan.

2   **jingle** *(n)* a short, memorable verse, tune or slogan. *(s)* ditty, song, refrain, chorus, rhyme.

3   **warble** *(v)* make a trilling (chirping) or quavering (wobbling) birdlike sound. *(s)* sing, tweet, chirrup.

4   **pixel** *(n)* one of many minute areas of illumination on a display screen. *(s)* dot.

5   **smuggled** *(adj)* brought in secretly. *(s)* sneaked in, hidden, rustled, slipped, stolen.

6   **savour** *(v)* taste and enjoy, especially by lingering over eating it. *(s)* relish, appreciate. *(ant)* detest.

7   **reassure** *(v)* remove doubt and fear. *(s)* assure, comfort, soothe, cheer. *(ant)* discourage, unnerve, alarm.

8   **conscientious** *(adj)* working well and thoroughly. *(s)* hardworking, dutiful, diligent, attentive. *(ant)* careless.

9   **meaningful** *(adj)* serious and worthwhile. *(s)* significant, consequential. *(ant)* insignificant, meaningless.

10   **study** *(n)* time and attention spent on learning a subject. *(s)* revision, homework, work.

11   **flutter** *(v)* flap or wave. *(s)* float, waft, drift, sail, glide, flitter, fall, ripple.

12   **shallow** *(adj)* having little depth. *(s)* light, thin, slight, superficial, depthless. *(ant)* deep, significant, profound.

FRIDAY

2. The Note

Claire shot upright. Streaks of sunshine sneaked through the gaps in her curtains, **projecting**[1] sparkling **shards**[2] that shimmered onto the wall.

Why's my lamp on? What time is it? she thought, trying to shake the fuzzy **haze**[3] from her head.

It looked too light outside and sounded too quiet inside. **Bleary**[4]-eyed, she cocked her ear towards her door; the silence bothered her. She concentrated harder and listened for the **hectic**[5] **pandemonium**[6] of morning, only none came. Diving out of bed, Claire snatched her clock. She was shocked to see it had stopped, and for the first time in her young life, she'd overslept.

'Weird, I must have been tired last night; I didn't eat my crisps.'

She'd trodden on them with a loud crunch. In a horrible **tizzy**[7], hopping and brushing cheesy crumbs from between her toes, she threw on her crinkled uniform, cleaned her teeth and scooted downstairs. She hoped she wasn't extremely late. Surely someone would have called her before they left. She was normally **punctual**[8] and hated being late. **Astonished**[9], Claire came down to

---

1   **project** *(v)* cause light or shadow to fall onto a surface (sometimes creating an image). *(s)* cast.

2   **shard** *(n)* a piece of something broken, creating sharp edges or fragments. *(s)* sliver, splinter, spike.

3   **haze** *(n)* mental confusion. *(s)* mist, blur, fog, obscurity, fuzziness, cloudiness. *(ant)* clarity, clearness, lucidity.

4   **bleary** *(adj)* unfocused and dull from sleeping. *(s)* hazy, fuzzy, blurry, sleepy, groggy, unclear. *(ant)* lively, clear.

5   **hectic** *(adj)* busy or frantic. *(s)* boisterous, chaotic, confused, frenetic, feverish. *(ant)* calm, orderly.

6   **pandemonium** *(n)* noisy disorder and confusion. *(s)* chaos, bedlam, mayhem, uproar, tumult. *(ant)* calm, order.

7   **tizzy** *(n)* nervous excitement or agitation. *(s)* flap, state, panic, dither. *(ant)* calm, control, ease, cheer.

8   **punctual** *(adj)* on time. *(s)* prompt, dependable, accurate, timely, ready. *(ant)* late, tardy, unpunctual.

9   **astonished** *(adj)* greatly impressed or surprised. *(s)* astounded, amazed, dumbfounded. *(ant)* underwhelmed.

find a **deserted**[1] house, and clean dishes. The kitchen looked just as she'd left it last night.

That's a first, she thought.

Not a **trace**[2] of breakfast or scattered make-up. Amazed by the tidiness, she gulped down some icy milk and wiped her mouth on her jumper. Slamming down the glass, she guessed they'd forgotten to wake her and left for the day. They never failed to surprise her.

'They're a right load of selfish goons,' she complained out loud, gathering her schoolbooks, wishing she'd packed them last night.

Rubbing today's toothpaste, and now milk, off her sleeve, Claire found her Tangle Teezer, and with a couple of strokes, she **tamed**[3] her **unruly**[4] waves. She pulled her hair into a ponytail and grabbed her coat and bag. After going back upstairs, twice, she finally managed to leave the house. Nagged by an unwelcome prickle of **anxiety**[5], she slammed the door and, **uncharacteristically**[6], ran all the way to Ben's.

*

'Odd,' Claire puffed as she knocked again. No one answered. Ben had left for school without her. *That's weird. Why didn't he ring me at home when I didn't show up?* she thought, hurt.

Realising she had no idea of the time, she headed for school, sprinting through the graveyard and up to Gladys's house. Panting, she stopped at the gate. Jack and Thomas sat **abnormally**[7] still, side by side like two **allied**[8] **sentries**[9] guarding the entrance. Gladys wasn't in the garden, and her front door gaped wide open.

Where's Gladys and her washing? she wondered, **squinting**[10] up and down the street. It wasn't raining, and if Jack was in the garden, Gladys was always with him.

---

1   **deserted** *(adj)* abandoned or left empty. *(s)* vacated, unoccupied. *(ant)* inhabited, full, crowded, populous.

2   **trace** *(n)* a mark or object indicating the passing or existence of something. *(s)* evidence, sign, hint.

3   **tame** *(v)* control. *(s)* curb, restrain, temper, train, subdue, moderate. *(ant)* unleash, liberate.

4   **unruly** *(adj)* disorderly and uncontrollable. *(s)* wild, unmanageable, wilful. *(ant)* orderly, well behaved.

5   **anxiety** *(n)* worried and nervous feeling. *(s)* apprehension, unease, disquiet. *(ant)* calmness, reassurance.

6   **uncharacteristically** *(adv)* in an uncharacteristic (unusual) way. *(s)* strangely, unexpectedly. *(ant)* typically.

7   **abnormally** *(adv)* in an abnormal (unusual) way. *(s)* oddly, peculiarly, uncharacteristically. *(ant)* normally.

8   **allied** *(adj)* joined together, cooperative in a friendly manner. *(s)* connected, associated. *(ant)* unrelated, hostile.

9   **sentry** *(n)* a soldier placed to guard. *(s)* lookout, sentinel, patrol, watchman.

10   **squint** *(v)* look with one's eyes screwed up or partly closed. *(s)* scan, peer, peek, glance.

Distracted[1], she felt something silky swish her shins. Thomas's slinky black body **weaved**[2] around her legs, tickling them with his tail. Jack yelped a **high-pitched**[3] yap and spun round and round her feet in impossibly tight circles.

'What are you doing, Jacky Boy?' Claire laughed, ruffling his coat. 'Gladys?' she called. 'Gladys?' No one answered.

She poked her head around the front door. 'Gladys?' she shouted again, taking a **tentative**[4] step into the hall. She peeped into the little lounge; Gladys wasn't there. She stuck her head around the kitchen door; no **customary**[5] teapot sat on the table, only the usual scattering of newspapers and **miscellany**[6]. Uneasy, she searched the entire house. Her **brow**[7] crinkled into a **disconcerted**[8] frown. *Gladys wouldn't leave the animals, and her door wide open. Could she have gone out and fallen somewhere?* she wondered.

She checked the tiny backyard, but Gladys wasn't outside. She ran upstairs again in case she'd missed something.

Just about sliding down the **steep**[9] stairs in a **panic**[10], Claire remembered Gladys was the only person she knew who didn't have a phone. Back in the kitchen, she slowed to collect her thoughts. She wasn't sure what to do or where to go, and she realised she was trembling. **Fraught**[11], she tried to contain herself.

'What about the animals? I can't go to school and leave you two here,' Claire said to them both. 'Thomas, what are you doing up there, boy?' she asked with an **affectionate**[12] prod. He'd jumped onto the kitchen table, purring. 'Thomas, what is it?' she asked, frowning.

The jet-black cat pawed at the table and twirled non-stop, moving in a dizzying figure of eight

---

1   **distracted** *(adj)* with diverted attention. *(s)* sidetracked, preoccupied, disturbed. *(ant)* focused, attentive.

2   **weave** *(v)* twist and turn while moving to avoid obstructions. *(s)* wind, entwine, lace, intermingle.

3   **high-pitched** *(adj)* high in pitch or sound frequency. *(s)* screechy, shrill, piercing. *(ant)* low-pitched, deep.

4   **tentative** *(adj)* done without confidence. *(s)* cautious, hesitating, faltering, reluctant, unsure. *(ant)* sure, certain.

5   **customary** *(adj)* usual or typical. *(s)* expected, habitual, characteristic. *(ant)* unusual, uncharacteristic.

6   **miscellany** *(n)* a group or mixture of different items. *(s)* assortment, collection, array, variety. *(ant)* uniformity.

7   **brow** *(n)* the area on the head comprising (consisting of) the forehead and temples.

8   **disconcert** *(v)* unsettle or confuse. *(s)* agitate, perturb, confound, fluster, discombobulate. *(ant)* reassure.

9   **steep** *(adj)* sharply rising or falling slope. *(s)* sheer, bluff, precipitous, vertical, vertiginous. *(ant)* gentle, gradual.

10   **panic** *(n)* uncontrollable anxiety or fear. *(s)* fright, dread, alarm, consternation, horror. *(ant)* calm, self-control.

11   **fraught** *(adj)* stressed and extremely anxious. *(s)* tense, apprehensive, troubled, upset, uptight. *(ant)* calm.

12   **affectionate** *(adj)* showing fondness and tenderness. *(s)* warm, friendly, demonstrative, kind. *(ant)* cold, unkind.

as a **constant**[1] buzz hummed from his throat. **Compelled**[2] to look closer, she watched, puzzled, as he paced faster and faster, his loud purr almost sounding like a growl. His **almond**[3] eyes, shining yellow-green, **bored**[4] into hers.

What is he doing? she thought. 'Thomas, what is it? Are you OK?' But he didn't stop.

Was he trying to get her attention? Had Jack tried to do the same, yapping at the gate and chasing his tail? Were they waiting for her? Then she saw it. Thomas stopped pacing but scraped and scratched at some old magazines. Something **jutted**[5] out from underneath, his claws lifting the edge off the table.

'What is it, Tommy Boy?' Claire gently moved him to one side. Intrigued, she slid something out from underneath an old cooking magazine. A neat **buff**[6] envelope, beautifully handwritten, said 'To Claire'.

'What? It's addressed to me!' Shocked, she picked it up.

Thomas stopped his clawing and purring. He sat stock-still on the table, gazing at her.

Claire flipped the envelope over, feeling its heavy luxury in her hand. Stunned, she stared at it, nervous of its contents. **Reticently**[7] she fingered the envelope, her hand trembling. In one leap, Jack joined Thomas on the table, and now they both sat side by side, their shining eyes appealing for something.

'What?' she asked them, not expecting an answer.

Trying to control her **tremor**[8], she opened the envelope and took out a piece of paper. It felt similar to **fabric**[9], thick and **velvety**[10], the **frayed**[11] edges **tinged**[12] brown, giving it an aged, grand

---

1   **constant** *(adj)* continuing without stopping. *(s)* consistent, continuous, steady, perpetual. *(ant)* intermittent, brief.

2   **compel** *(v)* force or oblige someone to do something. *(s)* impel, make, drive, obligate.

3   **almond** *(n)* the edible oval seed of an almond tree, the shape of an almond. *(s)* oval.

4   **bore** *(v)* drill a hole into (often used figuratively). *(s)* stare, pierce, penetrate, burrow, mine.

5   **jut** *(v)* protrude (stick out from). *(s)* poke out, project, extend, overhang. *(ant)* indent, depress, recede.

6   **buff** *(adj)* yellowish-beige colour. *(s)* fawn, manila, camel, off-white.

7   **reticently** *(adv)* in a reticent (hesitant) way. *(s)* warily, reluctantly, cagily, guardedly. *(ant)* easily, confidently.

8   **tremor** *(n)* an involuntary shake (tremble). *(s)* flutter, quake, wobble, quiver, vibrate.

9   **fabric** *(n)* cloth. *(s)* fibre, material, textile, drapery.

10   **velvety** *(adj)* like velvet cloth. *(s)* soft, smooth, silky, downy, furry. *(ant)* rough, coarse, bumpy, uneven.

11   **frayed** *(adj)* unravelled or worn. *(s)* tattered, distressed, eroded, shredded, deteriorated.

12   **tinge** *(v)* tint with a certain colour or shade. *(s)* stain, shade, colour, pigment, dye.

air. She unfolded it **delicately**[1], as if it might crumble into pieces. An impressive swirl of black letters lay before her, **gloriously**[2] formed **script**[3] handwritten in ink.

My dearest Claire,

*Do not be alarmed by my **absence**[4]. Your sister, Rebecca, is in danger. You cannot tell the police or involve others, not even your mother. You must trust us, sweet Claire. If you do as I ask, you will not be **endangered**[5]. I know the **enormity**[6] of this request.*

*You will find a train ticket and instructions in this envelope. **Abide**[7] by them and I will be waiting for you. More will be explained then.*

*Bring Jack; leave Thomas at home. Close the doors and take all the money from my tin on the Welsh **dresser**[8].*

Do not discuss this.

Be brave, Claire; Jack will help you.

*Make **haste**[9], and Cadwaladr will watch over you.*

Yours,

Gladys.

She read it twice.

'Cadwaladr! What does she mean by "watch over you"? And why does everyone spell my surname wrong?'

---

1   **delicately** *(adv)* in a delicate (careful) way. *(s)* daintily, precisely, dexterously, deftly, adroitly. *(ant)* clumsily.

2   **gloriously** *(adv)* in a glorious (magnificent) way. *(s)* splendidly, superbly, wonderfully, grandly. *(ant)* plainly.

3   **script** *(n)* handwriting. *(s)* words, calligraphy, lettering, inscription, text, print, font.

4   **absence** *(n)* the state of not being at an occasion or a place. *(s)* absenteeism, nonattendance. *(ant)* presence, attendance.

5   **endangered** *(adj)* in danger. *(s)* jeopardised, risked, threatened, compromised. *(ant)* protected, guarded.

6   **enormity** *(n)* scale and seriousness. *(s)* extent, size, magnitude, significance. *(ant)* insignificance, triviality.

7   **abide** *(v)* follow or accept. *(s)* adhere to, stick to, observe, comply with. *(ant)* flout, reject, disobey.

8   **dresser** *(n)* a sideboard with shelves. *(s)* cupboard, tallboy, cabinet.

9   **haste** *(n)* speed or urgency, hurry. *(s)* swiftness, briskness, dash, alacrity, rapidity. *(ant)* slowness, delay.

Claire **scoured**[1] the letter again and read the instructions. What did it all mean? If Rebecca was in danger, where was Gladys now? Why had the letter been hidden? Was somebody playing a trick on her?

She'd seen TV shows where people played **hoaxes**[2] on others – was a camera crew **poised**[3] to jump out and film her? But Jack and Thomas *had* tried to get her attention, hadn't they? And now this unusual letter with odd language and instructions to catch a train to somewhere called Bangor. Maybe it was all a joke.

She walked over to Gladys's dresser and opened the tin, half hoping it would be empty, but it wasn't. Two large pink notes lay in the tin. She'd never seen or held a fifty-pound note before. One hundred pounds – she checked it twice.

She read the letter again. If Gladys had written it, why had she used funny descriptions, calling her 'sweet Claire'? And what did 'Cadwaladr watching her' mean? She'd seen Gladys's writing before, and she didn't write in these twirling swirls. It made no sense.

She stuffed the fifty-pound notes deep into her school backpack. Digging like a **frantic**[4] rabbit, **rummaging**[5] through the dresser drawer, she searched for a lead for Jack. The only thing she could find was huge and would have fit a wolfhound.

'It will have to do,' she said, **adjusting**[6] it to its minimum. 'We're going, boy.'

Gladys never used a lead for Jack – her constant shadow didn't need one. Even so, Claire wouldn't take chances on a train. She kissed Thomas on his soot-black nose and closed the door. She left the house, **staving off**[7] a **queasy**[8] **unease**[9] that threatened to send her running home. But she didn't go.

With the **baffling**[10] letter and train ticket zipped away in her pocket, Claire headed for the tram that would take her to Victoria station in Manchester city centre. Jack trotted along on

---

1   **scour** *(v)* look or search thoroughly. *(s)* scrutinise, study, review, inspect, read, revise, rifle. *(ant)* overlook.

2   **hoax** *(n)* a deception, trick or deceit. *(s)* joke, jest, prank, ruse, con, fraud, swindle.

3   **poised** *(adj)* prepared. *(s)* primed, placed, positioned, ready, set, briefed, assembled.

4   **frantic** *(adj)* incredibly scared, anxious or worried. *(s)* panicky, desperate, hysterical, frenzied. *(ant)* calm.

5   **rummage** *(v)* search untidily through something. *(s)* hunt, dig, ransack, forage, delve.

6   **adjust** *(v)* alter or move slightly to fit. *(s)* tailor, adapt, change, modify, vary.

7   **stave off** *(v)* put off or delay something bad. *(s)* prevent, avert, counteract, foil, halt. *(ant)* assist, encourage.

8   **queasy** *(adj)* feeling slightly sick (nauseous) or uneasy. *(s)* odd, unsettled, troubled. *(ant)* well, untroubled.

9   **unease** *(n)* want or lack of ease. *(s)* anxiety, angst, apprehension, dread, foreboding, jitters. *(ant)* calmness, ease.

10   **baffling** *(adj)* difficult to understand. *(s)* confusing, perplexing, bewildering, befuddling. *(ant)* comprehensible.

his **ridiculously**[1] large lead, not minding this new **restriction**[2] at all. Doubting whether he'd travelled on a tram or a train before, she wondered how he might react. However, right now, Jack on the tram was the least of her worries.

'What's going on, Jacky Boy?' Claire asked the little dog, for now her **sole**[3] **companion**[4]. The morning sun had disappeared, and the **gloomy**[5] sky darkened to a **brooding**[6], **dismal**[7] grey, threatening rain. *What time is it?* she wondered. Too quiet for the morning rush hour; there was not a single passer-by. The tram was a fair walk away, so she put her head down and **stomped**[8] down the long road, Jack's legs at a **nippy**[9] trot beside her.

Puffed and sweating, she reached the tram station. A narrow, quiet area led onto a long, bare platform.

'Oh no!' Claire took out the money and stared at it. 'How am I going to pay?' Ticket machines didn't take the large notes. The distant rumble of a tram came rattling down the line. Squinting towards the sound, a tiny **speck**[10] **loomed**[11] larger as the tram slowed, approaching the station.

'What should we do, Jack? I shouldn't travel without a ticket, but we can't miss this tram.'

As if in response, Jack pulled on his lead, and although small, he was surprisingly strong and **insistent**[12]. An **obstinate**[13] terrier, he was making it crystal clear to Claire what course of action he preferred – to jump straight on the tram.

'OK, Jack. If an inspector boards, I'll offer to pay him with a fifty-pound note and beg for his **pity**[14].'

---

1   **ridiculously** *(adv)* in a ridiculous (silly) manner. *(s)* absurdly, comically, laughably. *(ant)* sensibly, reasonably.

2   **restriction** *(n)* a limiting condition. *(s)* constraint, control, restraint, limitation. *(ant)* freedom, liberation.

3   **sole** *(adj)* one and only. *(s)* solitary, single, individual, lone, solo. *(ant)* numerous, many.

4   **companion** *(n)* someone one spends time with. *(s)* friend, acquaintance, ally, buddy, chum. *(ant)* foe, enemy.

5   **gloomy** *(adj)* dark and dismal. *(s)* bleak, dreary, overcast, grey, miserable, ominous. *(ant)* bright, clear, sunny.

6   **brooding** *(adj)* darkly menacing. *(s)* threatening, ominous, gloomy, heavy, dark, dismal. *(ant)* bright, cheerful.

7   **dismal** *(adj)* dark and dreary, causing gloom or depression. *(s)* miserable, gloomy, dull. *(ant)* bright, light, clear.

8   **stomp** *(v)* tread heavily. *(s)* stamp, clump, plod, clomp, trudge, crush. *(ant)* tiptoe.

9   **nippy** *(adj)* quick and nimble. *(s)* fast, speedy, rapid, swift, fleet, sprightly, lithe, deft, hasty. *(ant)* slow, plodding.

10   **speck** *(n)* a tiny dot or particle. *(s)* fleck, spot, blot, blob, scrap, jot. *(ant)* mass.

11   **loom** *(v)* appear vaguely from the distance. *(s)* emerge, materialise, emanate, show. *(ant)* recede, leave.

12   **insistent** *(adj)* demanding something, not refusing. *(s)* assertive, resolute, unrelenting. *(ant)* weak, relenting.

13   **obstinate** *(adj)* not changing one's mind easily. *(s)* stubborn, determined, adamant. *(ant)* compliant, submissive.

14   **pity** *(n)* sorrow for the misfortunes of others. *(s)* sympathy, compassion, understanding, mercy. *(ant)* cruelty.

Claire knew that all journeys should be paid for **prior to**[1] boarding, as fines could be **levied**[2] on the spot. She crossed her fingers and sat down in the empty carriage, Jack glued to her heel. The tram **clattered**[3] through the **outskirts**[4] and on into the **dense**[5] city. They reached Victoria station without meeting an inspector, much to Claire's relief. *Come to think of it, without any other company at all,* she realised.

She'd been to Victoria station before with her mother, and it had **teemed**[6] with people; the **commuters**[7] and shoppers must have been at home today, because an **eerie**[8] hush filled the station **concourse**[9].

'Well, that part was easy, Jack.'

She rubbed his head, checking she'd picked up her bag. A huge, **elevated**[10] noticeboard flashed unknown places, platform numbers and ever-changing **departure**[11] times. The instructions stated to change trains at a place called Crewe and then board another train to Bangor. Feeling more **confident**[12], she stood up tall, squared her shoulders and headed for the train.

After triple-checking she wouldn't end up in Scotland, Claire scooped up Jack and **clambered**[13] on board. She didn't want him slipping down the scary gap onto the tracks. Plopping him down on the seat next to her, she crinkled her nostrils in disgust. It smelled worse than her mum's greasy chips. The old train screamed out for a proper scrub; discarded hamburger boxes and crushed beer cans lay strewn across the floor. She pulled Jack's nose away from the smells that disgusted her but proved **irresistible**[14] to him.

---

1   **prior to** *(prep)* before or previous to. *(s)* in advance of, earlier than, ahead of. *(ant)* later than, after.

2   **levy** *(v)* impose a fine or tax. *(s)* demand, charge, collect, gather, place, set. *(ant)* remit.

3   **clatter** *(v)* make a continuous rattling sound. *(s)* clack, clank, jangle, clash, bump, hurtle, clang.

4   **outskirts** *(n)* the outer parts of a town or city. *(s)* bounds, border, edge, suburbs, fringes, peripheries. *(ant)* centre.

5   **dense** *(adj)* crowded together. *(s)* populous, crammed, packed, full, compressed. *(ant)* sparse, empty.

6   **teem** *(v)* be full of or swarming with. *(s)* brim, bustle, crawl, overflow, abound. *(ant)* disperse, empty.

7   **commuter** *(n)* a person who regularly travels some distance to work. *(s)* traveller.

8   **eerie** *(adj)* strange and scary. *(s)* spooky, creepy, weird, uncanny, peculiar, paranormal. *(ant)* normal, earthly.

9   **concourse** *(n)* a large, accessible and open area. *(s)* foyer, entrance, forecourt, walkway.

10   **elevated** *(adj)* raised or in a higher position. *(s)* heightened, lifted, hoisted, aloft. *(ant)* lowered, dropped.

11   **departure** *(n)* the moment of leaving or starting a journey. *(s)* parting, exodus, exit, removal. *(ant)* arrival.

12   **confident** *(adj)* feeling certain about one's abilities. *(s)* self-assured, self-reliant, assertive. *(ant)* insecure, timid.

13   **clamber** *(v)* climb or move awkwardly. *(s)* scale, mount, crawl, scramble, ascend.

14   **irresistible** *(adj)* hard to resist (must-have). *(s)* tempting, enticing, tantalising. *(ant)* unappealing, resistible.

'Come on, Jack, we're moving.'

Traipsing[1] through the train, they found a cleaner carriage and settled down into a forward-facing window seat. As the train pulled away, an **elderly**[2] woman strolled down the **aisle**[3] and sat opposite them. She smiled and took a **tatty**[4] book from a large shopping bag and thumbed through the pages. Claire, on **heightened**[5] **alert**[6], decided she seemed harmless, **allaying**[7] her fears a little.

No one else entered the carriage, although an odd little man was sitting a few rows behind the elderly woman, on the opposite side of the aisle. She'd not seen him earlier. Trying to disguise her **curiosity**[8], Claire pretended to adjust Jack's collar whilst sneaking a peek at the stranger.

He wore a **bulky**[9] suit, coarse and dark, its cut **formal**[10]. The faded **hue**[11] and black tie gave him the **funereal**[12] air of a **Dickensian**[13] **undertaker**[14]. She struggled to **avert**[15] her eyes from the snowy layer of **scaly**[16] **scalp**[17] flakes that dusted his shoulders.

Yuck! she thought, turning back to Jack.

The train quickened, rocking a repetitive rhythm on its **parallel**[18] tracks. Putting on a **casual**[19]

---

1   **traipse** *(v)* move reluctantly or in a tired manner. *(s)* trudge, plod, lumber, amble.

2   **elderly** *(adj)* ageing or old. *(s)* aged, retired, grey, mature, senior. *(ant)* young, youthful, childlike.

3   **aisle** *(n)* a passageway between rows of seats. *(s)* walkway, gangway, corridor, lane, gap.

4   **tatty** *(adj)* shabby and worn. *(s)* scruffy, ragged, frayed, dog-eared, moth-eaten. *(ant)* smart, spruce, tidy.

5   **heightened** *(adj)* increased. *(s)* intensified, strengthened, amplified, enhanced. *(ant)* lessened, reduced.

6   **alert** *(n)* the state of watching for possible danger. *(s)* vigilance, readiness, observance. *(ant)* inattentiveness.

7   **allay** *(v)* calm or diminish a fear or worry. *(s)* dispel, alleviate, assuage, relieve, mollify. *(ant)* stimulate, incite.

8   **curiosity** *(n)* a desire to know or learn. *(s)* inquisitiveness, interest, nosiness. *(ant)* apathy, indifference.

9   **bulky** *(adj)* large and unwieldy. *(s)* cumbersome, heavy, awkward, substantial, ungainly. *(ant)* light, manageable.

10   **formal** *(adj)* official in attitude or appearance. *(s)* conventional, stiff, prim. *(ant)* informal, unconventional.

11   **hue** *(n)* colour, tone or shade. *(s)* complexion, aspect, tinge, tint.

12   **funereal** *(adj)* characteristic of a funeral. *(s)* mournful, melancholy, sombre, solemn. *(ant)* cheerful, bright.

13   **Dickensian** *(adj)* like or portraying similarity to the time of Charles Dickens. *(s)* Victorian.

14   **undertaker** *(n)* a person who prepares the dead for funerals. *(s)* mortician, embalmer.

15   **avert** *(v)* turn away. *(s)* turn aside, look away, divert.

16   **scaly** *(adj)* flaking because of dryness. *(s)* peeling, crusty, scabby, encrusted, scaling. *(ant)* smooth.

17   **scalp** *(n)* the skin that covers the head (not the face).

18   **parallel** *(adj)* side by side, having equal distance between. *(s)* aligned, lateral, alongside. *(ant)* perpendicular.

19   **casual** *(adj)* unconcerned and relaxed. *(s)* informal, laid back, nonchalant, cool. *(ant)* tense, concerned.

air[1], she unzipped her pocket and took out the letter. Twisting her shoulder towards the window, she shielded it from view. The woman didn't look up from her book, but through the gaps in the headrests, had she seen the **dour**[2] man twitch, flicking his glance her way?

With a **stealthy**[3] hop, Jack sneaked closer, snuggling into the space between her thigh and the window. She hoped no one would complain.

Claire read the letter again. What danger could Rebecca possibly be in?

'You must trust us.' Who the heck was 'us'? She hoped for some answers.

As the **absurdity**[4] of her situation sank in, she prayed Gladys would be waiting. She put the letter away and numbly stroked Jack as the landscape flashed by, the **obscured**[5] view **unique**[6] to train travellers.

The city, where **mere**[7] centimetres separated **clusters**[8] of buildings, vanished behind her. **Disused**[9] railway arches became scrapyards piled high with mangled cars; **graffiti**[10] **masterpieces**[11] sprayed onto brick and concrete opened out into gardens. Did people ever get used to the clatter of train noise invading their homes? She supposed they did – after all, she didn't notice planes over Chorlton any more.

The **uniformity**[12] of row after row of **suburban**[13] housing **dispersed**[14], opening into **lush**[15] countryside, so different from home. Her **limbs**[16] relaxed, and she slid lower in her seat, Jack

---

1   **air** *(n)* a portrayal, quality, manner or impression. *(s)* appearance, aura, mood, tone, look.

2   **dour** *(adj)* unfriendly, gloomy or miserable. *(s)* sour, stern, severe, grim. *(ant)* kindly, friendly, cheerful.

3   **stealthy** *(adj)* done so as not to be seen or heard. *(s)* quiet, cautious, covert, surreptitious. *(ant)* blatant, overt.

4   **absurdity** *(n)* something ridiculous or very unreasonable. *(s)* illogicality, irrationality. *(ant)* logic, sensibleness.

5   **obscured** *(adj)* concealed, not able to be seen. *(s)* hidden, veiled, covered, blocked, unclear. *(ant)* clear, distinct.

6   **unique** *(adj)* unlike anything else. *(s)* exclusive, distinctive, particular, individual, one-off. *(ant)* common.

7   **mere** *(adj)* having no greater extent than, barely. *(s)* meagre, measly, only, sheer.

8   **cluster** *(n)* similar things bunched or occurring together. *(s)* group, array, bunch, collection. *(ant)* dispersal.

9   **disused** *(adj)* no longer in use. *(s)* empty, abandoned, derelict, deserted, neglected. *(ant)* occupied, in use.

10   **graffiti** *(n)* writings or drawings illicitly (without permission) done in public spaces. *(s)* doodle.

11   **masterpiece** *(n)* an outstanding piece of art or work. *(s)* classic, treasure, masterstroke.

12   **uniformity** *(n)* the state or quality of being consistent (the same). *(s)* regularity, sameness. *(ant)* inconsistency.

13   **suburban** *(adj)* characteristic of a suburb (outlying residential district of a city). *(s)* outskirt. *(ant)* central, urban.

14   **disperse** *(v)* distribute, spread or scatter over a wide area. *(s)* separate, diffuse, dissipate. *(ant)* assemble.

15   **lush** *(adj)* (of grass) growing luxuriantly. *(s)* green, verdant, abundant, thriving, flourishing, fertile. *(ant)* barren.

16   **limb** *(n)* an arm, leg or wing. *(s)* appendage, member, offshoot.

cuddling in closer to her thigh.

After a short while, a low **gurgling**[1] noise bubbled from below, interrupting the **hypnotic**[2] rumble of a train on tracks. **Mortified**[3] and **initially**[4] thinking it was Jack growling, Claire realised it was her stomach grumbling.

How **embarrassing**[5]*!* she **cringed**[6] as her cheeks reddened and her temperature rose. She concentrated hard on the scene beyond the window, hoping the other passengers **assumed**[7] the sound was coming from Jack as he dreamed. The milk she had gulped earlier was long since **digested**[8], and now **ravenous**[9], she **fantasised**[10] about food.

Will do me the world of good to wait, Claire decided **stoically**[11] as her stomach rumbled on.

'Care for a nice sandwich, cariad?' the old woman asked Claire. 'They don't serve snacks on this train. You won't be able to buy food until Crewe,' she added, offering out a neat package wrapped in crisp greaseproof paper.

What did she call me? thought Claire. Her mouth watered as the woman **unveiled**[12] a bulging **wedge**[13] of bread. Jack's ears pricked upright. Wriggling closer to her outstretched hand, his nose twitched in **anticipation**[14].

Should I take it? agonised Claire. She hadn't talked to anyone other than Jack. Must she **abstain**[15], even from this **charitable**[16] old lady? She pictured Snow White and the poisoned apple.

---

1   **gurgling** *(n)* a hollow bubbling sound. *(s)* burble, murmur, rumble, splosh, slosh, ripple.

2   **hypnotic** *(adj)* making one feel sleepy (soporific). *(s)* mesmerising, rhythmic, repetitive. *(ant)* invigorating.

3   **mortified** *(adj)* embarrassed or ashamed. *(s)* humiliated, degraded, shamed, humbled. *(ant)* pleased, gratified.

4   **initially** *(adv)* at first, to begin with, at the start. *(s)* originally, firstly, primarily. *(ant)* finally, lastly, eventually.

5   **embarrassing** *(adj)* causing awkwardness or shame. *(s)* humiliating, mortifying, degrading. *(ant)* dignifying.

6   **cringe** *(v)* shiver inwardly with embarrassment or disgust. *(s)* wince, squirm, blush, recoil.

7   **assume** *(v)* suppose something to be the case without prior proof. *(s)* presume, think, believe. *(ant)* doubt.

8   **digest** *(v)* break down (food) in the body. *(s)* process, absorb, consume, burn, convert.

9   **ravenous** *(adj)* very hungry. *(s)* famished, starving, insatiable, rapacious, wanting. *(ant)* full, sated, satiated.

10   **fantasise** *(v)* daydream about something. *(s)* imagine, visualise, hallucinate, muse.

11   **stoically** *(adv)* in a stoic (tolerant) way. *(s)* tolerantly, coolly, enduringly, calmly, patiently. *(ant)* responsively.

12   **unveil** *(v)* reveal or uncover. *(s)* disclose, display, open, unwrap, divulge, expose, show. *(ant)* conceal, cover.

13   **wedge** *(n)* a solid piece, often triangular. *(s)* segment, hunk, chunk, sliver, slice, block. *(ant)* whole.

14   **anticipation** *(n)* the action of expecting something to happen. *(s)* expectation, hope.

15   **abstain** *(v)* stop oneself from doing or enjoying something. *(s)* cease, forgo, refrain. *(ant)* continue, accept.

16   **charitable** *(adj)* generous in giving to those in need. *(s)* altruistic, kind, benevolent. *(ant)* uncharitable, mean.

Abstinence[1] not being her **forte**[2], she hesitated for only a second, **relenting**[3] easily, her hunger **prevailing**[4] as she took the sandwich. Not wishing to appear **ungrateful**[5], she murmured a quiet thank-you, hoping a lightning **bolt**[6] wouldn't shoot from above and strike her where she sat.

Biting into the fresh, **succulent**[7] sandwich, she convinced herself the letter hadn't mentioned offerings of food from **generous**[8] people, and even if it had, she no longer cared. She was guilty but **famished**[9], so her stomach **invariably**[10] won the war. After all, Jack had **scoffed**[11] the piece she'd sneaked down to him without hesitating, and he would protect her, wouldn't he? As she sighed with pleasure at every mouthful, she thought it might be the **finest**[12] sandwich she'd ever tasted. Forgetting all fear of poisoning, she accepted the offer of a second and, to **alleviate**[13] her guilt, shared it with Jack.

Finishing the tasty lunch, Claire relaxed a **mite**[14] and rested her head against the window. She had no idea where Crewe or Bangor were. The woman opposite spoke with an unusual accent, and they were deep in the countryside. One of her classmates holidayed in Wales most summers – had she mentioned Bangor and something about a bridge to an island?

She smiled down at Jack. He'd rolled flat out onto his side, and his nose wiggled as he dozed.

The butty worked for you too, didn't it, boy? she thought, allowing herself a smile. *And thank goodness my stomach has shut up!*

---

1   **abstinence** *(n)* the action of restraining or not allowing oneself. *(s)* moderation, avoidance. *(ant)* excess, indulgence, greed.

2   **forte** *(n)* a great strength, something one excels at. *(s)* strong suit, speciality, thing. *(ant)* weakness, failing.

3   **relent** *(v)* give in to something. *(s)* capitulate, acquiesce, surrender, yield, concede, weaken. *(ant)* stand firm.

4   **prevail** *(v)* be superior or more powerful. *(s)* beat, win, succeed, triumph, dominate. *(ant)* fail, lose.

5   **ungrateful** *(adj)* not showing or feeling thanks. *(s)* unappreciative, churlish, rude. *(ant)* grateful, appreciative.

6   **bolt** *(n)* a jagged flash of lightning. *(s)* thunderbolt, thunderstroke, shaft.

7   **succulent** *(adj)* moist and tasty. *(s)* juicy, delicious, mouth-watering, yummy, lush, fresh. *(ant)* dry, unappetising.

8   **generous** *(adj)* eager to give (often pertaining to money). *(s)* kind, charitable, giving. *(ant)* mean, stingy.

9   **famished** *(adj)* very hungry. *(s)* ravenous, starving, underfed, unfed, empty, hollow. *(ant)* full, sated, satiated.

10   **invariably** *(adv)* on each occasion. *(s)* always, habitually, consistently, regularly. *(ant)* occasionally, erratically.

11   **scoff** *(v)* eat greedily and quickly, gobble food down. *(s)* guzzle, devour, bolt, wolf. *(ant)* nibble, pick.

12   **finest** *(adj)* best. *(s)* premium, top, quality, superior, supreme, deluxe, handpicked, optimum. *(ant)* worst.

13   **alleviate** *(v)* make a problem or suffering less severe. *(s)* ease, lessen, assuage, relieve. *(ant)* aggravate, worsen.

14   **mite** *(n)* a small amount. *(s)* tiny bit, little, dash, touch, tad, smidgen, mote. *(ant)* lot, loads, tons, heaps.

A full tummy and warm carriage worked like a sleeping **draught**[1]. Heavy and **leaden**[2], her eyelids closed, and she drifted off into tranquil peace … for about one **miserly**[3] second, until her dribble-soaked chin flopped against her chest and she jolted upright, hoping no one had seen. Flushing, she **fumbled**[4] around in her bag, pretending to fish something out, and quickly rubbed the slobbery **saliva**[5] from her chin.

How gross! she thought, cringing again, ashamed to lift her head out of her bag but wanting to laugh at the same time.

Sitting up, afraid of missing her stop, Claire tried to avoid eye contact with the woman but couldn't help snatching **curious**[6] **glimpses**[7]. The woman hadn't spoken again, and the odd man behind her faced blankly towards the window.

Still uncertain of the time, she guessed they'd travelled for an hour or so when the train slowed into Crewe station. Without looking at the woman, she grabbed her bag and left the carriage with a dozy Jack. She'd almost forgotten Gladys's letter and why she'd been in the warm, comfortable carriage, but as she stepped off the train, the **burden**[8] of it **jarred**[9] again.

Crewe was an **average**[10]-sized station, and Claire easily **located**[11] the platform for Bangor. Her train left in ten minutes, at 3.30 p.m.; at last she knew what time it was. It felt much later than the afternoon to her.

Finding an empty bench, she sat with Jack, opened her book and took a long gulp of water from her school bottle. But Claire was too distracted to read. She was putting her book away when two boys sat down beside her. Pulling Jack closer, she moved along the bench.

'Don't recognise that school uniform,' the boy next to her said, looking her up and down.

---

1   **draught** *(n)* liquid with medicinal properties. *(s)* medicine, dose, dosage, potion, elixir.

2   **leaden** *(adj)* heavy like lead. *(s)* weighty, sleepy, dragging, slow, laboured, sluggish. *(ant)* light, lively.

3   **miserly** *(adj)* small and inadequate. *(s)* meagre, piddling, paltry, mean, derisory, miserable. *(ant)* generous.

4   **fumble** *(v)* move the hands about clumsily. *(s)* scrabble, feel, search, root, dig, rummage.

5   **saliva** *(n)* watery liquid (spit) secreted from the mouth. *(s)* spittle, dribble, slaver, drool, slobber.

6   **curious** *(adj)* eager to learn or know something. *(s)* inquisitive, snooping, prying. *(ant)* apathetic, indifferent.

7   **glimpse** *(n)* a quick or partial view of something. *(s)* peep, flash, sight, peek, glance, shufti, look. *(ant)* stare.

8   **burden** *(n)* something that causes worry, hardship or distress. *(s)* problem, weight, affliction. *(ant)* relief.

9   **jar** *(v)* shock or disturb slightly. *(s)* shake, jolt, hit, rattle, irritate, disturb, perturb. *(ant)* appease, please.

10   **average** *(adj)* ordinary or standard. *(s)* normal, typical, regular, mediocre, middling. *(ant)* extraordinary.

11   **locate** *(v)* find the exact position or place of. *(s)* track down, detect, establish, discover, pinpoint. *(ant)* lose.

'Where you from?' the other one joined in.

Caught off guard by their **overfamiliarity**[1], Claire didn't answer.

'Where are you going?' the closest boy asked. 'And why have you got a dog with you?' he said, leaning nearer to her. Their questions felt too **probing**[2].

He was older than her and **encroaching**[3] on her **personal**[4] space. Unsure how to react, she pretended she hadn't heard.

'Sorry?' she asked, buying some time. They were about Rebecca's age, and their **audacious**[5] **manner**[6] alarmed her.

'Where are you going?' the boy closest repeated.

Claire was used to the likes of Becca and Drane, but outnumbered here, and without Ben for backup, she quickly decided to act **coy**[7] and just gave a small smile as **reserved**[8] **acknowledgement**[9] of him.

'Cat got your tongue?' he said, **shifting**[10] even closer.

Jack stiffened against her calf and growled.

'It's OK, boy,' she said automatically, but knew it wasn't.

Out of the corner of her eye, she spotted the elderly woman from the train.

'There's my grandma,' she said, grabbing her bag and standing up. 'Oh, and by the way, my dog bites,' she added, **striding**[11] off towards the woman as the train pulled into the station.

Ignoring what the letter had said, Claire marched straight up to her. 'Let me help you with that bag,' she offered. She hoped those boys weren't right behind her. She hoped they weren't getting the train to Bangor.

---

1   **overfamiliarity** *(n)* an inappropriately informal manner. *(s)* immodesty, presumption. *(ant)* formality, reserve.

2   **probing** *(adj)* enquiring closely (nosy). *(s)* invasive, prying, personal, impertinent. *(ant)* restrained, discreet.

3   **encroach** *(v)* advance gradually but beyond acceptable limits. *(s)* intrude, infringe, invade. *(ant)* respect.

4   **personal** *(adj)* affecting or belonging to a certain person (yours). *(s)* own, private, intimate, special. *(ant)* public.

5   **audacious** *(adj)* daring and bold or showing a lack of respect. *(s)* brave, overconfident. *(ant)* reticent, respectful.

6   **manner** *(n)* the way in which something happens or is done. *(s)* conduct, behaviour, demeanour.

7   **coy** *(adj)* making a pretence of modesty or shyness. *(s)* bashful, timid, evasive, demure, reserved. *(ant)* brazen.

8   **reserved** *(adj)* slow to reveal opinions or emotions. *(s)* reticent, aloof, unfriendly, diffident. *(ant)* outgoing.

9   **acknowledgement** *(n)* recognition or acceptance. *(s)* admission, appreciation, awareness. *(ant)* denial.

10   **shift** *(v)* move. *(s)* budge, shuffle, swing, relocate, drift, alter, deviate, change.

11   **stride** *(v)* walk in long marching steps. *(s)* tread, stomp, pace, pound, stamp. *(ant)* dawdle, drag, shuffle.

'Thank you, cariad,' said the woman as Claire lifted her bag onto the train, Jack hopping up behind her.

Plonking herself down by a window, Claire felt a surprising comfort as the woman sat opposite her again, smiling. Claire returned a **brief**[1] grin, then looked away, **discouraging**[2] conversation and feeling **a tad**[3] guilty at only having helped her in order to **dupe**[4] the boys.

The woman's features vaguely reminded her of someone. As the empty train pulled away, Claire **racked her brains**[5], sure she knew her yet unable to place her. She patted the seat, and Jack jumped up. Relieved there was no sign of the two boys, she relaxed a little.

✳

Claire's head whacked the window, and she woke **disorientated**[6]. They had stopped at a station with an **unpronounceable**[7] name – Penmaenmawr. Convinced it was Welsh, she sat up, amazed she'd nodded off, and **niggled**[8] because Jack lay opposite her with the woman, his head resting on her lap.

'Are you all right, Jack?' He belonged to her today, and Claire made sure this woman knew it. She patted the seat beside her, and he hopped right back. Wide awake now, she began to worry whether Gladys would be at the station. This whole **scenario**[9] was **insane**[10] and **increasingly**[11] scary.

What am I doing here? she thought. Doubt hit her even harder.

As the journey continued, Claire enjoyed the unfamiliar and **sedate**[12] **rural**[13] views. Snaking

---

1   **brief** *(adj)* not lasting for long. *(s)* short, fleeting, momentary, swift, temporary, passing. *(ant)* lasting, lengthy.

2   **discourage** *(v)* persuade against an action. *(s)* dissuade, deter, prevent, curb, oppose, stop. *(ant)* encourage.

3   **a tad** *(adv)* by a small amount or extent. *(s)* a touch, somewhat, slightly. *(ant)* profoundly, considerably.

4   **dupe** *(v)* deceive and trick. *(s)* fool, hoodwink, mislead, cheat, delude, beguile, bamboozle, con.

5   **rack one's brains** *(v)* make an effort to think or remember. *(s)* concentrate, think hard.

6   **disorientated** *(adj)* confused. *(s)* confounded, thrown, puzzled, baffled. *(ant)* clear, lucid.

7   **unpronounceable** *(adj)* difficult to say. *(s)* unsayable, unutterable, inexpressible. *(ant)* pronounceable.

8   **niggled** *(adj)* slightly irritated. *(s)* bothered, troubled, worried, annoyed. *(ant)* at ease, alleviated, appeased.

9   **scenario** *(n)* a development of events. *(s)* situation, state, set-up, consequence, circumstance.

10   **insane** *(adj)* foolish, mad and irrational. *(s)* crazy, idiotic, irresponsible, senseless. *(ant)* sensible, rational.

11   **increasingly** *(adv)* more and more. *(s)* gradually, progressively, mountingly. *(ant)* less, decreasingly.

12   **sedate** *(adj)* unhurried and tranquil. *(s)* quiet, peaceful, calm, placid, serene. *(ant)* boisterous, busy.

13   **rural** *(adj)* of the countryside. *(s)* agricultural, rustic, idyllic, provincial, bucolic. *(ant)* metropolitan, urban.

into a dim tunnel, the train snatched the scenes away, and she marvelled at how this **subway**[1] carved its way through the rock, **dissecting**[2] the side of the mountain. **Emerging**[3] on the other side, she saw **undulating**[4] hills, dotted with grazing sheep, rising to her left, and the **choppy**[5] blue-green sea stretching all the way to the **horizon**[6]. The **glorious**[7] sights lifted her **spirits**[8], and for a second, she forgot her **predicament**[9]. It felt like the first week of the summer holidays. The sun and Penmaenmawr reminding her of a British holiday town, run-down yet inviting in a bed-and-breakfast kind of way.

The mountains and the sea occupied the view for the rest of the journey. **Unbeknown**[10] to Claire, sighting the Isle of Anglesey and its smaller neighbour, Puffin Island, was a sure sign her arrival in the Welsh city of Bangor was **imminent**[11].

As the train crawled into Bangor station, Claire **peered**[12] through the window, looking for Gladys, but couldn't see her.

'Come on, Jack.' She clicked her tongue and tugged his lead. Looking down at him to avoid saying goodbye to the woman, she grabbed her belongings and left.

As she **disembarked**[13], a fresh, salty breeze whipped up the platform, and shivering, she zipped her coat against the chill. Scanning everywhere for Gladys, she noticed all the signs were written in Welsh and English.

'*Diolch*, cariad,' said the ticket collector as Claire passed between the **barriers**[14], flashing her ticket.

---

1   **subway** *(n)* a tunnel under a road or underground. *(s)* underpass, passageway, channel. *(ant)* overground, flyover.

2   **dissect** *(v)* cut up or through something. *(s)* divide, separate, part, disjoin. *(ant)* combine, connect, join.

3   **emerge** *(v)* move out of or through something. *(s)* appear, arise, arrive, surface. *(ant)* disappear, submerge.

4   **undulating** *(adj)* rising and falling. *(s)* rolling, wave-like, flowing, swelling, heaving. *(ant)* flat, level.

5   **choppy** *(adj)* having small, rough waves. *(s)* shifting, ripply, uneven, irregular. *(ant)* smooth, regular, flat.

6   **horizon** *(n)* the place where the surface of the earth and the sky appear to meet. *(s)* skyline.

7   **glorious** *(adj)* striking and beautiful. *(s)* magnificent, superb, splendid, wonderful. *(ant)* dull, awful, atrocious.

8   **spirit** *(n)* feelings and mood. *(s)* emotion, attitude, air, energy, enthusiasm, morale, heart.

9   **predicament** *(n)* a difficult or embarrassing situation. *(s)* dilemma, crisis, plight. *(ant)* walkover, doddle.

10   **unbeknown** *(adj)* without having knowledge of. *(s)* unknown, undetermined, undiscovered. *(ant)* known.

11   **imminent** *(adj)* about to happen. *(s)* pending, expected, looming, forthcoming, likely, immediate. *(ant)* remote.

12   **peer** *(v)* look with concentration. *(s)* stare, scrutinise, gaze, scan, focus, examine, study, rake. *(ant)* glance.

13   **disembark** *(v)* leave (usually some form of transport). *(s)* alight, land, arrive, get off. *(ant)* embark, board.

14   **barrier** *(n)* an obstacle to prevent movement through or across. *(s)* obstruction, boundary, limit.

Acknowledging him with a bob of her head, she sighed, relieved Jack hadn't needed a ticket after all.

'Cariad' – had the woman said that on the train? she wondered, still hunting for Gladys. She couldn't find her anywhere.

'Where's the way out, Jack?' Claire asked the terrier, scouring the station. 'Come on, boy, it's this way,' she said, answering her own question and tugging his lead towards the exit.

As they were leaving, she almost bumped into someone **straying**[1] into her path. She ducked sideways, shocked to realise it was the same man who had sat behind the old lady **en route**[2] to Crewe. Ignoring him, she stared straight ahead, striding on, pretending to know her route. Her skin had **bristled**[3] as he'd brushed by, and for a moment, she thought he was heading for her. **Unnerved**[4], she **heaved**[5] an **audible**[6] sigh of relief as she headed away from him. Then she saw the two boys from the bench, and they *were* heading straight towards her.

Making an about-turn, Claire hoped there was another exit. The station was emptying, and the ticket collector had gone. She ran back through an open barrier and along the platform towards some steep stairs leading to a bridge that **spanned**[7] the tracks. Not daring to look back, but hearing the boys' quickening footsteps behind her, she took the stairs two at a time. She sprinted across the bridge and ran down the stairs on the other side, leaping down the last four in one – Jack in tow.

Panic-stricken[8] and **smothering**[9] the **urge**[10] to cry, she tried to gain her **bearings**[11]. Then suddenly Jack pulled so hard on his lead that she lost her grip and let go of him. Off balance, Claire stumbled around to see the woman from the train bent over and petting a wildly **enthusiastic**[12]

---

1   **stray** *(v)* wander or roam. *(s)* drift, meander, err, swerve, deviate, diverge, digress, turn.

2   **en route** *(adv)* on the way. *(s)* on the road, on the move, on the journey.

3   **bristle** *(v)* recoil or react defensively. *(s)* stiffen, prickle, shiver, flinch, object, blench. *(ant)* calm.

4   **unnerved** *(adj)* made to lose confidence or courage. *(s)* alarmed, daunted, flustered. *(ant)* calm, encouraged.

5   **heave** *(v)* produce (a sigh). *(s)* breathe, exhale, emit, utter, huff, puff, billow.

6   **audible** *(adj)* able to be heard. *(s)* detectable, discernible, noticeable, clear, distinct. *(ant)* inaudible.

7   **span** *(v)* cross or extend from side to side. *(s)* bridge, cover, traverse, connect, link. *(ant)* disconnect, unlink.

8   **panic-stricken** *(adj)* affected by panic. *(s)* scared, frightened, anxious, alarmed. *(ant)* calm, confident.

9   **smother** *(v)* suppress a feeling. *(s)* stifle, oppress, choke, quash, restrain, conceal. *(ant)* express, show.

10   **urge** *(n)* a sudden or strong impulse or desire. *(s)* need, wish, compulsion, appetite. *(ant)* disinclination, dislike.

11   **bearing** *(n)* direction or position. *(s)* heading, orientation, location, course.

12   **enthusiastic** *(adj)* eager. *(s)* keen, excited, fervent, animated, exuberant. *(ant)* apathetic, indifferent.

Jack, whose **traitorous**[1] tail wagged **furiously**[2]. Claire glanced around, weak with relief, but the boys had gone. Maybe they weren't chasing her after all, and she'd **overreacted**[3] because she was alone. She wouldn't usually feel so threatened by two teenage boys.

The lady spoke in what Claire assumed was Welsh, because the one word she understood was 'Jack'. Speechless, she watched as he sprang **comically**[4] on all fours, **lapping**[5] his wet tongue over the woman's face.

Unhurried, the woman straightened and smiled at Claire.

'Hello, Claire. My name is Anwen, and I am the sister of Gladys.'

'What?' Claire stepped back, stunned. Trying to **absorb**[6] this, she **stuttered**[7], 'What are you talking about? Where's Gladys?' she demanded.

The lady carried on smiling at her, Jack's tail still whirring in frantic circles.

'See how Jack welcomes me, Claire,' replied the woman. 'He knows me.'

'Hang on. Gladys hasn't got a sister. She'd have told Ben and me if she did. We'd have met her,' **contradicted**[8] Claire.

'Do you think a dog as **intuitive**[9] as Jack would welcome me like this?' the woman asked gently. 'Would he have slept by me, Claire? He wouldn't have taken my food, nor would he have let you take it either if I **intended**[10] harm, cariad,' she added.

Claire frowned, **stumped**[11] by a happy Jack. Far from **fickle**[12], he wouldn't take to just anyone.

---

1   **traitorous** *(adj)* characteristic of a traitor (disloyal person). *(s)* two-faced, false, duplicitous. *(ant)* faithful, loyal.

2   **furiously** *(adv)* in a furious (energetic) manner. *(s)* energetically, feverishly, frantically. *(ant)* slowly, calmly.

3   **overreact** *(v)* respond more forcibly or emotionally than needed. *(s)* overdramatise, overplay. *(ant)* underplay.

4   **comically** *(adv)* in a funny or amusing way. *(s)* hilariously, entertainingly. *(ant)* seriously, solemnly.

5   **lap** *(v)* slurp and move the tongue like an animal drinking. *(s)* lick, slosh, swill, slap.

6   **absorb** *(v)* take in and understand. *(s)* assimilate, follow, comprehend, get. *(ant)* miss, misunderstand.

7   **stutter** *(v)* struggle to say one's words. *(s)* stammer, splutter, falter, mumble, hesitate. *(ant)* enunciate.

8   **contradict** *(v)* deny the truth, assert the opposite. *(s)* oppose, counter, dispute, refute. *(ant)* agree, confirm.

9   **intuitive** *(adj)* tending to use one's feelings to judge. *(s)* instinctive, insightful, discerning. *(ant)* non-intuitive.

10   **intend** *(v)* plan to do or have. *(s)* try, mean, aim, expect, attempt, propose.

11   **stump** *(v)* cause to be at a loss. *(s)* baffle, bewilder, confuse, confound, mystify. *(ant)* clarify, explain.

12   **fickle** *(adj)* often changing one's feelings or affections. *(s)* changeable, indecisive, erratic. *(ant)* constant, stable.

He was a **seasoned**[1] judge of character, **engaging**[2] both his nose and brain. Her **resolve**[3] melted away, unveiling a surprised relief. What choice did she have? She had to trust this woman, for now.

'Shall we go?' The woman turned, **gesturing**[4] to the exit.

Claire followed, expecting to be led to a car or a bus stop. **Astounded**[5], she stopped. In the road stood a beautiful pony **harnessed**[6] to a **rickety**[7] wooden **trap**[8]. The horse's long tail swished towards a thickset, **grim**[9]-faced man sitting in the front on a thin bench seat, holding the **reins**[10]. **Plumes**[11] of smoke puffed and **billowed**[12] from a **stout**[13] pipe held between his lips; he neither moved nor spoke. **Thunderstruck**[14], Claire's mouth fell open, and stayed open.

'Jack will sit with Gwilym,' said the woman, nodding towards the miserable-looking man as he gathered the reins. Then, with a **nimble**[15] hop, the woman climbed up into the trap like it was her usual **mode**[16] of transport and sat behind the man.

Jack pulled away, his lead slipping from Claire's hand and dangling behind him. Much to Claire's astonishment, he jumped up and sat upright on the **stern**[17] man's lap, ready to go. The old woman held out a hand to Claire, who struggled to climb up. Claire plonked down onto the hard bench, leaving as much distance as possible between herself and the woman. She was

---

1   **seasoned** *(adj)* experienced and accustomed to certain conditions. *(s)* veteran, expert. *(ant)* inexperienced.

2   **engage** *(v)* put into use. *(s)* employ, enlist, appoint, involve, draw from. *(ant)* disengage.

3   **resolve** *(n)* firm determination. *(s)* firmness, resolution, steadfastness, tenacity, doggedness. *(ant)* indecision.

4   **gesture** *(v)* move (usually the head or hand) to express something. *(s)* gesticulate, signal, nod.

5   **astounded** *(adj)* shocked or greatly surprised. *(s)* amazed, astonished, stunned, stupefied. *(ant)* unimpressed.

6   **harness** *(v)* yoke (attach) to a harness to pull something. *(s)* connect, bind, hitch. *(ant)* unharness, detach.

7   **rickety** *(adj)* likely to collapse, poorly manufactured. *(s)* wobbly, unstable, unsound. *(ant)* reliable, sound.

8   **trap** *(n)* a two-wheeled carriage pulled by a pony or horse. *(s)* cart, gig, hansom.

9   **grim** *(adj)* serious or gloomy. *(s)* stern, dour, severe, surly, morose, unkind. *(ant)* kind, pleasant, cheerful.

10   **rein** *(n)* a long, narrow strap used when leading, guiding or riding a horse. *(s)* lead.

11   **plume** *(n)* a long puff of smoke. *(s)* trail, cloud, curl, spiral, column.

12   **billow** *(v)* move or flow outwards with undulating motions. *(s)* undulate, puff, balloon, rise, waft.

13   **stout** *(adj)* heavily built. *(s)* strong, solid, big, sturdy, robust, heavy-duty. *(ant)* flimsy, thin, slight.

14   **thunderstruck** *(adj)* shocked or surprised. *(s)* astonished, incredulous, flabbergasted. *(ant)* unsurprised.

15   **nimble** *(adj)* light and quick in movement. *(s)* agile, sprightly, lithe, deft, lissom. *(ant)* awkward, clumsy.

16   **mode** *(n)* the usual way or manner of something. *(s)* kind, method, means, type, fashion.

17   **stern** *(adj)* serious and strict. *(s)* severe, firm, formidable, dour, uncompromising. *(ant)* cheerful, lenient.

neither **amenable**[1] to nor trusting of these people, yet.

The woman reached down and took out a thick, colourful blanket from her **voluminous**[2] bag.

'We'll put this over our feet and knees, cariad.' She spread it out over them both and tucked it snugly under their legs. 'Gets a bit **draughty**[3], so it does, especially on the bridge.'

Claire **appreciated**[4] the **instant**[5] warmth seeping through to her legs under the rug.

'Welsh lambswool **woven**[6] with the finest quality **mohair**[7], there's nothing that works better to warm you through,' the woman patted her knees, smiling.

The miserable man, who until now had not uttered a peep, **scowled**[8], mumbled something **inaudible**[9] followed by a loud tut, then unhooked Jack's **oversized**[10] lead and collar. With a look of **disdain**[11], he dropped them both onto the floor in the back of the trap, shouted, 'Yarrhhh, Lady!' and tapped the long reins against the pony's athletic round **rump**[12]. With a jerk, they were off, trotting forward into the complete unknown, Jack standing on the man's lap, nose in the air, his proud figure at the **helm**[13].

---

1   **amenable** *(adj)* responsive and open. *(s)* agreeable, cooperative, willing, biddable. *(ant)* stubborn, unwilling.

2   **voluminous** *(adj)* having much fabric, loose and full. *(s)* ample, spacious, roomy. *(ant)* slight, lacking, small.

3   **draughty** *(adj)* cold due to currents of cool air. *(s)* chilly, breezy, windy, gusty, blowy. *(ant)* cosy, warm.

4   **appreciate** *(v)* recognise and be grateful for. *(s)* welcome, acknowledge, enjoy, cherish. *(ant)* disparage.

5   **instant** *(adj)* happening at once. *(s)* immediate, rapid, swift, prompt, direct, instantaneous. *(ant)* gradual.

6   **weave** *(v)* interlace thread to form cloth (past participle: *woven*). *(s)* intertwine, interweave. *(ant)* unravel.

7   **mohair** *(n)* a yarn or fabric made from the hair of the angora goat mixed with wool.

8   **scowl** *(v)* frown in an angry way. *(s)* glare, glower, disapprove, lour, grimace. *(ant)* smile, approve, praise.

9   **inaudible** *(adj)* unable to be heard. *(s)* hushed, imperceptible, muffled, indistinct. *(ant)* audible, perceptible.

10   **oversized** *(adj)* larger than the usual size. *(s)* enormous, jumbo, whopping, massive. *(ant)* mini, undersized.

11   **disdain** *(n)* the feeling that something is unworthy of respect. *(s)* contempt, derision, scorn. *(ant)* admiration.

12   **rump** *(n)* the hind part or backside of a mammal. *(s)* rear, bottom, behind, beam, buttocks.

13   **helm** *(n)* a position of leadership (the front). *(s)* command, reins, controls.

3. An Old Betrayal

The **colossal**[1] man driving the trap remained silent, staring **steadfastly**[2] ahead with his **canine**[3] co-driver. He clucked an occasional sound **encouraging**[4] the pony's pace to pick up, but nothing more.

His **sculpted**[5], **chiselled**[6] features glowed a **ruddy**[7] red, and his hands, the size of shovels, were tinged a purple hue in the chilly air. His Roman nose jutted out from his face at a proud angle above weathered skin mapped with **intricate**[8] veins and **craggy**[9] **etchings**[10]. His full mouth and lips **divulged**[11] no **emotion**[12]. Claire guessed he might be a farmer; his **tweed**[13] clothes and flat cap looked well-worn and in need of a wash. Despite his frayed **attire**[14], he exuded an **indescribable**[15]

---

1   **colossal** *(adj)* exceptionally large or great. *(s)* gargantuan, immense, huge, mammoth. *(ant)* little, small.

2   **steadfastly** *(adv)* in a steadfast (firm) way. *(s)* unwaveringly, persistently, staunchly. *(ant)* weakly, irresolutely.

3   **canine** *(adj)* relating to or like a dog. *(s)* doggy, doggish, doglike, dogly, hound-like.

4   **encourage** *(v)* persuade or support. *(s)* urge, push, spur, excite, boost, goad. *(ant)* dissuade, discourage.

5   **sculpted** *(adj)* well shaped, like a good sculpture. *(s)* chiselled, carved, angled, defined. *(ant)* uncarved.

6   **chiselled** *(adj)* strongly and clearly defined (as if carved with a chisel). *(s)* rugged, carved. *(ant)* undefined.

7   **ruddy** *(adj)* having a reddish colour to the face. *(s)* blooming, florid, flush, rosy, bronzed. *(ant)* pale.

8   **intricate** *(adj)* detailed and complicated. *(s)* complex, labyrinthine, elaborate, obscure. *(ant)* plain, simple.

9   **craggy** *(adj)* rugged and rough but in an attractive sort of way. *(s)* weathered, lined. *(ant)* smooth, even.

10   **etching** *(n)* an engraving or carving on a surface. *(s)* mark, impression, imprint, inscription, score, scratch.

11   **divulge** *(v)* make known. *(s)* disclose, reveal, show, exhibit, tell, confess. *(ant)* conceal, hide, protect.

12   **emotion** *(n)* one's feelings, mood or mental state. *(s)* sentiment, reaction, sensation.

13   **tweed** *(n)* a rough cloth (originating from Scotland) flecked with colours.

14   **attire** *(n)* clothes. *(s)* clothing, dress, outfit, apparel, garb, garments, wardrobe.

15   **indescribable** *(adj)* too difficult or unusual to describe. *(s)* indefinable, intense, powerful. *(ant)* definable.

air. Claire imagined he'd **tolerate**[1] little nonsense. Jack hadn't **budged**[2] an inch from this solid man's lap during the entire journey.

Claire's **equine**[3] experience **amounted to**[4] nothing, yet she found this **unforeseen**[5] ride **exhilarating**[6]. The pony's coat was the colour of Victorian red brick, yet gleamed as richly as a **buffed**[7], polished chestnut. A muscular, arched neck held a proud, pretty head crowned **nobly**[8] by a long sandy mane. This soft cream trim matched the silken tail, whose flowing ribbons of hair billowed in the wind. **Soothed**[9] by the simple rhythmic clip-clop of hooves on the road, her spirits lifted a touch.

So much nicer than cars, she thought as the trap bumped along the deserted road. *But where are* all the cars? she wondered. It struck her that none had overtaken them. *How weird! Is Wales always this quiet?* she asked herself.

The road narrowed; a **sinister**[10] dusk fell as **gnarled**[11], twisted trees lined and **canopied**[12] their way. The trap's wheels sank into deep **potholes**[13], squirting sloppy mud up the sides, spraying the passengers. Claire rubbed at her mouth, spitting out specks of gritty dirt.

As quickly as it had narrowed, the road widened and eased. She stretched her cold, stiff fingers, **kneading**[14] some life back into her creaky white knuckles. Without moving her head, she swivelled her eyes and sneaked a **furtive**[15] glance at the two strangers. What she'd missed on

---

1   **tolerate** *(v)* put up with or allow to happen. *(s)* endure, stand, abide, accept, sanction. *(ant)* forbid, stop.

2   **budge** *(v)* move a small amount. *(s)* inch, nudge, dislodge, shift, stir.

3   **equine** *(adj)* relating to horses. *(s)* equestrian, horsey.

4   **amount to** *(v)* come to a total of. *(s)* tally, constitute, total, equal, number.

5   **unforeseen** *(adj)* not predicted, expected or anticipated. *(s)* surprising, unanticipated. *(ant)* foreseen.

6   **exhilarating** *(adj)* causing thrill or excitement. *(s)* animating, invigorating, uplifting. *(ant)* depressing, boring.

7   **buffed** *(adj)* polished until smooth, shining or gleaming. *(s)* brushed, shiny, burnished, glossy. *(ant)* unpolished.

8   **nobly** *(adv)* in a noble (grand) way. *(s)* splendidly, majestically, magnificently, stately. *(ant)* humbly.

9   **soothe** *(v)* gently calm or quieten. *(s)* allay, alleviate, assuage, mollify, console. *(ant)* aggravate, exacerbate.

10   **sinister** *(adj)* indicating imminent misfortune. *(s)* ominous, eerie, menacing. *(ant)* unthreatening, auspicious.

11   **gnarled** *(adj)* twisted and knobbly, usually with age. *(s)* knotted, contorted, deformed. *(ant)* straight, smooth.

12   **canopy** *(v)* cover with a canopy (of trees). *(s)* enclose, shroud, blanket. *(ant)* expose, open.

13   **pothole** *(n)* a hole in the surface of a road. *(s)* cavity, crater, depression, gap, pocket.

14   **knead** *(v)* squeeze and massage with the hands. *(s)* blend, press, mix, work, rub, mould, manipulate.

15   **furtive** *(adj)* secret or sneaky. *(s)* stealthy, clandestine, sly, surreptitious, cautious, covert. *(ant)* overt.

the train became **blatantly**[1] obvious: the **resemblance**[2] between Gladys and this woman, Anwen, her sister. Jack perched on the man's knee, seeming so content Claire felt certain he'd done this before.

Then, catching her unaware, the road narrowed again, **veering**[3] a **precipitous**[4] curve to the right, then to the left, thrusting her sideways. She held tight, stopping herself from spilling out over the trap's side. The pony's shoes skidded on the road, and sparks flew as the metal struck stone. Without warning, the tight, steep **zigzag**[5] then **plateaued**[6] to reveal a **vast**[7] structure of grey metal and stone.

What? Where did that come from? thought Claire as an **imposing**[8] bridge **towered**[9] before them, **majestically**[10] spanning what looked like a huge river. She **ogled**[11] in wonder, absorbing the beauty as they trotted across the open and **exposed**[12] **expanse**[13], the wind whipping in wild gusts past their heads.

'Hold on to the blanket, Claire,' Anwen said, pushing **flyaway**[14] **strands**[15] of grey hair from her forehead. 'It gets blowy up here.'

Claire's head whirled from side to side, **desperate**[16] to take in the splendid **vista**[17]. She gasped, marvelling at the dark, threatening water swirling below her as the rush of salty wind **buffeted**[18]

---

1 **blatantly** *(adv)* in a blatant (obvious) way with no shame. *(s)* flagrantly, manifestly, palpably. *(ant)* furtively.

2 **resemblance** *(n)* similarity to something or someone else. *(s)* likeness, congruity, closeness. *(ant)* dissimilarity.

3 **veer** *(v)* suddenly change direction. *(s)* turn, depart, deviate, diverge, divert, swerve.

4 **precipitous** *(adj)* steep, sheer or high. *(s)* abrupt, dizzying, lofty, vertical, arduous. *(ant)* gentle, flat, gradual.

5 **zigzag** *(n)* a course with alternate right and left turns. *(s)* wiggle, squiggle. *(ant)* straight.

6 **plateau** *(v)* flatten or level out. *(s)* even, straighten, smooth, plane. *(ant)* undulate, bump, roughen.

7 **vast** *(adj)* large or immense. *(s)* enormous, broad, extensive, colossal, huge, gigantic. *(ant)* small, insignificant.

8 **imposing** *(adj)* impressive, striking and grand in appearance. *(s)* commanding, monumental. *(ant)* modest.

9 **tower** *(v)* soar above, rise or reach to a great height. *(s)* dominate, ascend, overlook. *(ant)* descend, decline.

10 **majestically** *(adv)* in a majestic (grand) manner. *(s)* resplendently, magnificently, imposingly. *(ant)* humbly.

11 **ogle** *(v)* stare admiringly at something. *(s)* eyeball, observe, watch, gawk, gaze, goggle, gawp.

12 **exposed** *(adj)* bared to the elements (weathered). *(s)* unprotected, open, unsheltered. *(ant)* sheltered.

13 **expanse** *(n)* a stretch or wide area of something. *(s)* span, breadth, width, distance, reach. *(ant)* enclosure.

14 **flyaway** *(adj)* light, airy and difficult to control. *(s)* unruly, unmanageable. *(ant)* manageable, controlled.

15 **strand** *(n)* a single or thin lock of hair (also pertaining to thread or fibre). *(s)* string, wisp.

16 **desperate** *(adj)* having a great desire or need. *(s)* eager, raring, bursting, impatient. *(ant)* loath, reluctant.

17 **vista** *(n)* a lovely view. *(s)* panorama, outlook, scene, landscape, perspective.

18 **buffet** *(v)* strike or batter against. *(s)* pound, clobber, pummel, whack, bash.

against the steel that supported this **feat**[1] of **engineering**[2]. The beautiful curves and arches of this road bridge stood in **stark**[3] **contrast**[4] to the **industrial**[5], **functional**[6] lines of the railway bridge adjacent. It was so stunningly **scenic**[7] she wished she could capture it on a postcard to Ben. All too soon they had reached the end, and straining her neck, she turned back, savouring one last look as the memorable scene melted from view.

'Don't worry, I'm sure you'll cross the Menai Bridge again,' smiled Anwen. 'Below is the Menai Strait, and now we are on Ynys Môn. That is the Welsh for "Anglesey", cariad,' smiled Anwen.

Claire frowned. *There's that odd word again. Maybe it's Welsh for 'Claire',* she thought.

She didn't much care right now as she **inhaled**[8] the fresh air and, **momentarily**[9] **banishing**[10] her **woes**[11], enjoyed the journey. The roads were still deserted, not like in Chorlton, where traffic crawled and constantly **queued**[12]. They were trotting gently along a wide, straight stretch surrounded by **acres**[13] of flat green fields when the idyllic peace was interrupted by the distant sound of **accelerating**[14] engines.

Short-lived[15] *peace,* thought Claire as she heard the **whine**[16] of **revving**[17] motorbikes in the distance. Thinking nothing more of it, she soaked up the **scenery**[18], ignoring the two people in

---

1   **feat** *(n)* a great achievement requiring courage, skill or strength. *(s)* accomplishment, deed, effort. *(ant)* failure.

2   **engineering** *(n)* the design and manufacture of complex structures. *(s)* construction, fabrication, architecture.

3   **stark** *(adj)* sharply clear. *(s)* crisp, distinct, obvious, sheer, blatant, glaring. *(ant)* indistinct, ambiguous.

4   **contrast** *(n)* a difference in comparison. *(s)* distinction, contradiction, opposition, disparity. *(ant)* similarity.

5   **industrial** *(adj)* relating to industry, appearing to be functional and manufactured. *(s)* technical. *(ant)* domestic.

6   **functional** *(adj)* practical and useful rather than attractive. *(s)* utilitarian, unadorned. *(ant)* impractical, ornate.

7   **scenic** *(adj)* pretty, impressive or beautiful (of scenery or views). *(s)* picturesque, charming, lovely. *(ant)* unsightly.

8   **inhale** *(v)* breathe in. *(s)* suck in, respire, smell, gulp, snort, sniff, gasp. *(ant)* exhale, breathe out.

9   **momentarily** *(adv)* for a moment in time. *(s)* fleetingly, briefly, temporarily. *(ant)* indefinitely, permanently.

10   **banish** *(v)* get rid of. *(s)* dismiss, dispel, eject, eliminate, eradicate, exclude, isolate, exile. *(ant)* accept, allow.

11   **woe** *(n)* great distress, misery or sorrow. *(s)* anguish, burden, despair, gloom, misfortune. *(ant)* happiness, joy.

12   **queue** *(v)* wait in a line. *(s)* line up, queue up, file, stream.

13   **acres** *(n)* a large expanse or quantity of something. *(s)* large extent, vast expanse, great estate.

14   **accelerate** *(v)* increase speed. *(s)* quicken, hasten, escalate. *(ant)* decelerate, slow.

15   **short-lived** *(adj)* lasting a brief time. *(s)* fleeting, ephemeral, momentary, transient. *(ant)* long-lasting.

16   **whine** *(n)* a high-pitched, unpleasant sound. *(s)* drone, hum, whir.

17   **rev** *(v)* increase engine speed by accelerating. *(s)* race, roar, scream. *(ant)* decelerate.

18   **scenery** *(n)* natural and picturesque features of a landscape. *(s)* surroundings, backdrop, setting, panorama.

the trap. She would talk when Gladys appeared. For now, she remained **resolutely**[1] **mute**[2].

'Yarrhhh, Lady!' barked the man **brusquely**[3] at the pony, his tone commanding.

The trap **lurched**[4] as the pony's pace increased. Anwen tucked the blanket further under her knees, then gripped the side of the trap with one hand, and the bench seat with the other. Jack jumped down from the front, disappearing somewhere under the man's feet.

Why the sudden hurry? thought Claire. She glanced at the sky; it didn't look like rain, and neither of them had **indicated**[5] a need to rush, but they were rattling fast along the flat stretch now. No wonder Jack had taken cover – he'd have been **catapulted**[6] off the front seat at this rate.

The clattering of hooves became drowned out by the sound of two motorbikes that had caught up behind the trap. Too proud to **overrule**[7] her **self-imposed**[8] speech ban, Claire frowned, glancing sideways at Anwen as both bikes then accelerated alongside. Fully expecting them to overtake, Claire hoped they'd get on with it. The bikes puffed out **noxious**[9] fumes, and the high-pitched **thrum**[10] of the engine noise was increasingly annoying.

Fully **moulded**[11] helmets and black **visors**[12] **concealed**[13] the bikers' faces; judging by their build, Claire reckoned they were male. She'd seen lads like this racing around on similar types of off-road scrambling bikes at home, and she thought they were **immature**[14] too.

Just get going, you pair of show-offs, she thought as they continued revving their engines, riding even closer. But they weren't moving forward or overtaking. They drove **precariously**[15]

---

1   **resolutely** *(adv)* in a resolute (firm) manner. *(s)* steadfastly, staunchly, stubbornly, decisively. *(ant)* irresolutely.

2   **mute** *(adj)* remaining speechless. *(s)* silent, voiceless, taciturn, dumb, wordless, quiet. *(ant)* vocal, speaking.

3   **brusquely** *(adj)* in a brusque (rude or off-handed) manner. *(s)* tersely, abruptly, gruffly, roughly. *(ant)* gently.

4   **lurch** *(v)* move in an abrupt, unsteady or uncontrolled way. *(s)* jerk, lean, reel, falter.

5   **indicate** *(v)* mention, show, suggest or point out. *(s)* signify, display, announce, demonstrate. *(ant)* conceal.

6   **catapult** *(v)* hurl, propel or launch (as if from a catapult). *(s)* shoot, throw, project, toss, slingshot.

7   **overrule** *(v)* use one's authority to reject or disallow something. *(s)* overturn, override, reverse. *(ant)* allow.

8   **self-imposed** *(adj)* imposed on or done to oneself. *(s)* chosen, voluntary, self-inflicted. *(ant)* enforced.

9   **noxious** *(adj)* harmful, poisonous or unpleasant. *(s)* toxic, deadly, lethal, foul. *(ant)* harmless, pleasant.

10   **thrum** *(n)* a continuous humming sound. *(s)* hum, vibration, drone, whir, whine, buzz.

11   **moulded** *(adj)* formed or cast into a shape using malleable (bendable) material. *(s)* fashioned, shaped, sculpted.

12   **visor** *(n)* the movable part of a helmet, pulled down to cover and protect the face. *(s)* mask, shade.

13   **conceal** *(v)* hide or disguise. *(s)* screen, shroud, cloak, cover, camouflage, obscure, veil. *(ant)* reveal, uncover.

14   **immature** *(adj)* undeveloped, childish or infantile. *(s)* young, puerile, adolescent, juvenile. *(ant)* mature.

15   **precariously** *(adv)* in a precarious (unstable) way. *(s)* shakily, unsteadily, perilously. *(ant)* securely, steadily.

close alongside the trap, and Claire saw the bikes didn't have number plates.

'Yarrhhh, Lady!' **bellowed**[1] the man again, and the pony broke into what Claire assumed was a gallop. They shot forward at such speed that Claire was **thrust**[2] against the back of the trap, and she, too, like Anwen, gripped its sides and the bench's edge.

The thundering of hooves **pounding**[3] the road, the roar of the bikes' engines and the swerving trap were scary. Suddenly they were **hurling**[4] along the road so fast Claire feared she would fall out. Assuming a horse could never **outrun**[5] a motorbike, she **jammed**[6] her foot against the side of the trap and **hunkered**[7] down as best she could. But the bikes stayed alongside, almost **ramming**[8] into the trap with a **precision**[9] that showed their riders were obviously not a couple of **joyriding**[10] **juveniles**[11].

Deciding to break her silence, Claire shouted to Anwen, 'What's happening?' but her voice was lost in the **tumult**[12]. The woman was crouched over, like Claire, clinging on for what seemed like dear life. The trap shook and rattled so much Claire felt it might fall apart and **disintegrate**[13] at any moment, **ejecting**[14] them into the road and the direct path of the motorbikes.

'Stop!' she screamed at the top of her voice. 'Stop!' She didn't know who she was screaming at, whether it was the man driving the trap or the motorbikes, but she screamed **regardless**[15]. She was too scared to cry. This couldn't end well; she thought she was going to die.

Suddenly, out of nowhere, an ear-splitting noise roared through the air around and above

---

1   **bellow** *(v)* shout loudly and deeply. *(s)* holler, bark, roar, cry, yell. *(ant)* whisper.

2   **thrust** *(v)* advance or move with force. *(s)* push, throw, chuck, jam, shove, force, propel. *(ant)* pull.

3   **pound** *(v)* hit heavily and repeatedly. *(s)* beat, batter, hammer, clobber, pummel.

4   **hurl** *(v)* impel or throw with force. *(s)* fling, heave, lob, launch, pitch, dash, fire. *(ant)* hold, catch.

5   **outrun** *(v)* escape from, run faster than. *(s)* elude, flee, excel, outpace, outclass, beat, exceed. *(ant)* lose.

6   **jam** *(v)* force into a position or space. *(s)* cram, thrust, ram, press, stuff, wedge, squash. *(ant)* free, release.

7   **hunker** *(v)* crouch down or squat low. *(s)* bend, cower, dip, duck, hunch, huddle. *(ant)* straighten, face.

8   **ram** *(v)* crash into something. *(s)* bump, butt, hit, collide, strike, slam, pound, impact. *(ant)* retreat.

9   **precision** *(n)* an instance of exactness or preciseness. *(s)* accuracy, exactitude, sureness. *(ant)* inaccuracy.

10   **joyriding** *(n)* the act of driving dangerously in a stolen car for enjoyment. *(s)* carjacking, speeding, hijacking.

11   **juvenile** *(n)* a young person. *(s)* adolescent, teenager, youth, minor, youngster, kid. *(ant)* adult, senior.

12   **tumult** *(n)* a confused and loud noise. *(s)* commotion, chaos, disturbance, maelstrom, furore. *(ant)* peace.

13   **disintegrate** *(v)* break into small parts or fragments. *(s)* crumble, shatter, dismantle. *(ant)* combine, integrate.

14   **eject** *(v)* forcibly expel in a sudden or violent way. *(s)* fire, evict, discharge, banish. *(ant)* accept, inject.

15   **regardless** *(adv)* not caring about the circumstances or outcomes. *(s)* anyway, nevertheless.

them, **decibels**[1] louder than the screaming motorbikes. A sound so **invasive**[2], so loud, it **reverberated**[3] through the trap. The noise was excruciating. Her ears hurt so much she tried to shield them with her arms whilst still holding on to the **careering**[4] trap.

The thunderous roar came over her head again, **soaring**[5] and fading so quickly above her. Even when she managed a peek, she barely caught sight of what it was. But it was flying; it was fast; and it made the loudest noise she'd ever heard.

Rigid[6], **tense**[7] and frozen with fear, Claire didn't initially feel the trap easing slightly as the pony's gallop slowed to a canter, then, in turn, slowed to a fast trot. She couldn't hear where the motorbikes were, because the noise rumbling around the sky was still too deafening.

Her ears were ringing like **pealing**[8] bells when she felt a prodding in her right side. She ignored it at first; then she realised she was no longer being flung around in her seat. The noise in the sky had faded off into the distance, and she saw the motorbikes were gone. The prodding became a gentle shake, and she slowly lifted her head to see Anwen looking concerned and gently holding her by the arm.

Reeling[9], Claire tried to make sense of what had just happened. The pony was sweating, and Jack was back at the helm. They hadn't travelled that far, because they were still moving along the straight expanse of road where the bikes had **harassed**[10] them. There wasn't a house in sight, and the road was **flanked**[11] on both sides by flat fields, but to their **immediate**[12] right, Claire saw a huge industrial-looking building surrounded by large tarmacked areas. She wasn't sure what it was, maybe some sort of **warehouse**[13]. *Could it be a runway?* she thought.

---

1   **decibel** *(n)* a unit to measure the intensity of sound (loudness).

2   **invasive** *(adj)* intruding undesirably (difficult to ignore). *(s)* intrusive, persistent. *(ant)* non-invasive, restrained.

3   **reverberate** *(v)* repeat as an echo or pulsating vibration. *(s)* resonate, resound, ring, rebound.

4   **career** *(v)* move in a quick, uncontrolled manner. *(s)* hurtle along, race, tear, gallop, dash, rush. *(ant)* dawdle.

5   **soar** *(v)* climb or fly rapidly above usual levels. *(s)* ascend, escalate, rise. *(ant)* decline, descend, plummet.

6   **rigid** *(adj)* not flexible, unable to be bent. *(s)* stiff, inflexible, firm, unbending. *(ant)* floppy, flexible, pliable.

7   **tense** *(adj)* unable to relax due to tension, rigid or tight. *(s)* edgy, stressed, overwrought, anxious. *(ant)* relaxed.

8   **peal** *(v)* ring (of a bell or bells). *(s)* chime, clang, sound, reverberate, resound, resonate, ding.

9   **reel** *(v)* feel bewildered and shocked. *(s)* falter, lurch, wobble, shake, spin, stagger. *(ant)* steady, stabilise.

10   **harass** *(v)* pressure, intimidate or trouble someone. *(s)* annoy, pester, bother, badger, hassle. *(ant)* help.

11   **flank** *(v)* be on each side or on one side of. *(s)* border, edge, skirt, fringe, line, verge.

12   **immediate** *(adj)* next to or nearest in space or time. *(s)* direct, near, close, nearby. *(ant)* distant, far.

13   **warehouse** *(n)* a large storage building for materials. *(s)* depot, repository, storehouse.

'Whoa!' the man barked unexpectedly. They were approaching what looked like a railway level crossing, only there were no train tracks leading from them. Warning lights on both sides of the road were flashing **intermittently**[1] red.

'Whoa, Lady,' he grunted, pulling the horse to a **halt**[2] before the flashing lights. The pony snorted, shifting impatiently on the spot, awaiting her next command.

'Stand, Lady, stand,' said the man.

'Have your ears recovered?' Anwen asked.

Claire nodded, poking inside both ears with her **index fingers**[3].

'What was all that about?' blurted Claire. 'Who was chasing us, and where have they gone, and what the heck was flying around, making that noise?'

'Get ready to stick your fingers in your ears again, cariad,' Anwen said. 'You'll soon see.'

The now-familiar noise rumbled deep in the distance. If Claire hadn't known better, she'd have **sworn**[4] it was thunder.

As the waves of sound grew louder, Claire glanced at the trap's **occupants**[5], then at the flashing lights in front of them. The direction of the noise was difficult to **pinpoint**[6], seeming to constantly change **orientation**[7], but as it came nearer, Claire turned to her left to see a black dot in the distance. Within seconds, she could see it was a black fighter jet.

'What the …?' mouthed Claire, sealing her ears with her fingers as the noise grew louder.

Jack stood on the man's lap; the pony didn't **flinch**[8], but her ears flattened backwards. Anwen's hands were now clamped over her ears. The jet was about one hundred metres away and, Claire reckoned, only about one hundred metres high but still **descending**[9] towards them. As it neared, she could see it wasn't going to hit them but was only metres out in front of them. It was so close

---

1   **intermittently** *(adv)* in an intermittent (not continuous) way. *(s)* sporadically, alternatingly. *(ant)* constantly.

2   **halt** *(n)* an abrupt stop. *(s)* standstill, pause, cessation, stand, freeze, break, wait, rest. *(ant)* continuation.

3   **index finger** *(n)* the first finger (the one next to the thumb). *(s)* pointer, forefinger, indicator.

4   **swear** *(v)* promise something is the case (past participle: *sworn*). *(s)* vow, affirm, proclaim, attest, declare.

5   **occupant** *(n)* a person who resides (exists) in a place. *(s)* incumbent, inhabitant, resident.

6   **pinpoint** *(v)* identify or find with accuracy and precision. *(s)* locate, isolate, determine, place. *(ant)* lose.

7   **orientation** *(n)* direction or position in relation to something. *(s)* placement, bearing. *(ant)* disorientation.

8   **flinch** *(v)* shy away from instinctively. *(s)* move, withdraw, twitch, recoil, start, baulk, wince. *(ant)* stand firm.

9   **descend** *(v)* move or fall downwards. *(s)* plunge, dip, swoop, dive, plummet. *(ant)* ascend, climb.

the **force**[1] and **vibration**[2] of its power **resonated**[3] and reverberated right through her.

The jet was **magnificent**[4], like a giant **streamlined**[5] bird of **prey**[6]. Almost **skimming**[7] the flashing lights, it **decelerated**[8], flying in front of them and right across the road towards what must be a runway on their right. The jet was so close Claire could see the pilot's helmet through the **cockpit**[9] glass. As it flew past, the pilot raised his right arm and **saluted**[10] at the trap. Then the jet briefly touched its wheels down onto the vast tarmac runway, before the forward thrust of engines roared into life, and it lifted straight back off, up into the sky.

In **awe**[11], and still **partially**[12] deafened by the now-**decreasing**[13] engine noise, Claire watched the jet's **rear**[14] flashing white tail light as it disappeared into the distance. At that moment, the red warning lights in front of them stopped flashing, and the man slapped the reins onto the pony's **rear**[15], and they were off again at a fast trot, as if nothing had happened.

'What was *that* all about?' demanded Claire directly of Anwen. 'That was mad. What just happened?' she asked, not giving Anwen time to answer. 'Where did that plane come from? Did it scare those motorbikes off?' Claire stared at Anwen, not realising she was waiting for her to stop speaking.

'Yes, Claire, it did. It came to help us. We have **dependable**[16] friends.'

'Friends? Friends in fighter jets? How did they even know to come? We're in the middle of nowhere.'

---

1   **force** *(n)* energy or strength from physical action. *(s)* brunt, clout, feel, dynamism, effort. *(ant)* weakness.

2   **vibration** *(n)* an instance of vibrating (shaking or trembling). *(s)* tremor, shuddering, throb. *(ant)* stillness.

3   **resonate** *(v)* (of a sound) cause to prolong, echo or resound. *(s)* reverberate, vibrate, oscillate.

4   **magnificent** *(adj)* spectacular, impressive and awesome. *(s)* superb, superlative, brilliant. *(ant)* unimpressive.

5   **streamlined** *(adj)* designed to reduce air (or water) resistance. *(s)* aerodynamic, sleek, slick. *(ant)* cumbersome.

6   **prey** *(n)* an animal that is hunted and killed by another for food. *(s)* quarry, game, kill. *(ant)* predator, hunter.

7   **skim** *(v)* pass over (a surface) nearly or lightly touching it. *(s)* glide, graze, brush, glance.

8   **decelerate** *(v)* reduce speed, slow down. *(s)* brake. *(ant)* accelerate, increase, speed up.

9   **cockpit** *(n)* a compartment for a pilot. *(s)* flight deck.

10   **salute** *(v)* raise the hand to the head formally in recognition. *(s)* acknowledge, greet, wave. *(ant)* shun.

11   **awe** *(n)* respect and wonderment. *(s)* admiration, amazement, surprise. *(ant)* contempt, indifference.

12   **partially** *(adv)* to a partial (limited) extent. *(s)* partly, somewhat, moderately. *(ant)* completely, totally.

13   **decrease** *(v)* become smaller or fewer. *(s)* lessen, reduce, dwindle, diminish, decline, subside. *(ant)* increase.

14   **rear** *(adj)* placed at the back part of something. *(s)* posterior, hind, aft. *(ant)* front, fore, anterior.

15   **rear** *(n)* backside. *(s)* hindquarters, buttocks, rump, behind, butt. *(ant)* front, fore, forepart.

16   **dependable** *(adj)* reliable and trustworthy. *(s)* unfailing, steadfast, loyal, staunch. *(ant)* unreliable.

'See over there, that big building? That is an aircraft **hangar**[1], and the control tower is just behind it. Can you see?' said Anwen.

Claire could just make out glass windows to the top right-hand side of the hangar that she had thought was a warehouse, but she would never have guessed had she not been told.

'That was an RAF Hawk T1; they help us look after our own hawk.'

'Your hawk?' asked Claire, wondering what the **batty**[2] woman was talking about. *What are these people involved in*? she thought, impressed a little and scared a lot.

'You're telling me eighty-odd-year-old Gladys Jones knows people who can call on fighter jets when they need to?' Claire had raised her voice loud enough for the man driving the trap to hear, but he didn't react. 'You've got to be kidding. I don't believe you,' Claire said, shaking her head. But there was no **denying**[3] what she'd just **witnessed**[4].

'OK, I give in,' said Claire. 'You win. Tell me what the heck is going on here. I can't wait until we see Gladys. What's happening?' she shouted at them both.

'Your sister is in danger,' said Anwen, looking straight at Claire. 'And you can help us all.'

Claire's heart lurched so hard she coughed. 'Help you all?' she spluttered.

'Rebecca is **innocently**[5] **embroiled**[6] in something we have feared for many years,' Anwen said, waiting for Claire to digest the words.

'What?' asked Claire. 'Go on.'

Anwen continued. 'It all goes back to a Welsh **folk**[7] story so famous we have a village in Snowdonia named after it, Beddgelert. It tells of a **twelfth**[8]-century Welsh **sovereign**[9], Prince Llywelyn, and his **faithful**[10] hound, Gelert. Do you know this story, Claire?'

Claire shook her head.

---

1   **hangar** *(n)* a large building, usually for housing aircraft. *(s)* shed, shelter, store.

2   **batty** *(adj)* mentally unsound. *(s)* bonkers, barmy, potty, eccentric, crackers, nuts, insane. *(ant)* sane, rational.

3   **deny** *(v)* refuse to admit the truth or existence of. *(s)* contradict, contest, oppose. *(ant)* accept, confirm.

4   **witness** *(v)* see something happen. *(s)* observe, view, watch, perceive, eyeball, notice. *(ant)* ignore, overlook.

5   **innocently** *(adv)* in a naive and simple manner. *(s)* unknowingly, gullibly, guiltlessly. *(ant)* knowingly.

6   **embroil** *(v)* involve in a difficult situation. *(s)* enmesh, entangle, ensnare, entrap, catch up. *(ant)* exclude.

7   **folk** *(n)* people. *(s)* society, inhabitants, citizenry, public, population, community.

8   **twelfth** *(adj)* occupying position twelve in a sequence.

9   **sovereign** *(n)* a ruler, monarch or ultimate power. *(s)* potentate, king, queen, emperor, empress.

10   **faithful** *(adj)* remaining loyal, steadfast, constant and true. *(s)* dedicated, dependable, reliable. *(ant)* disloyal.

'Whilst out hunting one day, the prince noticed Gelert's unusual absence. On returning, he found his baby's **crib**[1] empty as his bloodstained hound greeted him. In a **reckless**[2] fury, assuming Gelert had killed his son, the frantic father drew his sword and, **in one fell swoop**[3], killed his dog.'

'Hang on a minute. What has any of this got to do with my sister, or me?' Claire asked, feeling more scared than she revealed.

'There are things you need to understand. Let me continue,' said Anwen.

Claire nodded.

'As his dog lay dead, the prince heard a cry from beneath the crib. There, wrapped in bloodstained, torn sheets, partially covered by the body of a dead wolf, lay his baby son. Horrified, the prince realised at once his mistake. He had killed his faithful dog, who had saved his child from the jaws of a **mighty**[4] wolf. **Besieged**[5] with emotion, he sank to the floor, cradling his son in one arm, and his dead dog's head in the other. **Legend**[6] says, from that moment on, he never smiled again.'

'Is it true?' asked Claire. 'I've heard stories like this before.'

'Yes, it is,' replied Anwen.

'Well, it's a sad story, but what has it got to do with me?' asked Claire.

'We're nearly there now, cariad. Gladys will be waiting for us; she will tell you more.'

'Where are we going?' asked Claire, desperate to know.

'We're going to a farm where we'll be safe,' replied Anwen as they continued onwards.

*

After a while of travelling in silence, the man slowed the pony to a walk and turned off the long straight, onto a narrower stretch. They **trundled**[7] on down the **meandering**[8] road, its sides

---

1   **crib** (*n*) a baby's bed. (*s*) cot, cradle, bassinet.

2   **reckless** (*adj*) heedless of danger or the consequences of an action. (*s*) irresponsible, wild, rash. (*ant*) cautious.

3   **in one fell swoop** (*adv*) in a single blow. (*s*) with one strike.

4   **mighty** (*adj*) strong and powerful, especially due to size. (*s*) forceful, huge, almighty. (*ant*) weak, insignificant.

5   **besiege** (*v*) overwhelm or surround. (*s*) afflict, beleaguer, plague, trouble, harass. (*ant*) abandon, assist.

6   **legend** (*n*) a story of the past, often fictitious (untrue). (*s*) fable, myth, tale, folklore.

7   **trundle** (*v*) move slowly and heavily. (*s*) drive, roll, rattle, wheel, labour, traipse, wander.

8   **meandering** (*adj*) following a winding, twisting course. (*s*) zigzagging, bendy, curvy, twisty, snaky. (*ant*) straight.

hemmed[1] by low walls of grey stones expertly[2] piled and held in place by their own weight. Beyond, the setting sprawled[3], wild and green, interrupted by solitary[4] cottages dotted here and there, chimney smoke carried off on the breeze. Cows and sheep, seemingly ubiquitous[5] in Wales, grazed[6] in peaceful, unending pastures[7].

Occasionally they passed other grazing horses, and when they did, the pony's trot transformed into a proud circus prance[8], boastfully[9] lifting her knees. Her ears pricked forward, and she snorted low communicative[10] whinnies[11] to her fellow[12] beings, encouraging them to trot alongside, until the field's boundaries[13] prevented them from going on.

Tapering[14] further, the lane descended into a single steep track. Stark stone walls merged[15] into thick, spiky gorse bushes. Their yellow flowers disguising thousands of miniature[16] daggers, minuscule[17] weapons primed[18] to attack whatever dared to brush past them. Cloggy mud squelched thick and deep, but the brave pony's feet soldiered on, not once losing their expert footing. The man slowed to a safer, steadier walk, cautiously entering a dense wooded area that seemed to appear from nowhere.

---

1   **hem** *(v)* surround and restrict. *(s)* enclose, border, edge.

2   **expertly** *(adv)* done in an expert (skilful) way. *(s)* adeptly, proficiently, capably, well. *(ant)* badly, poorly.

3   **sprawl** *(v)* spread out over a wide area. *(s)* stretch, extend, cover, ramble. *(ant)* shrink, compress.

4   **solitary** *(adj)* isolated or secluded, existing alone. *(s)* individual, single, remote. *(ant)* accompanied.

5   **ubiquitous** *(adj)* present everywhere. *(s)* abundant, omnipresent, pervasive. *(ant)* absent, limited, rare, scarce.

6   **graze** *(v)* eat grass in a field or pasture. *(s)* browse, feed, forage, crop.

7   **pasture** *(n)* land covered with plants and grass for animals. *(s)* field, meadow, prairie, herbage.

8   **prance** *(n)* movement with springy steps. *(s)* dance, gambol, bound, skip, caper, frisk, frolic. *(ant)* trudge, plod.

9   **boastfully** *(adv)* in a boastful (show-off) manner. *(s)* immodestly, bigheadedly, vainly. *(ant)* modestly.

10   **communicative** *(adj)* able to talk and share information. *(s)* expressive, open, forthcoming. *(ant)* taciturn.

11   **whinny** *(v)* noise made by a horse (a high-pitched neighing sound). *(s)* nicker, whicker, bray.

12   **fellow** *(n)* a person or a thing like or associated with another. *(s)* equivalent, companion, friend. *(ant)* stranger.

13   **boundary** *(n)* a line that marks the limit or border of an area. *(s)* confines, perimeter, frontier, edge.

14   **taper** *(v)* narrow, diminish or reduce in thickness towards one end. *(s)* contract, decrease. *(ant)* thicken, expand.

15   **merge** *(v)* blend or mingle into something else. *(s)* meld, mix, combine, unify, conflate. *(ant)* separate, diverge.

16   **miniature** *(adj)* small compared to others. *(s)* tiny, minute, mini, baby, minuscule, diminutive. *(ant)* giant.

17   **minuscule** *(adj)* incredibly small. *(s)* tiny, minute, microscopic, infinitesimal, diminutive. *(ant)* gigantic, vast.

18   **primed** *(adj)* made ready for use or action. *(s)* prepared, set, braced, loaded, poised. *(ant)* unprepared.

Claire's mouth opened, shocked at this sudden barrier of spiny **shrubs**[1], fern **fronds**[2] and giant trees standing before them. Certain the woods hadn't been there a moment ago, she turned to ask Anwen where they were, but Jack answered her question – he knew this place.

Jack was **fidgeting**[3], his tail was wagging, and his legs **jigged**[4] on the man's lap as they continued winding down a steep **ravine**[5].

As they navigated the **treacherous**[6] hill, branches and **barbs**[7] scratched at the trap. Claire's hands gripped the sides as she searched the others' faces for the fear she'd seen earlier when the bikes had chased them. She **detected**[8] none as the dark woods opened into a surprise clearing, and there, **nestled**[9] amongst a cluster of trees, sat a stone house flanked by **dilapidated**[10] buildings and a **ramshackle**[11] barn. It was thoroughly **secluded**[12], and the one sign of life was the smoke curling from the chimney in grey **coils**[13], which spread amongst the branches before anyone beyond this space would ever see.

'Whoa, Lady,' grunted the man as he pulled the pony to a halt in front of the **modest**[14] house. Jack sprang in one leap to the ground and ran yapping towards the narrow wooden front door. To Claire's **utter**[15] relief, the door opened, and Gladys appeared. Jack sprang straight up into her arms. Forgetting herself, and with tears blinding her, she ran and flung herself at Gladys too.

For a while, Claire was unable to speak as Gladys held on to them both, Jack attempting to

---

1   **shrub** (*n*) a woody plant smaller than a tree. (*s*) bush, shrubbery, thicket, brier, undergrowth.

2   **frond** (*n*) a leaf like a fern or a palm.

3   **fidget** (*v*) make small, nervous or impatient movements. (*s*) fret, fiddle, twiddle, twitch. (*ant*) sit still, relax.

4   **jig** (*v*) move in jerky, dance-like movements. (*s*) caper, hop, bounce, prance, skip, spring.

5   **ravine** (*n*) a deep and narrow gorge with steep sides. (*s*) gulley, canyon, valley, rift, abyss. (*ant*) mountain, hill.

6   **treacherous** (*adj*) presenting hidden or unforeseen dangers. (*s*) hazardous, precarious, perilous. (*ant*) safe.

7   **barb** (*n*) a spiky hook or thorn-like object. (*s*) arrow, dart, bristle, prong, point, prickle, tip, spur, needle, spine.

8   **detect** (*v*) discern the presence of something. (*s*) notice, sense, perceive. (*ant*) miss, overlook.

9   **nestle** (*v*) be situated. (*s*) lie, hide, shelter, settle, huddle, burrow.

10   **dilapidated** (*adj*) needing repair due to age. (*s*) run-down, tumble-down, shabby, decaying. (*ant*) pristine.

11   **ramshackle** (*adj*) in a state of disrepair. (*s*) rickety, tumble-down, dilapidated, derelict, decrepit. (*ant*) sturdy.

12   **secluded** (*adj*) private and sheltered. (*s*) concealed, undisturbed, isolated, segregated, quiet. (*ant*) public, busy.

13   **coil** (*n*) an object made of or consisting of concentric rings. (*s*) loop, curl, spiral, twirl, helix.

14   **modest** (*adj*) not elaborate, large or expensive. (*s*) ordinary, humble, plain, simple. (*ant*) flashy, excessive.

15   **utter** (*adj*) absolute. (*s*) unconditional, total, complete, downright, unreserved. (*ant*) partial.

cover their ears with wet licks. Then everything overflowed at once; **multiple**[1] questions tumbled from Claire's mouth in senseless **gibberish**[2].

'Come in, cariad, and we will explain as much as possible,' soothed Gladys. 'How about we start with a nice cup of tea?'

In this unfamiliar kitchen, Claire spotted the cooking range first. **Identical**[3] to Ben's mum's, it brought a **blunt**[4], **melancholic**[5] ache to her chest, and suddenly she **yearned**[6] for her family and best friend. Stifling a choke, she fought back tears. Gladys busied herself, allowing Claire time to gather her emotions. Using a thick cloth to protect her hand from the heat, Gladys lifted a fat black kettle and poured boiling water into a waiting, warmed teapot.

'Would you like a piece of buttered bread, cariad? I baked it earlier; it's still warm.'

Why's Gladys talking in that odd voice? thought Claire as she replied, 'Yes, please.'

The aroma of freshly baked bread filled the air. Starving, she sniffed the wonderful, sweet smell, reminding herself she'd not eaten a morsel since the sandwich on the train.

Anwen joined them, carrying in some bags from outside. The solemn-faced man, Gwilym, was nowhere to be seen. The **congenial**[7] kitchen **conveyed**[8] a cosy warmth: a dresser on one side **adorned**[9] with blue-and-white plates; a round table covered by a **chequered**[10] cloth; and a stout butcher's block stood upright in the corner. The cooking range **dominated**[11] one wall, **circulating**[12] a constant heat, gratefully felt where they sat with their hands wrapped around mugs of hot tea.

'We **presume**[13] you are bursting with questions, Claire, but please, listen for a moment,' said Gladys.

---

1   **multiple** *(adj)* numerous and usually varied. *(s)* many, various, legion, manifold, different. *(ant)* few, one, same.

2   **gibberish** *(n)* nonsense talk. *(s)* prattle, babble, drivel, twaddle, garbage, rot, claptrap. *(ant)* sense, reason.

3   **identical** *(adj)* similar in every way. *(s)* equal, indistinguishable, duplicate, alike, like, matching. *(ant)* different, separable.

4   **blunt** *(adj)* not sharp. *(s)* dull, rounded, deadened, worn, edgeless, stubby. *(ant)* sharp, pointed, severe, harsh.

5   **melancholic** *(adj)* feeling sadness. *(s)* unhappy, gloomy, forlorn, despondent, nostalgic, lamenting. *(ant)* happy.

6   **yearn** *(v)* really want something. *(s)* long, ache, pine, crave, desire, hanker, thirst. *(ant)* reject, abjure.

7   **congenial** *(adj)* pleasing and pleasant. *(s)* agreeable, convivial, welcoming, friendly. *(ant)* unfriendly.

8   **convey** *(v)* make known or understandable. *(s)* deliver, transmit, exude, communicate. *(ant)* obscure, conceal.

9   **adorn** *(v)* make more attractive or beautiful. *(s)* decorate, embellish, ornament, enhance. *(ant)* strip.

10   **chequered** *(adj)* in a pattern made of squares (like a chessboard). *(s)* plaid, tartan, checked, squared.

11   **dominate** *(v)* be the most conspicuous (stand out most). *(s)* command, overshadow, prevail, dwarf, dictate.

12   **circulate** *(v)* move freely in a closed area or system. *(s)* flow, travel, distribute, spread.

13   **presume** *(v)* suppose or imagine that something is the case. *(s)* believe, assume, guess, gather. *(ant)* doubt.

'Gladys, I don't want to listen. I've been *listening* to your letter all morning. I need to ask one thing first: what does *cariad* mean, and why didn't you tell me you had a sister, and why have I come to Wales, and how the heck can you lot call on fighter jets?' she blurted in one long breath, gasping as she finished.

'That's more than one thing!' Gladys laughed.

'*Cariad* is Welsh for "love", and in Wales it's used a lot. I am Welsh, Claire, not from Lancashire, as you thought. What we tell you now will be difficult for you, as it swims against the **tide**[1] of **normality**[2].'

'You mean that story about the dog? What's that got to do with me or Rebecca being in danger?' Claire's mouth moved to speak again, but this time, Gladys would not be interrupted.

'So my sister, Anwen, has told you of Beddgelert?' asked Gladys.

'Yes. Some old dead prince killed his dog. So what?' said Claire, **confounded**[3] as to where any of this was leading. Aware Gladys had not brought her all this way to **recount**[4] Welsh **folklore**[5], she shrugged her shoulders and, with a tone as sharp as a **thistle**[6], said, 'Well?'

She'd never been cheeky to Gladys before, and immediately **regretted**[7] being so.

'Well, a more troubling truth **taints**[8] this story. That day, something was taken from the prince's child that would lead to **devastating**[9] effects.'

'Is this true?' asked Claire, her bread suddenly forgotten, her tea cooling – untouched.

'Yes, cariad, it is.'

Jack skipped in and hopped up onto Claire's lap. He sat upright and cocked his head towards Gladys.

'That **fateful**[10] day, the Gwalch Gem bracelet was stolen from the baby prince.'

---

1   **tide** *(n)* the alternate rise and fall of the sea (usually twice a day). *(s)* flow, current, drift.

2   **normality** *(n)* the condition of being normal or usual. *(s)* ordinariness, routine, normalcy. *(ant)* abnormality.

3   **confounded** *(adj)* surprised or confused. *(s)* muddled, puzzled, baffled, perplexed, bemused. *(ant)* clear.

4   **recount** *(v)* tell someone about something. *(s)* narrate, describe, depict, convey, story-tell.

5   **folklore** *(n)* traditional belief in a custom or story. *(s)* legends, myth, mythology, fiction. *(ant)* non-fiction.

6   **thistle** *(n)* spiky plant. *(s)* barb, bramble, brier.

7   **regret** *(v)* feel sad about something one has done or failed to do. *(s)* lament, bemoan, rue. *(ant)* cherish.

8   **taint** *(v)* spoil because of an undesirable (unwanted) quality. *(s)* blemish, contaminate, pollute. *(ant)* enhance.

9   **devastating** *(adj)* destructive, causing grief or shock. *(s)* harmful, distressing, detrimental. *(ant)* constructive.

10   **fateful** *(adj)* involving far-reaching consequences. *(s)* significant, pivotal, consequential. *(ant)* insignificant.

Claire **started**[1], afraid Gladys had something life-threatening **lodged**[2] in her throat. To her **unaccustomed**[3] ears, the ending of the word *gwalch*, when **pronounced**[4] in Welsh, sounded like an **exaggerated**[5] and **accentuated**[6] ending of the Scottish word *loch*. It **grated**[7] like **abrasive**[8] sandpaper.

'What did you call it? You sound as if you're choking, Gladys,' said Claire.

'I'm fine, cariad,' answered Gladys as her **temples**[9] and cheeks **wrinkled**[10] into amused **furrows**[11]. Welsh sounded most unusual to the **untuned**[12] ear.

'The Gwalch Gem is an **exquisite**[13] **emerald**[14], cut to the shape of a hawk. It is **embedded**[15] in a bracelet of unique Welsh gold mined from a **covert**[16] **location**[17] by ancient knights. The **combination**[18] of this gem and the gold give it special powers, but with power comes **responsibility**[19] and, sadly, also **corruption**[20] and greed.'

'But, how do you know all this?' interrupted Claire, shaking her head.

'There exists an ancient **order**[21] **entitled**[22] the Knights Hawk. They walk amongst us today,

---

1   **start** *(v)* jerk or jump with alarm. *(s)* jolt, flinch, twitch, react, blanch, bounce. *(ant)* stand firm.

2   **lodge** *(v)* firmly wedge, embed or stick in a place. *(s)* catch, fix, plant, jam. *(ant)* dislodge.

3   **unaccustomed** *(adj)* not used to or familiar with. *(s)* untuned, unfamiliar, unacquainted. *(ant)* accustomed.

4   **pronounce** *(v)* sound out. *(s)* say, speak, utter, enunciate, articulate. *(ant)* mispronounce.

5   **exaggerated** *(adj)* increased beyond normal proportions. *(s)* overstated, embellished. *(ant)* understated.

6   **accentuated** *(adj)* made prominent or noticeable. *(s)* emphasised, highlighted, stressed. *(ant)* played down.

7   **grate** *(v)* make a rasping sound. *(s)* abrade, chafe, catch, scratch. *(ant)* please, soothe, pacify.

8   **abrasive** *(adj)* capable of polishing by rubbing or grinding. *(s)* rough, scratchy, coarse, rasping. *(ant)* smooth.

9   **temple** *(n)* the flat part of the head situated between the forehead and the ear.

10   **wrinkle** *(v)* make lines or folds in. *(s)* crease, furrow, crinkle, rumple, pucker, scrunch. *(ant)* smooth, straighten.

11   **furrow** *(n)* a wrinkle, crease or line on a person's face. *(s)* undulation, crinkle, crow's foot. *(ant)* smoothness.

12   **untuned** *(adj)* not properly adjusted or tuned (not used to). *(s)* unaccustomed, unfamiliar. *(ant)* accustomed.

13   **exquisite** *(adj)* extremely beautiful. *(s)* wonderful, perfect, delightful, superb, flawless. *(ant)* ugly, flawed.

14   **emerald** *(n)* a bright green precious stone. *(s)* jewel, gem, treasure, gemstone, rock, sparkler.

15   **embed** *(v)* fix into surrounding mass. *(s)* insert, implant, sink, surround, inlay. *(ant)* dislodge, extract.

16   **covert** *(adj)* not openly displayed or acknowledged. *(s)* secret, underground, concealed. *(ant)* obvious, overt.

17   **location** *(n)* a specific position or place. *(s)* site, setting, scene, locality, whereabouts, situation, spot, area.

18   **combination** *(n)* a mixing of things that remain individually distinct. *(s)* arrangement, grouping. *(ant)* division.

19   **responsibility** *(n)* a moral obligation to respect, behave or care for. *(s)* duty, accountability. *(ant)* immorality.

20   **corruption** *(n)* dishonest behaviour by those in power. *(s)* exploitation, fraud, immorality. *(ant)* honesty.

21   **order** *(n)* a society of knights bound by a common rule of life. *(s)* organisation, company, group.

22   **entitle** *(v)* give a title (name) to someone or something. *(s)* label, designate, call, dub.

though perhaps not as you might imagine.'

'What do you mean, Knights Hawk?' Claire interrupted again.

'They are not **clad**[1] in **armour**[2] and **chain mail**[3], **wielding**[4] swords, as history **portrays**[5]; they **blend**[6] in unnoticed. My surname is Cadwaladr. I am a Keeper of the Gwalch Gem bracelet, and I am also **honoured**[7] to be a Knight Hawk.'

'Cadwallader?' **exclaimed**[8] Claire. 'But my name's Cadwallader; yours is Jones!'

'My family name is Cadwaladr; it sounds the same as yours,' Gladys **reiterated**[9].

'How come we've got the same surname now?' asked Claire.

'Because you, too, are a Keeper,' replied Gladys, **observing**[10] Claire's stunned reaction, 'though your name is spelled differently. Until you earn your **Instinct**[11], you cannot be **knighted**[12] as a true Cadwaladr. Only then can you take the Welsh **title**[13], once it is deserved. All Cadwaladr folks born with Instinct are Keepers of the gem, and **potential**[14] Knights Hawk.'

'What do you mean, a Keeper? A keeper of what? And being knighted? What are you on about, Gladys?' asked Claire, **confused**[15].

'We don't expect you to understand yet.' Anwen joined in the **exchange**[16]. 'Keepers earn their Instinct in order to guard the Gwalch Gem bracelet, **ensuring**[17] its **benevolence**[18]. In fair hands,

---

1   **clad** *(adj)* clothed or dressed. *(s)* attired, covered, cloaked, garbed, disguised. *(ant)* unclothed, undressed.

2   **armour** *(n)* metal coverings worn in battle to protect the body. *(s)* shield, shell, defence.

3   **chain mail** *(n)* flexible armour made of small metal rings that link together.

4   **wield** *(v)* hold and wave a weapon with intent to use it. *(s)* brandish, manipulate, carry, sport.

5   **portray** *(v)* represent or describe something in a certain way. *(s)* depict, show, reveal. *(ant)* obscure.

6   **blend** *(v)* mix in without being noticed. *(s)* merge, combine, mingle, unify, meld, amalgamate. *(ant)* stick out.

7   **honoured** *(adj)* regarded with gratitude and respect. *(s)* privileged, grateful, pleased, thrilled. *(ant)* insulted.

8   **exclaim** *(v)* cry out suddenly. *(s)* blurt, proclaim, declare, shout, call, yell. *(ant)* whisper, mutter.

9   **reiterate** *(v)* say again for emphasis or clarity. *(s)* repeat, restate, recap, retell.

10   **observe** *(v)* watch carefully. *(s)* inspect, note, regard, scrutinise, monitor, study, survey. *(ant)* ignore, overlook.

11   **instinct** *(n)* an innate (inbuilt) ability. *(s)* talent, aptitude, character, flair, intuition, sense. *(ant)* knowledge.

12   **knight** *(v)* give someone the title of knight. *(s)* ennoble, dub, entitle, designate. *(ant)* revoke, renounce.

13   **title** *(n)* a name to describe someone's position or job. *(s)* label, rank, entitlement, designation, epithet.

14   **potential** *(adj)* having the possibility of being. *(s)* possible, budding, prospective, probable. *(ant)* unlikely.

15   **confused** *(adj)* bewildered or perplexed. *(s)* puzzled, baffled, mystified, bamboozled. *(ant)* enlightened, clear.

16   **exchange** *(n)* a short conversation. *(s)* discussion, talk, chat, interchange, altercation.

17   **ensure** *(v)* make certain. *(s)* guarantee, assure, safeguard, confirm, warrant, protect. *(ant)* undermine, weaken.

18   **benevolence** *(n)* goodwill and kindness. *(s)* compassion, goodness, altruism. *(ant)* malevolence.

peace and **prosperity**[1] **reign**[2], but in **malevolent**[3] hands, it is **destructive**[4].'

'Hang on a minute! Destructive? What do you mean?' asked Claire, picking out the only part she'd understood.

Her eyes **flitted**[5] between the two women, feeling horribly out of her depth and regretting her decision to come.

As if sensing her fear, the trap driver's solid figure entered the kitchen. **Possessing**[6] a **graceful**[7] **gait**[8] for someone so **sturdy**[9], he settled at the table, and Jack jumped straight off Claire's lap and onto his. His presence **encompassed**[10] them, smothering the room in an awkward silence.

Claire glanced around **sheepishly**[11], looking everywhere except at him. His **proximity**[12] unnerved her. Self-consciously she sipped her now-cold tea to fill the silence. She hated cold tea – but swallowed it anyway.

Despite herself, she **submitted**[13] to her curiosity and risked a poorly disguised peek at Gwilym over the top of her mug. As he stroked Jack's head, she studied him, certain he'd looked older before. His skin seemed smoother, less lined, and his hair thicker and darker somehow.

Maybe it's the light, she thought.

He was, in fact, a **handsome**[14] man, and now wearing jeans and a T-shirt, he didn't resemble a farmer at all. Come to that, did Gladys appear younger too?

Am I going bonkers? she thought, thrown by this **subtle**[15] change of appearance and the strange

---

1   **prosperity** *(n)* the state of having money or success. *(s)* wealth, affluence, opulence, riches. *(ant)* poverty.

2   **reign** *(v)* be the dominant feature of a situation. *(s)* rule, dominate, prevail, control, lead. *(ant)* submit, yield.

3   **malevolent** *(adj)* wishing or showing evil. *(s)* malicious, spiteful, wicked, nasty, vindictive. *(ant)* benevolent.

4   **destructive** *(adj)* causing huge damage. *(s)* calamitous, detrimental, injurious. *(ant)* constructive, beneficial.

5   **flit** *(v)* move swiftly. *(s)* dart, dip, flicker, sweep, fly, skim, flutter, flash. *(ant)* dawdle.

6   **possess** *(v)* have or own a characteristic or thing. *(s)* acquire, occupy, carry, obtain, maintain. *(ant)* lack.

7   **graceful** *(adj)* having grace, elegance and poise (not stiff and ungainly). *(s)* agile, nimble, fluid. *(ant)* clumsy.

8   **gait** *(n)* the way a person walks or strides. *(s)* step, manner, posture, bearing, style, carriage, movement.

9   **sturdy** *(adj)* strong and solidly built. *(s)* robust, durable, substantial, rugged, muscular, burly. *(ant)* weak, frail.

10   **encompass** *(v)* surround, enclose or hold within. *(s)* circle, envelop, contain, hold, wrap, swathe. *(ant)* exclude.

11   **sheepishly** *(adv)* in an embarrassed or unconfident way. *(s)* awkwardly, uncomfortably. *(ant)* confidently.

12   **proximity** *(n)* nearness. *(s)* closeness, immediacy, vicinity, adjacency. *(ant)* remoteness, distance.

13   **submit** *(v)* give in to. *(s)* succumb, acquiesce, yield, surrender, defer, buckle, capitulate. *(ant)* defy, resist.

14   **handsome** *(adj)* good-looking. *(s)* attractive, fetching, striking, appealing, fine. *(ant)* ugly, unattractive, plain.

15   **subtle** *(adj)* delicate or difficult to detect. *(s)* slight, faint, indistinct, imperceptible. *(ant)* obvious.

shape of a partly concealed **tattoo**[1] poking out from under his sleeve. He reminded her of an actor her mum **fawned**[2] over, whose name escaped her.

'Claire, I am Gwilym Cadwaladr, and you are my niece.'

Claire nearly spat her tea at him but ended up choking on it instead.

'What are you talking about? I haven't got an uncle!' she blurted, glaring at all three people in turn.

'You are an Instinctive Cadwallader,' he explained. 'All Cadwallader people born with Instinct **hail from**[3] the Knights Hawk. You are my niece, though not in the true sense as you **perceive**[4] it.'

'What? How can you be my uncle when I don't have an uncle, and why did my mum not tell me about you if you are my uncle?' she continued, her honest eyes challenging his.

'I mined the Welsh gold in which the Gwalch Gem is embedded. In Welsh the word *gwalch* means "hawk", Claire.'

'Sorry?' she asked, even more confused.

'Legend tells of **mortals**[5] searching for a rare Welsh gold, one **deemed**[6] to be the purest on earth. Folklore speaks of this gold and the Hawk Gem in combination possessing powers to change men forever, *but* only if **coupled**[7]; alone, they are powerless.'

Reading her **expression**[8], aware his **statements**[9] were difficult to **comprehend**[10], he paused to let them sink in before continuing.

'Prince Llywelyn's family possessed the gem for **generations**[11]. Llywelyn tasked his most trusted knights to **unearth**[12] the gold in a quest to prove the claims. When I did, I became a

---

1   **tattoo** *(n)* an indelible (permanent) mark on the skin from injecting pigment (colour). *(s)* brand, mark.

2   **fawn** *(v)* flatter and give excessive attention to. *(s)* court, pander, cajole, crawl, grovel, butter up. *(ant)* belittle.

3   **hail from** *(v)* originate from. *(s)* come from, have one's roots in, be a native of.

4   **perceive** *(v)* interpret or view in a particular way. *(s)* see, comprehend, regard, consider. *(ant)* misinterpret.

5   **mortal** *(n)* a human who will eventually die. *(s)* person, individual, man, woman, child. *(ant)* immortal.

6   **deem** *(v)* consider, judge or regard in a specified way. *(s)* assume, believe, reckon, suppose. *(ant)* misjudge.

7   **couple** *(v)* combine or link together with something else. *(s)* pair, join, attach, team, unite, match. *(ant)* separate.

8   **expression** *(n)* a look that conveys (shows) a certain emotion. *(s)* face, appearance, air.

9   **statement** *(n)* a clear expression of something that is said or written. *(s)* account, speech.

10   **comprehend** *(v)* understand. *(s)* follow, get, realise, fathom, grasp, twig. *(ant)* misunderstand, misinterpret.

11   **generations** *(n)* a period of time encompassing many steps in a line of descent. *(s)* ages, years, aeons.

12   **unearth** *(v)* discover by searching or investigating. *(s)* uncover, excavate, exhume, find, expose. *(ant)* bury.

Knight Hawk. You are of my **lineage**[1] and you have the gift.'

'What gift? What do you mean, gift?' she asked.

'The gift of Instinct,' he answered patiently. 'However, not all Cadwaladr **descendants**[2] are born with Instinct, Claire.'

'Are you Rebecca's "uncle" too? Does she have a gift?'

'No, and she will never earn the true Cadwaladr name.'

'The true Cadwallader name – what exactly do you mean?' she asked, **ruffled**[3].

Gwilym reached over and picked up something from the dresser. He put a notepad down and wrote 'Cadwaladr'.

Claire picked it up.

'You've written that wrong,' she said **flippantly**[4], pointing to it.

The man's features softened.

'This is how the Welsh write your surname, Claire, and it means "battle leader". Your present spelling **heralds from**[5] the true word but is a **derivative**[6]. *Only* when you have earned it, and *only* if you are knighted as a Knight Hawk, can you take our **authentic**[7] version of Cadwaladr.'

'Battle leader?' She shook her head, mouthing the surprising **translation**[8]. 'Really? Battle leader. Is that what my name means?'

'Yes, Claire.'

'Me being a knight. Are you lot human?' Claire asked, the thought jarring her.

'Yes. We are mortal, though we do **tend**[9] to live a long time. We are rare.'

'I'm rare?' she asked, screwing up her face.

'Yes, Claire, very.'

---

1   **lineage** *(n)* direct descent from an ancestor. *(s)* ancestry, family, line, heredity, roots, origin.

2   **descendant** *(n)* a person descended (coming) from an ancestor. *(s)* offspring, progeny, child. *(ant)* ancestor.

3   **ruffled** *(adj)* upset or disturbed. *(s)* vexed, perturbed, unsettled, distressed, irritated, irked. *(ant)* calm.

4   **flippantly** *(adv)* in a disrespectful or unserious way. *(s)* frivolously, offhandedly, jokingly, cheekily. *(ant)* seriously.

5   **herald from** *(v)* originate from. *(s)* come from, have roots in, hail from.

6   **derivative** *(n)* something derived (coming) from another. *(s)* descendant, offshoot, spin-off. *(ant)* original, root.

7   **authentic** *(adj)* genuine, original or traditional. *(s)* valid, accurate, real, legitimate. *(ant)* false, fake.

8   **translation** *(n)* the act of changing one language into another. *(s)* conversion, interpretation. *(ant)* original.

9   **tend** *(v)* be likely to possess certain characteristics. *(s)* be prone to, be liable to, have a propensity.

For a short while, nobody spoke. Claire fiddled with the notepad on the table, looking at the way he'd printed her **supposed**[1] name.

'So, if I *do* have this Instinct thingy, what does it mean?' she asked.

'You have an **innate**[2] **flair**[3], although its **benefits**[4] are not **infinite**[5] or free. You are born with the *potential* of Instinct, but *you alone* must earn it; we cannot train you.'

'Not free?' she asked. 'If you can't train me, how do I get it?'

'By being brave and **defending**[6] what is right. True Instinct, *good* Instinct, can only be used in defence, never to **provoke**[7] or attack,' said Gwilym, **stressing**[8] the word *never*.

'Provoke an attack?' she asked, raising her voice. 'I don't like the sound of this.'

'Your Instinct will **evolve**[9] and **thrive**[10] if you work for it and deserve it, but **moreover**[11], when you *need* it. One day, you might become a Knight Hawk and use the authentic spelling of our great name: Cadwaladr. True Instinctives are kind, **loyal**[12] and must possess **profound**[13] **integrity**[14]. But most of all, we are brave. You could have refused to come today, but you didn't.'

Gwilym's voice tailed off, his expression distant. Claire waited, wondering where his thoughts had strayed. This all sounded **preposterous**[15], yet she wanted to believe him, although she'd already had enough of being brave for one day.

'Gwilym,' said Gladys, nudging him from his **reverie**[16], offering him tea.

---

1   **supposed** *(adj)* assumed to be true. *(s)* presumed, claimed, apparent, alleged. *(ant)* real.

2   **innate** *(adj)* naturally occurring. *(s)* inborn, intuitive, instinctive, inherent, characteristic, intrinsic. *(ant)* learned.

3   **flair** *(n)* an instinctive ability or aptitude for doing something well. *(s)* talent, skill, gift, finesse. *(ant)* ineptitude.

4   **benefit** *(n)* an advantage or profit. *(s)* value, help, boon, perk, reward, bonus. *(ant)* detriment, disadvantage.

5   **infinite** *(adj)* never-ending or impossible to calculate. *(s)* unlimited, endless, boundless. *(ant)* finite, limited.

6   **defend** *(v)* protect from harm or resist an attack. *(s)* preserve, uphold, secure, shield, guard. *(ant)* attack.

7   **provoke** *(v)* deliberately cause or stimulate something (often unwelcome). *(s)* aggravate, incite. *(ant)* allay.

8   **stress** *(v)* emphasise or give importance to. *(s)* accentuate, highlight, affirm. *(ant)* understate, mumble.

9   **evolve** *(v)* develop gradually over time. *(s)* grow, change, progress, advance, thrive, flourish. *(ant)* regress.

10   **thrive** *(v)* do well. *(s)* flourish, grow, prosper, advance, succeed, blossom. *(ant)* wither, decline, deteriorate.

11   **moreover** *(adv)* even more so, as a further matter. *(s)* in addition, furthermore, also.

12   **loyal** *(adj)* remaining consistent and true. *(s)* trusty, reliable, dependable, faithful, constant. *(ant)* disloyal.

13   **profound** *(adj)* intense, deep or great (feelings, qualities, or emotions). *(s)* sincere. *(ant)* superficial, shallow.

14   **integrity** *(n)* soundness of moral principle. *(s)* truthfulness, honour, reliability. *(ant)* dishonesty, corruption.

15   **preposterous** *(adj)* utterly nonsensical. *(s)* stupid, ridiculous, absurd, ludicrous. *(ant)* sensible, reasonable.

16   **reverie** *(n)* a state of being lost in thought. *(s)* daydream, musing, contemplation, fantasy. *(ant)* concentration.

He eventually picked up his mug and returned his gaze to Claire, who now couldn't contain herself. 'What could I do if I get this Instinct thing? Fly?' she asked, grinning. But Gwilym remained **sombre**[1].

'I cannot **foresee**[2] your **capabilities**[3]. What is it that you would **realistically**[4] like to achieve? What would you improve, Claire, given the **opportunity**[5]? To a young Instinctive, talents are usually **limited**[6] to two or three **elements**[7]; we are not superheroes. If we **strive**[8] for **knowledge**[9] and **proficiency**[10], we advance. That is all I know.'

'How's my sister involved in all this?' asked Claire, remembering what had brought her here in the first place.

'I will come to your sister shortly.'

'Oh, OK,' she said.

'Hundreds of years ago, commanded by Prince Llywelyn, I was a **valiant**[11] young knight tasked with discovering the legend's truth. I led the quest to find the **elusive**[12] Welsh gold that, if proved true, would **empower**[13] the Gwalch Gem.'

Enthralled[14], Claire leaned towards him; good stories captivated her. Only this wasn't a story.

'Suffering **immense**[15] losses, we located and **extracted**[16] the gold for Llywelyn, who

---

1   **sombre** *(adj)* deeply serious or sad (feeling or looking). *(s)* melancholy, solemn, grave, sober. *(ant)* cheerful.

2   **foresee** *(v)* be aware of beforehand (see something coming). *(s)* predict, forecast, prophesy.

3   **capability** *(n)* someone's or something's abilities. *(s)* skill, competence, proficiency, aptitude. *(ant)* inability.

4   **realistically** *(adv)* in a realistic (true and accurate) way. *(s)* practically, sensibly, logically. *(ant)* unrealistically.

5   **opportunity** *(n)* the chance to be able to do or achieve something. *(s)* prospect, occasion.

6   **limit** *(v)* restrict (prevent from obtaining or achieving more). *(s)* curb, cap, restrain. *(ant)* exceed.

7   **element** *(n)* an essential part or characteristic of something. *(s)* bit, component, constituent. *(ant)* whole.

8   **strive** *(v)* make huge efforts to obtain or achieve something. *(s)* aim, struggle, endeavour, try. *(ant)* shirk, quit.

9   **knowledge** *(n)* skills or awareness gained by study or practice. *(s)* expertise, wisdom. *(ant)* ignorance.

10   **proficiency** *(n)* great skill or expertise. *(s)* ability, talent, aptitude, competence. *(ant)* incompetence.

11   **valiant** *(adj)* showing determination or courage. *(s)* brave, heroic, gallant, intrepid. *(ant)* cowardly, craven.

12   **elusive** *(adj)* difficult to achieve, find, catch or remember. *(s)* evasive, fleeting, tricky. *(ant)* accessible.

13   **empower** *(v)* give power to. *(s)* energise, enliven, rouse, enable, charge, endow. *(ant)* disempower, inhibit.

14   **enthral** *(v)* capture or fascinate. *(s)* rivet, captivate, engross, grip, transfix. *(ant)* bore.

15   **immense** *(adj)* large in scale or degree (huge). *(s)* great, immeasurable, enormous, boundless. *(ant)* tiny.

16   **extract** *(v)* remove or take out, often with huge effort or force. *(s)* obtain, mine, unearth. *(ant)* implant, bury.

crafted[1] it into the bracelet that still holds the Gwalch Gem today. The **extensive**[2] power of the bracelet quickly became **apparent**[3].'

'What can it do?' asked Claire, intrigued.

'Well,' said Gwilym, 'it **initiated**[4] our powers of Instinct, and we became the Knights Hawk, but moreover, and more **significantly**[5], it **enables**[6] the user to **manipulate**[7] time.'

'Wow,' said Claire. 'Change time – that's pretty cool.'

'Llywelyn used it wisely, for only **virtuous**[8] **deeds**[9]. However, he suspected certain **courtiers**[10] **coveted**[11] it for their own **avaricious**[12] gain, and he feared even some of his most trusted allies were **plotting**[13] to steal the bracelet, to **profit**[14] from its power.'

Gladys leaned over, topping up their mugs.

'Not for me, thanks,' Claire **declined**[15], putting her hand over the top of hers.

'Llywelyn **governed**[16] fairly, but palaces **harbour**[17] **traitors**[18]. Whilst away hunting one day, he **entrusted**[19] his wife and younger brother with **tending**[20] his son and guarding the bracelet,

---

1   **craft** *(v)* make an object with great skill and care, often by hand. *(s)* fashion, create, shape. *(ant)* destroy.

2   **extensive** *(adj)* on a large scale, covering or affecting a large area. *(s)* far-reaching, wide. *(ant)* narrow, limited.

3   **apparent** *(adj)* obvious, visible or understood. *(s)* clear, evident, plain, discernible, perceptible. *(ant)* unclear.

4   **initiate** *(v)* cause an action or a process to begin. *(s)* start, instigate, commence, instruct. *(ant)* stop.

5   **significantly** *(adv)* in a significant (important) way. *(s)* crucially, notably, radically. *(ant)* insignificantly.

6   **enable** *(v)* allow or make possible to do something. *(s)* empower, permit, facilitate. *(ant)* prevent.

7   **manipulate** *(v)* alter, control or influence. *(s)* direct, affect, change, exploit, manoeuvre.

8   **virtuous** *(adj)* having high moral standards. *(s)* honest, righteous, honourable, ethical. *(ant)* bad, dishonest.

9   **deed** *(n)* a performance or action. *(s)* feat, act, endeavour, accomplishment, achievement, effort.

10   **courtier** *(n)* a person who attends a royal court. *(s)* aristocrat, noble, peer, attendant.

11   **covet** *(v)* long to have something (often when it belongs to another). *(s)* yearn, envy, crave. *(ant)* reject, abjure.

12   **avaricious** *(adj)* greedy for wealth or material gain. *(s)* rapacious, grasping, materialistic. *(ant)* generous.

13   **plot** *(v)* devise a harmful or secret plan (often as a group). *(s)* conspire, connive, contrive, scheme.

14   **profit** *(v)* gain an advantage, benefit or money. *(s)* prosper, thrive, exploit, strengthen, earn. *(ant)* lose.

15   **decline** *(v)* refuse politely. *(s)* reject, abstain, desist, refrain, spurn, turn down, pass up. *(ant)* accept.

16   **govern** *(v)* rule with authority. *(s)* oversee, head, reign, dominate, regulate, manage. *(ant)* mismanage.

17   **harbour** *(v)* give refuge to. *(s)* accommodate, defend, hide, conceal, shelter, protect. *(ant)* hand over.

18   **traitor** *(n)* someone who betrays (double-crosser). *(s)* conspirator, turncoat, collaborator, snitch. *(ant)* loyalist.

19   **entrust** *(v)* assign (give) responsibility and trust. *(s)* charge, delegate, allocate, authorise. *(ant)* mistrust.

20   **tend** *(v)* look after, care for. *(s)* watch over, attend to, keep, protect, cultivate, nurture. *(ant)* neglect, harm.

which they knew was hidden in his son's **chamber**[1]. **Traumatised**[2] at having killed Gelert, the prince didn't notice the theft immediately. He called to his wife, but **alas**[3], she did not come. He cried out to his brother; still no one came. In the **ensuing**[4] silence, Llywelyn realised the enormity of the **betrayal**[5] and agony he would **endure**[6]. The Gwalch Gem bracelet had gone. Just two people knew it had been **tethered**[7] around his son's thigh. The two people who Llywelyn had trusted with his life: his wife and his brother.'

Again this **gruff**[8] man paused, **wistfully**[9] searching an unknown **yonder**[10]. Claire was desperate to **intrude**[11], to question him, but she bit at her lip, knowing she shouldn't interrupt until he **rejoined**[12] the present and **resumed**[13] his tale.

'The prince cried as he kissed Gelert's lifeless head, inhaling the **scent**[14] of his dead friend before it faded forever. The people he loved and trusted most had **lured**[15] a wolf into his baby's chamber to distract Gelert, knowing he would protect the baby and bracelet with his life, and this he had done.'

As tears **welled**[16], Claire swallowed hard, trying her **utmost**[17] not to downright **blub**[18]. She'd never owned a pet, but she adored Jack and Thomas, and had fallen in love with the pony who'd brought them here.

---

1   **chamber** *(n)* a compartment or private room (especially a bedroom). *(s)* cubicle, space, cell.

2   **traumatise** *(v)* subject to lasting shock from bad experience or injury. *(s)* devastate, torment. *(ant)* soothe.

3   **alas** *(int)* used to express pity, regret, grief, disappointment or concern.

4   **ensuing** *(adj)* happening afterwards due to something else. *(s)* resulting, consequent. *(ant)* preceding.

5   **betrayal** *(n)* the action of being gravely disloyal (untrue) to someone. *(s)* duplicity, treachery. *(ant)* loyalty.

6   **endure** *(v)* suffer pain or difficulty patiently. *(s)* bear, tolerate, undergo, withstand. *(ant)* succumb.

7   **tether** *(v)* tie something up to restrict movement, fix securely. *(s)* fasten, bind, truss, fetter. *(ant)* untie, release.

8   **gruff** *(adj)* rough and deep (voice), or abrupt in manner. *(s)* brusque, curt, surly, stern, blunt. *(ant)* friendly.

9   **wistfully** *(adv)* done in a wistful (regretful, longing or yearning) manner. *(s)* sadly, pensively. *(ant)* contentedly.

10   **yonder** *(n)* far distance. *(s)* faraway place, distant land, yon, beyond. *(ant)* surroundings, vicinity.

11   **intrude** *(v)* disrupt without invitation. *(s)* interrupt, interfere, encroach, infringe, disturb. *(ant)* withdraw, avoid.

12   **rejoin** *(v)* return to, come back. *(s)* resume, regain, revert.

13   **resume** *(v)* continue or begin again (after pausing or an interruption). *(s)* restart, recommence. *(ant)* stop.

14   **scent** *(n)* a distinctive smell (often a pleasant one). *(s)* trace, whiff, aroma, perfume. *(ant)* stench, stink.

15   **lure** *(v)* tempt to do something, often by offering a reward. *(s)* entice, ensnare, trap, persuade. *(ant)* dissuade.

16   **well** *(v)* rise to the surface and sometimes spill out or over. *(s)* brim, overflow, gush, flood, surge. *(ant)* subside.

17   **utmost** *(n)* the most extreme extent or amount. *(s)* greatest, best, supreme, maximum, uttermost. *(ant)* least.

18   **blub** *(v)* cry uncontrollably and noisily. *(s)* sob, weep, blubber, bawl, howl, yowl. *(ant)* smile, laugh.

'Llywelyn's wife fled with his brother, choosing power and greed over her husband and child. Had they planned for Llywelyn to return and see Gelert covered in blood, mistaking his dog's **heroic**[1] deed? Had they intended such hurt for Llywelyn, or was the killing of Gelert a **harsh**[2] twist of timing and **unintended**[3], a young father's **impulsive**[4] and **volatile**[5] temper leading him to **lash out**[6] without thought? The truth may remain **undetermined**[7]. The one part of this legend that is **wholly**[8] **factual**[9], however, is Prince Llywelyn never smiled again.'

Blinking back tears, but keeping her eyes on Gwilym, Claire wiped her cheek on her grubby sleeve.

'Dark years ensued. Prince Llywelyn's brother and wife used the bracelet's time-changing abilities for **selfish**[10] and malevolent gain. I **pledged**[11] I would not rest until I returned the bracelet to its **rightful**[12] keeper. When at last it was, Llywelyn **avowed**[13] that it must never fall into **untrustworthy**[14] hands again, that it be **sequestered**[15] and **isolated**[16] from **temptation**[17]. Together with my Knights Hawk sisters, Gladys and Anwen Cadwaladr, I must ensure it remains forever under lock and key, **segregated**[18], shut away from the hands of **unscrupulous**[19] individuals, so none will ever be tempted by its powers again.'

---

1   **heroic** *(adj)* having brave and courageous characteristics. *(s)* gallant, valiant, epic, intrepid. *(ant)* craven.

2   **harsh** *(adj)* unpleasant, cruel, grim and unpalatable. *(s)* severe, callous, ruthless, unkind. *(ant)* gentle, kind.

3   **unintended** *(adj)* not planned or meant to happen. *(s)* unintentional, accidental, chance. *(ant)* intentional.

4   **impulsive** *(adj)* done without thinking about beforehand. *(s)* rash, spontaneous, reckless, hasty. *(ant)* cautious.

5   **volatile** *(adj)* displaying random and quick changes of emotion. *(s)* explosive, impulsive. *(ant)* placid, stable.

6   **lash out** *(v)* hit out quickly and violently. *(s)* strike, blow, attack, slam, knock, impact, pound, thrash.

7   **undetermined** *(adj)* not known. *(s)* unknown, undiscovered, unspecified, uncertain. *(ant)* known, definite.

8   **wholly** *(adv)* in a way that is whole. *(s)* completely, entirely, absolutely, totally, fully, altogether. *(ant)* partially.

9   **factual** *(adj)* concerned with what is true. *(s)* accurate, genuine, authentic, truthful, real. *(ant)* fictional, untrue.

10   **selfish** *(adj)* lacking consideration for others. *(s)* egotistical, greedy, self-serving. *(ant)* selfless, altruistic.

11   **pledge** *(v)* promise solemnly to do something. *(s)* swear, vow, guarantee, assure.

12   **rightful** *(adj)* having a deserved or legitimate right to something. *(s)* correct, true, apt, lawful. *(ant)* wrongful.

13   **avow** *(v)* confess or assert openly. *(s)* declare, profess, state, affirm, maintain, insist, confirm. *(ant)* deny.

14   **untrustworthy** *(adj)* not to be trusted. *(s)* dishonest, unreliable, deceitful, disloyal. *(ant)* dependable, honest.

15   **sequester** *(v)* keep apart or hide away from. *(s)* isolate, seclude, cloister, segregate. *(ant)* reveal, integrate.

16   **isolate** *(v)* set apart from the rest. *(s)* separate, confine, sequester, detach, insulate, seclude. *(ant)* integrate.

17   **temptation** *(n)* a thing that tempts or attracts someone. *(s)* lure, enticement, attraction, bait. *(ant)* aversion.

18   **segregate** *(v)* set apart from the rest. *(s)* disconnect, divide, isolate, separate, dissociate. *(ant)* integrate.

19   **unscrupulous** *(adj)* not fair or honest, having poor morals. *(s)* dishonest, corrupt, immoral. *(ant)* honest.

'So, what *exactly* is a Keeper?' Claire asked, getting the **gist**[1] of things but still **lagging**[2].

'Cadwalladers born of potential Instinct, who then earn and develop it, help *keep* the gem safe; it is our duty.'

'How has Rebecca got anything to do with this?'

'Ah, yes, Rebecca,' Gwilym replied, sighing.

---

1   **gist** *(n)* the general meaning of speech or text. *(s)* essence, idea, point, upshot, nub, basis.
2   **lag** *(v)* fall behind, not keep up with. *(s)* trail, dally, straggle, crawl, slow, wane, dawdle. *(ant)* lead, keep up.

4. Hidden in Plain Sight

Class 10J were chattering loud, **raucous**[1] nonsense and fidgeting incessantly. **Boisterous**[2] and impossible to control, they chucked rubbish and messed around as the ancient school bus limped along with the rush hour through town. **Disobeying**[3] **numerous**[4] **cautions**[5] to put away their phones, they sniggered at photos and texts, hiding them from view. They were en route to a museum, supposedly to help with their history exam, but to them, the study part would be no fun.

Rebecca Cadwallader's mouth opened and closed like a feeding fish. She chomped shamelessly on a piece of **prohibited**[6] gum, surrounded by her gang of **doting**[7] admirers. They hung on her every word as she gossiped and whinged, **criticising**[8] the trip. Next to her **slouched**[9] the source of her ill-placed **arrogance**[10], a smiling **youth**[11] named Josh Drane.

In constant trouble and regularly **suspended**[12] from school, Drane **revelled**[13] in the fear he

---

1   **raucous** *(adj)* making a harsh, loud noise. *(s)* wild, boisterous, unruly, disorderly. *(ant)* orderly, placid.

2   **boisterous** *(adj)* noisy and energetic (usually cheerfully). *(s)* lively, animated, rowdy, unruly. *(ant)* placid, quiet.

3   **disobey** *(v)* fail to obey (not do as one is asked). *(s)* defy, flout, violate, challenge, contravene. *(ant)* obey.

4   **numerous** *(adj)* many. *(s)* frequent, plentiful, abundant, various, copious, several, diverse. *(ant)* few, one.

5   **caution** *(n)* a warning. *(s)* ultimatum, reprimand, rebuke, telling-off, advice, reproof.

6   **prohibited** *(adj)* not permitted. *(s)* banned, forbidden, barred, vetoed, disallowed, outlawed. *(ant)* permitted.

7   **doting** *(adj)* showing excessive (too much) fondness. *(s)* adoring, idolising, besotted, indulgent. *(ant)* stony.

8   **criticise** *(v)* indicate faults in a disapproving way. *(s)* censure, condemn, malign, denounce. *(ant)* praise.

9   **slouch** *(v)* move, sit or stand in a drooping or lazy manner. *(s)* slump, stoop, hunch, sprawl. *(ant)* straighten.

10   **arrogance** *(n)* an exaggerated sense of one's importance. *(s)* big-headedness, conceit, pride. *(ant)* humility.

11   **youth** *(n)* a young person. *(s)* teenager, adolescent, junior, youngster, juvenile. *(ant)* adult, old person.

12   **suspend** *(v)* temporarily prevent or exclude from (school or job). *(s)* remove, reject, evict. *(ant)* include.

13   **revel** *(v)* gain pleasure from. *(s)* delight, bask, luxuriate, wallow, glory, enjoy, savour, relish. *(ant)* dislike, hate.

instilled[1] in his contemporaries[2], enjoying the effect he had on them. He skulked[3] in school corridors, shrouded[4] in hoodies, taunting teachers. He wore banned designer[5] trainers, knowing he'd be sent home, and smoked openly in the grounds, enticing[6] the younger kids to join in. There were rumours[7] of worse. Other schools refused to take him, so for now, he went unchecked[8]. Despite many ugly traits, he radiated[9] an odd attraction[10] to which Rebecca had recently become inexplicably[11] drawn.

'Do you want a Snickers, Becca?' Drane asked. 'I nicked two from the shop before we got on the bus. He's a right old dodderer[12], that shopkeeper. Dead easy to pinch[13] from.' The boy grinned.

Rebecca nodded an enthusiastic yes at him. Repulsed[14] by her, he felt his skin crawl as she gnawed[15] her grey gum, then blew a bubble. Her pathetic[16] bovine[17] expression reminded him of a cow chewing the cud[18].

Such a gullible fool, he thought smugly[19], hiding his contempt[20] for this girl.

He'd easily wrapped this one around his finger to do his bidding[21]. He'd practised for years,

---

1   **instil** *(v)* establish and fix an attitude in someone's mind. *(s)* implant, impress, introduce, induce. *(ant)* remove.

2   **contemporary** *(n)* a person around the same age as another. *(s)* peer, fellow, associate.

3   **skulk** *(v)* move furtively and stealthily, not wanting to be seen. *(s)* lurk, prowl, loiter. *(ant)* appear, materialise.

4   **shroud** *(v)* envelop or cover to prevent from being seen. *(s)* conceal, mask, hide, veil, swathe. *(ant)* reveal.

5   **designer** *(adj)* designed by a famous fashion designer. *(s)* trendy, fashionable, branded. *(ant)* unbranded.

6   **entice** *(v)* tempt or attract. *(s)* lure, cajole, invite, persuade, seduce, inveigle. *(ant)* dissuade, deter.

7   **rumour** *(n)* a circulating story of little or doubtful truth. *(s)* gossip, tale, anecdote, tittle-tattle. *(ant)* fact.

8   **unchecked** *(adj)* not restrained or controlled. *(s)* free, unimpeded, unhindered, unrestricted. *(ant)* checked.

9   **radiate** *(v)* emanate (give off) a feeling or quality. *(s)* transmit, exude, emit, circulate, shine. *(ant)* absorb.

10 **attraction** *(n)* a feature or quality that attracts interest or liking. *(s)* magnetism, appeal. *(ant)* repulsion.

11 **inexplicably** *(adv)* in an unexplainable way. *(s)* mysteriously, unaccountably, puzzlingly. *(ant)* explicably.

12 **dodderer** *(n)* a person who moves slowly or totters, typically because of old age. *(s)* codger. *(ant)* youngster.

13 **pinch** *(v)* take without permission. *(s)* steal, thieve, nab, nick, pilfer, swipe, snatch. *(ant)* purchase, buy, give.

14 **repulse** *(v)* cause to feel intense distaste, displeasure or disgust. *(s)* repel, sicken, revolt. *(ant)* attract.

15 **gnaw** *(v)* chew persistently. *(s)* bite, nibble, champ, chomp, masticate, munch, crunch.

16 **pathetic** *(adj)* arousing pity, inadequate. *(s)* pitiful, useless, laughable, weak. *(ant)* admirable, respectable.

17 **bovine** *(adj)* relating to (like) a cow or cattle, or stupid. *(s)* dim-witted, dim, dense, dull. *(ant)* intelligent.

18 **cud** *(n)* partly digested food from the stomach of a ruminant (animal that chews). *(s)* chewed food.

19 **smugly** *(adv)* in a smug (self-satisfied) way. *(s)* arrogantly, conceitedly, haughtily, snootily. *(ant)* humbly.

20 **contempt** *(n)* the feeling that someone or something is worthless. *(s)* disdain, dislike, scorn. *(ant)* admiration.

21 **bidding** *(n)* the asking or ordering of someone to do something. *(s)* request, command, behest.

and his master had taught him well; this dumb girl would do whatever he demanded of her. He ground his teeth and flashed her another fake smile. She beamed back.

'Ta, Josh,' **tittered**[1] Rebecca, **batting**[2] her mascara-caked lashes.

'It's gonna be, like, soooo boring today,' she said, fluttering her spidery lashes again. As if **oblivious**[3] to his disdain, which **bordered**[4] dangerously on hatred, her **vacuous**[5] eyes gazed an adoring look into his.

'Yeah, rubbish,' he lied, curling his lip, pretending to agree.

Staring out of the window, he silently **mocked**[6] her **banal**[7], **tedious**[8] remarks. **Compassion**[9] and **sympathy**[10] were alien to him; all his actions were a **calculated**[11] means to an end. He had planned the day with **meticulous**[12] precision, and failure was not an option. He would allow nothing to **interfere**[13] with his **preparation**[14]; he admired his master too greatly to fail him.

Using Rebecca Cadwallader had been Drane's idea. She would be their **insurance**[15] **policy**[16]. The Mal-Instinctives suspected the other sister, Claire, may have Instinct, and having a Cadwallader as a **hostage**[17] would make it difficult for the knights to save the gem and easier for his master to steal it. The Knights Hawk protected their own.

Sentimental[18] *old idiots*, he thought, spitting onto the floor.

---

1   **titter** *(v)* giggle or laugh. *(s)* snigger, snicker, chortle, cackle, chuckle, guffaw. *(ant)* cry, sob, weep.

2   **bat** *(v)* (of eyelashes) open and close in fluttering movements. *(s)* flicker, blink, flap, wink.

3   **oblivious** *(adj)* unaware or unconcerned about what is happening. *(s)* ignorant, unconscious. *(ant)* conscious.

4   **border** *(v)* come close to or be developing into. *(s)* verge, approach, near, resemble, encroach. *(ant)* differ.

5   **vacuous** *(adj)* having or showing lack of intelligence or thought. *(s)* empty, dim, inane, vacant. *(ant)* intelligent.

6   **mock** *(v)* tease or make fun of. *(s)* ridicule, deride, scorn, insult, taunt. *(ant)* praise, compliment, flatter.

7   **banal** *(adj)* boring or obvious from lack of originality. *(s)* trite, predictable, unimaginative. *(ant)* original.

8   **tedious** *(adj)* tiresome or monotonous. *(s)* long, slow, dull, boring, dreary, uninteresting. *(ant)* interesting.

9   **compassion** *(n)* sympathy and concern for the sufferings of another. *(s)* care, empathy. *(ant)* indifference.

10   **sympathy** *(n)* feelings of sorrow and pity for the misfortunes of another. *(s)* empathy. *(ant)* callousness.

11   **calculated** *(adj)* done with full awareness of the consequences. *(s)* deliberate, planned. *(ant)* spontaneous.

12   **meticulous** *(adj)* showing great attention to detail. *(s)* careful, precise, exact, scrupulous. *(ant)* careless, sloppy.

13   **interfere** *(v)* prevent from being carried out or continuing. *(s)* hamper, hinder, restrict, impede. *(ant)* assist.

14   **preparation** *(n)* something done to get ready for an event or undertaking. *(s)* planning. *(ant)* unreadiness.

15   **insurance** *(n)* protection against a possible outcome. *(s)* assurance, cover. *(ant)* endangerment, vulnerability.

16   **policy** *(n)* a contract of insurance between individuals or groups. *(s)* scheme, plan.

17   **hostage** *(n)* someone unwillingly held to be exchanged for something else. *(s)* captive, detainee. *(ant)* captor.

18   **sentimental** *(adj)* having nostalgic or sugary feelings. *(s)* soppy, mawkish, romantic. *(ant)* cynical, unemotional.

*

The museum exuded a quaint and **parochial**[1] **atmosphere**[2], and although it was large and **housed**[3] some **unrivalled**[4] **antiquities**[5], its tired **veneer**[6] needed **investment**[7] and modern **refurbishment**[8].

The Gwalch Gem bracelet lay in a low-key glass case, its resting place for many years. This innocent home was a perfect disguise for its **dazzling**[9] **supremacy**[10], the power it granted its wearer recognised by only a rare few.

To the average **spectator**[11], the bracelet passed as a pretty piece of gold-and-emerald jewellery. Nice but nothing special or, indeed, **priceless**[12], its real value and power **deliberately**[13] concealed. The Keepers engineered it this way, intending **minimal**[14] attention to be drawn to their secret force. They **shunned**[15] bulletproof glass and laser-beam protection, and purposely **stowed**[16] the gem in an open, public place. There they could guard it, and no one could wear it.

Mostly it was local schools and **pensioners**[17] who visited this museum. A lack of modern **installations**[18] did not attract **the masses**[19] but rather just a **meagre**[20] trickle of local people and

---

1   **parochial** *(adj)* with limited or narrow outlook or scope (small-town-like). *(s)* provincial, insular. *(ant)* broad.

2   **atmosphere** *(n)* the tone, mood or ambience. *(s)* impression, feeling, air, character.

3   **house** *(v)* provide space for or accommodate (keep in a certain place). *(s)* store, hold, retain. *(ant)* evict, expose.

4   **unrivalled** *(adj)* better than everything or everyone else. *(s)* unequalled, unique, matchless. *(ant)* inferior, poor.

5   **antiquity** *(n)* something from the ancient past. *(s)* relic, artefact, antique. *(ant)* novelty, modernity.

6   **veneer** *(n)* the outside layer or appearance of something. *(s)* cladding, covering, coating, front.

7   **investment** *(n)* time or money spent to gain or improve a result. *(s)* finance, expenditure. *(ant)* withdrawal.

8   **refurbishment** *(n)* improvement to make good again. *(s)* redecoration, renovation, restoration, repair, refit.

9   **dazzling** *(adj)* amazing or overwhelming due to an impressive quality. *(s)* stunning, overpowering. *(ant)* boring.

10   **supremacy** *(n)* the state of being supreme (superior) to all others. *(s)* dominance, superiority. *(ant)* inferiority.

11   **spectator** *(n)* someone who watches an event, game, show or thing. *(s)* onlooker, viewer. *(ant)* participant.

12   **priceless** *(adj)* so precious that a value cannot be put on it. *(s)* invaluable, rare, high-priced. *(ant)* worthless.

13   **deliberately** *(adv)* done in a deliberate (on purpose) way. *(s)* intentionally, knowingly. *(ant)* accidentally.

14   **minimal** *(adj)* of the smallest degree, quantity or amount. *(s)* least, slightest. *(ant)* maximum, most.

15   **shun** *(v)* ignore, avoid or reject with persistence. *(s)* evade, eschew, reject, spurn. *(ant)* seek, accept, welcome.

16   **stow** *(v)* store, pack or keep neatly in a specific place. *(s)* stash, secrete, tuck, deposit. *(ant)* unload, remove.

17   **pensioner** *(n)* a person who receives a pension (money invested or saved). *(s)* retiree.

18   **installation** *(n)* an art exhibition in a gallery or museum. *(s)* display, presentation, placing.

19   **the masses** *(n)* ordinary people. *(s)* the populace, the multitude, the public. *(ant)* the elite.

20   **meagre** *(adj)* inadequate or scant amount. *(s)* small, measly, derisory, paltry, insufficient. *(ant)* plentiful.

hordes[1] of bored schoolkids. This humble museum, tucked away in an **inconspicuous**[2] part of town, proved the perfect resting place for the Gwalch Gem bracelet.

*

'Come on, you lot, look lively! Switch off your phones, and if anyone's chewing gum, please **refrain**[3] by getting rid of it in that bin over there,' ordered Mr Hollie.

Mr Hollie taught 10J history, and Josh Drane didn't **faze**[4] him. No, indeed. **Hence**[5] the school **consenting**[6] to Drane's presence today. Mr Hollie had **assured**[7] the headmistress he could handle him, so she had relaxed the rules, hoping the **gesture**[8] of **independence**[9] might improve Drane's **attitude**[10] and, moreover, his behaviour. Mr Hollie had decided that if it came to it, he would **flex**[11] his **authoritative**[12] muscles today. This group was **infamous**[13] for its **notoriously**[14] challenging behaviour. The headmistress was often called in to **monitor**[15] tricky lessons. Today she had entrusted him to take this **problematic**[16] class on the field trip, and he was **determined**[17] to impress her.

Drane, Rebecca and their **dubious**[18] **cohort**[19] **reluctantly**[20] **trudged**[21] after their teacher. They

---

1   **horde** *(n)* a large group of people. *(s)* crowd, throng, mass, gathering, mob, host, multitude. *(ant)* few, one.

2   **inconspicuous** *(adj)* not clearly visible or attracting attention. *(s)* ordinary, quiet. *(ant)* conspicuous.

3   **refrain** *(v)* stop oneself from doing something. *(s)* desist, abstain, cease, resist, halt. *(ant)* persist, continue.

4   **faze** *(v)* disconcert or disturb. *(s)* bother, deter, daunt, intimidate, discourage. *(ant)* encourage.

5   **hence** *(adv)* for this reason or because of. *(s)* therefore, consequently, thus, so.

6   **consent** *(v)* grant permission or agreement to. *(s)* comply, permit, allow, sanction. *(ant)* dissent, forbid.

7   **assure** *(v)* tell someone something to dispel doubt. *(s)* promise, reassure, convince, persuade. *(ant)* worry.

8   **gesture** *(n)* an action to convey a feeling or intention of something. *(s)* act, indication, sign.

9   **independence** *(n)* freedom from the control of others. *(s)* self-rule, liberty, autonomy. *(ant)* dependence.

10   **attitude** *(n)* a way of thinking, feeling or acting. *(s)* approach, outlook, manner, mindset, opinion.

11   **flex** *(v)* cause muscles to stand out by contracting and tensing them. *(s)* activate, expand, tighten. *(ant)* relax.

12   **authoritative** *(adj)* commanding and likely to be respected and obeyed. *(s)* firm, imposing, decisive. *(ant)* weak.

13   **infamous** *(adj)* known for a bad quality, deed or behaviour. *(s)* notorious, disreputable, shady. *(ant)* reputable.

14   **notoriously** *(adv)* in a notorious (widely known) way. *(s)* flagrantly, infamously, overtly. *(ant)* obscurely.

15   **monitor** *(v)* observe and review, watch over. *(s)* check, supervise, control, scrutinise. *(ant)* ignore, mismanage.

16   **problematic** *(adj)* causing a problem. *(s)* difficult, tricky, challenging, awkward. *(ant)* easy.

17   **determined** *(adj)* having or displaying resolve. *(s)* resolute, intent on, firm, unwavering. *(ant)* irresolute.

18   **dubious** *(adj)* not to be relied upon. *(s)* questionable, untrustworthy, reluctant, shady. *(ant)* trustworthy.

19   **cohort** *(n)* a group of people with a shared characteristic. *(s)* gang, unit, troop, partnership. *(ant)* hotchpotch.

20   **reluctantly** *(adv)* in a reluctant (hesitant or unwilling) way. *(s)* half-heartedly, grudgingly. *(ant)* willingly.

21   **trudge** *(v)* walk slowly. *(s)* lumber, plod, trail, trek, tramp, traipse, slog. *(ant)* run, sprint, tiptoe.

spat out gum and threw drink cans into an overflowing bin at the museum's **unremarkable**[1] entrance. Drane's **haughty**[2] swagger and lack of interest hid **attuned**[3] **senses**[4] that operated on high alert. His tense limbs, his brain **adhering**[5] to his mental list, his **animosity**[6] towards Rebecca: all concealed an **acute**[7] **efficiency**[8] **simmering**[9] beneath his **brash**[10] **exterior**[11]. He **glowered**[12] with blatant **disrespect**[13] as the unsuspecting teacher **briefed**[14] his class.

'Right, you've got your notepads and pencils, so *actually* make some notes. We're meeting the **curator**[15], Mr Evans, in five minutes. As we're part of the local **community**[16], he's **graciously**[17] offered to give us a guided tour, which, I might add, is a **privilege**[18] not offered to everyone. I expect **exceptional**[19] behaviour, not **impudence**[20], and show some **gratitude**[21], will you?' lectured Mr Hollie to his mostly **disinterested**[22] pupils. 'Mr Evans is no **amateur**[23]; he knows his facts inside out. I suggest you make the most of it and listen. You'll be writing this up in our next

---

1   **unremarkable** *(adj)* not interesting or surprising (not noteworthy). *(s)* ordinary, average. *(ant)* extraordinary.

2   **haughty** *(adj)* high in one's own estimation. *(s)* arrogant, superior, disdainful, conceited. *(ant)* modest, humble.

3   **attuned** *(adj)* adjusted or acclimatised to something (used to). *(s)* accustomed, adapted. *(ant)* maladapted.

4   **sense** *(n)* a faculty of the body that perceives the external environment. *(s)* awareness, ability, perception.

5   **adhere** *(v)* follow closely or stick to something. *(s)* obey, abide, observe. *(ant)* abandon, disobey.

6   **animosity** *(n)* a strong hostility or aversion. *(s)* hatred, loathing, enmity, rancour. *(ant)* goodwill, friendship.

7   **acute** *(adj)* highly developed (on the ball). *(s)* clever, keen, sharp, shrewd, astute. *(ant)* blunt, stupid.

8   **efficiency** *(n)* maximum productivity with minimum waste. *(s)* competence, proficiency. *(ant)* inefficiency.

9   **simmer** *(v)* exist in a repressed (pushed down or hidden) state. *(s)* bubble, churn, fester.

10   **brash** *(adj)* cocky and overbearing. *(s)* arrogant, cheeky, brazen, pushy, impudent. *(ant)* self-effacing, mild.

11   **exterior** *(n)* (of a person) demeanour and behaviour. *(s)* air, bearing, appearance, front. *(ant)* interior.

12   **glower** *(v)* scowl angrily or sullenly (glare daggers at). *(s)* stare, frown, gloom. *(ant)* beam, smile.

13   **disrespect** *(n)* a lack of courtesy or respect. *(s)* contempt, disregard, boldness, insolence. *(ant)* respect.

14   **brief** *(v)* inform and instruct in preparation. *(s)* advise, explain, prime, direct, prepare, update.

15   **curator** *(n)* a person who looks after a collection of things or a museum. *(s)* caretaker, warden, supervisor.

16   **community** *(n)* a place and its inhabitants of similar characteristics. *(s)* area, district, neighbourhood.

17   **graciously** *(adv)* in a gracious (courteous) manner. *(s)* kindly, decently, generously. *(ant)* rudely, meanly.

18   **privilege** *(n)* a special honour (not simply a right). *(s)* benefit, treat, favour, advantage, boon. *(ant)* burden.

19   **exceptional** *(adj)* in a way that is unusually good. *(s)* outstanding, remarkable, excellent, great. *(ant)* bad, poor.

20   **impudence** *(n)* the quality of being rude. *(s)* audacity, insolence, impertinence, disrespect, cheek. *(ant)* respect.

21   **gratitude** *(n)* the quality of being thankful and showing appreciation. *(s)* thanks, gratefulness. *(ant)* ingratitude.

22   **disinterested** *(adj)* having no interest, being indifferent to something. *(s)* bored, apathetic. *(ant)* interested.

23   **amateur** *(n)* a person who is inept or incompetent (not good at). *(s)* novice, beginner, apprentice. *(ant)* expert.

lesson,' he continued in his **long-winded**[1] way. Mr Hollie was not known for being **pithy**[2], often appearing to overly enjoy the sound of his own voice.

As Mr Hollie paused, Josh Drane inhaled a **resoundingly**[3] noisy sniff, then let out the loudest, longest burp he could **muster**[4]. All eyes turned to him and then back to Mr Hollie. Looking **incensed**[5], the teacher whirled around as if to **chastise**[6] Drane but stopped **abruptly**[7] as a short, slight man clothed in a **fusty**[8] dark suit appeared and **extended**[9] his hand.

'Hello. You must be Mr Hollie from Chorlton High. I'm Robert Evans, the curator here. A pleasure to **make your acquaintance**[10],' he said to the obviously fuming teacher.

Mr Hollie glared at Drane, quickly switching to an **affable**[11] smile for Mr Evans. 'Um, hello, Mr Evans,' replied Mr Hollie, **flustered**[12]. 'Yes. And thank you so much for agreeing to give us a guided tour of your museum today. Meet my history pupils.' He waved an **imperious**[13] gesture at the now-silent kids. 'Oh, and this is Miss Malik, my assistant,' he added with a dismissive wave.

Josh Drane watched them, welcoming this attention, **precisely**[14] as planned. He intended all eyes to be **levelled**[15] his way for as long as possible. If they were too busy worrying what he was up to, they wouldn't catch anyone else, would they? Drane had spotted Evans's **baleful**[16] eyes watching him from the moment he'd entered the hall. Couldn't the Knights Hawk produce a

---

1   **long-winded** *(adj)* continuing at a boring length. *(s)* tedious, lengthy, pompous. *(ant)* concise, pithy.

2   **pithy** *(adj)* terse (short) and expressive. *(s)* brief, succinct, witty, concise. *(ant)* long-winded.

3   **resoundingly** *(adv)* in a resounding (emphatic, loud) manner. *(s)* sonorously, forcefully. *(ant)* weakly.

4   **muster** *(v)* summon up (a response, attitude or feeling). *(s)* gather, collect, rally, raise, call on. *(ant)* disperse.

5   **incensed** *(adj)* incredibly angry. *(s)* enraged, infuriated, exasperated, riled, annoyed. *(ant)* placated, calm.

6   **chastise** *(v)* scold (tell off) in a harsh manner. *(s)* berate, reprimand, discipline, rebuke, censure. *(ant)* praise.

7   **abruptly** *(adv)* in an abrupt (unexpected and sudden) way. *(s)* hastily, quickly, immediately. *(ant)* gradually.

8   **fusty** *(adj)* old-fashioned and outdated (not modern). *(s)* stuffy, dull, boring, conservative, musty. *(ant)* trendy.

9   **extend** *(v)* hold out towards (stretch or stick out). *(s)* offer, proffer, give, present. *(ant)* withdraw, retract.

10   **make someone's acquaintance** *(v)* meet someone for the first time.

11   **affable** *(adj)* amiable or cordial. *(s)* courteous, friendly, genial, pleasant, jovial, warm. *(ant)* unfriendly, cold.

12   **flustered** *(adj)* agitated and confused. *(s)* unsettled, alarmed, disconcerted, perturbed. *(ant)* calm.

13   **imperious** *(adj)* bossy and high-handed. *(s)* domineering, arrogant, superior. *(ant)* subservient, humble.

14   **precisely** *(adv)* in a precise (exact) way. *(s)* meticulously, absolutely, strictly, just, without doubt. *(ant)* vaguely.

15   **level** *(v)* direct or aim towards. *(s)* point, turn, cast, address, incline, train, focus. *(ant)* avert.

16   **baleful** *(adj)* menacing or threatening harm. *(s)* unfriendly, hostile, vindictive, malevolent. *(ant)* benevolent.

superior[1] shield for their precious bracelet, rather than some **decrepit**[2] old **intellectual**[3]? This task would be easier than he'd thought.

'Follow me, please,' said Mr Evans through barely **visible**[4] lips and crooked, yellowing teeth. 'We have our cinema, where we show visitors an **introductory**[5] film of the museum's history and its **resident**[6] pieces. It also highlights the **pertinent**[7] safety aspects of today's visit. Come this way,' he continued, leading Mr Hollie and his pupils through the exhibition hall and towards a tired-looking side room.

Josh Drane bent down, pretending to tie a lace on his **forbidden**[8] trainers; he knew he wouldn't be sent home today for rule-breaking. Standing up slowly, he patted his pocket, the flick knife he'd concealed safely stowed away, its blade **retracted**[9] for now.

'Come on, Becs, you're sittin' with me,' he said, grabbing her arm and pulling her to the back row.

*

As the **rowdy**[10] kids **filed**[11] into the cinema, squabbling over seats, no one noticed a **nondescript**[12] boy peel off from the back of the line and walk away. They were all too **preoccupied**[13] with Drane and his giggling girlfriend.

No one noticed the tall, suited man slip into the museum as the security guard nipped to the loo to check messages on his phone.

No one noticed the soot-black cat slink silently through the entrance, weaving its way amongst the **maze**[14] of glass showcases scattered throughout the exhibition hall.

---

1   **superior** *(adj)* greater in power or size (better than). *(s)* finer, worthier, advanced, improved. *(ant)* inferior.

2   **decrepit** *(adj)* elderly and infirm. *(s)* old, creaky, deteriorated, feeble, rickety, frail. *(ant)* hearty, vigorous.

3   **intellectual** *(n)* a person possessing a highly developed intellect. *(s)* scholar, academic, erudite. *(ant)* ignoramus.

4   **visible** *(adj)* able to be seen. *(s)* noticeable, evident, perceptible, obvious. *(ant)* invisible, imperceptible.

5   **introductory** *(adj)* serving as an opening or an introduction. *(s)* preliminary, initial. *(ant)* concluding.

6   **resident** *(adj)* living or staying somewhere on a long-term basis. *(s)* occupying, residing. *(ant)* transient.

7   **pertinent** *(adj)* appropriate, applicable or relevant. *(s)* apposite, apt, suitable, fitting. *(ant)* irrelevant.

8   **forbidden** *(adj)* not allowed. *(s)* banned, prohibited, stopped, disallowed, denied, vetoed. *(ant)* allowed.

9   **retract** *(v)* draw back into something. *(s)* withdraw, pull in, sheathe. *(ant)* extend.

10   **rowdy** *(adj)* loud and noisy. *(s)* disorderly, unruly, raucous, disruptive, boisterous, rebellious. *(ant)* restrained.

11   **file** *(v)* walk behind one another in a line (single file). *(s)* march, troop, trail, parade, funnel. *(ant)* crowd.

12   **nondescript** *(adj)* lacking interesting or distinguishing features. *(s)* unremarkable, ordinary. *(ant)* special.

13   **preoccupied** *(adj)* engrossed in thought or mentally distracted. *(s)* absorbed, concerned. *(ant)* unconcerned.

14   **maze** *(n)* a puzzling network of something (paths, passages, etc.). *(s)* warren, web, labyrinth.

In the stale-smelling cinema, Mr Evans had started the film. It creaked and whirred into life. From the tiny screening space, the exhibition hall remained fully visible; it allowed only one way in and one way out. The boy Drane would be clearly seen if he left the cinema.

*

The teachers and pupils finally settled down to watch the film – that is, all except one.

'Here, Becs, have some of this; Hollie won't see,' said Drane, furtively handing Rebecca a can of drink.

'Ta, Josh. Don't care if he sees it, anyway,' she replied, **guzzling**[1] the drink.

'Yeah, too right,' he replied, smirking a grin of **encouragement**[2].

The powder Drane had poured into the can was completely tasteless.

---

1   **guzzle** *(v)* eat or drink greedily. *(s)* gulp, swig, wolf, swallow, consume, swill, devour. *(ant)* nibble, sip.
2   **encouragement** *(n)* the act of supporting someone. *(s)* endorsement, support, reassurance. *(ant)* discouragement.

5. Worse than Cross-Country

Whilst Rebecca and most of the class were **ensconced**[1] in the museum's cinema, Claire was sitting in the cosy kitchen in Anglesey, the true reason for her being there about to unfold.

'Ah, yes, Rebecca,' replied Gwilym, sighing.

Claire knew Gwilym's story would **inevitably**[2] lead to her sister. Biting her lip, she searched Gwilym's face for clues, dreading what he might say next.

'Rebecca is being held by Mal-Instinctives **intent**[3] on stealing the Gwalch Gem bracelet. We must help her and protect the bracelet.'

'The Mal-whats? What are they? Why do they want my sister?' screeched Claire.

'To distract us,' replied Gwilym.

'From what?' said Claire, gnawing at her fingernails.

'In gratitude for finding the gold, Llywelyn granted his most trusted knights the gift of Instinct, and we became the Knights Hawk. But when Llywelyn's **callous**[4] brother stole the bracelet, he controlled it. He gave *his* followers Instinct but, **regrettably**[5], Instinct of a different kind – one of **malice**[6]. Mal-Instinctives are our enemies. They seek to find and control the bracelet with a **fanatical**[7] and enduring **tenacity**[8], and we must stop them.'

---

1   **ensconce** *(v)* settle in a safe or comfortable place. *(s)* entrench, install, establish, situate.

2   **inevitably** *(adv)* in an inevitable (unavoidable) way. *(s)* certainly, definitely, inescapably. *(ant)* doubtfully.

3   **intent** *(adj)* determined to do something. *(s)* decided, resolute, resolved, committed. *(ant)* reluctant.

4   **callous** *(adj)* having a cruel and heartless disregard for others. *(s)* hard, unfeeling, uncaring. *(ant)* caring.

5   **regrettably** *(adv)* with regret (sadness). *(s)* unfortunately, undesirably, deplorably, woefully. *(ant)* fortunately.

6   **malice** *(n)* the desire to hurt or harm someone. *(s)* spite, animosity, malevolence, evil, hate. *(ant)* kindness.

7   **fanatical** *(adj)* obsessively concerned with something. *(s)* dedicated, extreme, fervent, fixated. *(ant)* indifferent.

8   **tenacity** *(n)* the quality of being determined and persistent. *(s)* stubbornness, resolve, diligence. *(ant)* irresolution.

An **uptight**[1] silence **stifled**[2] the air.

'So you're saying there are people that look like you and me out there, but they're bad, really bad, and they've got Rebecca?' Claire asked, gnawing at her skin now.

'Yes, cariad,' replied Gladys, joining in. 'They have Rebecca.'

Claire stared at the three people. 'I got here by listening to a cat, following a dog, being pulled along by a horse,' she **ranted**[3], 'and you've been lying to me for ages, Gladys.' She pointed at her and stood up.

Tears of **frustration**[4] brimmed as she spoke, but an impatient **rapping**[5] at the door stopped her from crying. Shocked, she stared around the table.

'Who's that?' she asked.

They'd not mentioned anyone else. She'd heard no one approach. Jack hadn't barked.

Without answering or hesitating, Gwilym opened the door.

A man of **hulking**[6] **stature**[7] bowed his head under the doorframe. His **khaki**[8] **overalls**[9] were tucked into heavy, muddy boots. A black visor pulled up over a green helmet revealed his face. Chunky headphones sat over the top, and a miniature microphone **protruded**[10] from the side, covering his mouth. Claire gawped at him; she'd spent a lot of time speechless today.

'Come, Claire, I can explain more on our way; we must go,' said Gwilym.

'I'm not going anywhere with you,' she snapped. 'Tell me how I can get the train back home.'

'Claire, it's time to leave,' repeated Gwilym.

'Leave to go where? I don't even know why you dragged me all this way in the first place. You could have told me all this at home, Gladys.'

---

1 **uptight** *(adj)* tense or angry, but controlled. *(s)* edgy, uneasy, anxious, bothered. *(ant)* calm, composed, cool.

2 **stifle** *(v)* constrain, prevent or choke. *(s)* hinder, hamper, suppress, smother, withhold. *(ant)* release, relieve.

3 **rant** *(v)* speak or shout in a lengthy and passionate way. *(s)* bluster, yell, bellow, rage, go on. *(ant)* sweet-talk.

4 **frustration** *(n)* an upset or annoyance. *(s)* aggravation, irritation, exasperation. *(ant)* success, satisfaction.

5 **rapping** *(n)* an act of repeated striking against a hard surface. *(s)* knocking, tapping, thumping, thwacking.

6 **hulking** *(adj)* (of a person) large and heavy. *(s)* bulky, colossal, massive, gargantuan, imposing. *(ant)* dainty.

7 **stature** *(n)* a person's natural height, size or build. *(s)* physique, figure, tallness, form, shape, frame.

8 **khaki** *(n)* fabric of a dull greenish or brownish-yellow colour (often military clothing).

9 **overalls** *(n)* a one-piece garment (clothing) worn over ordinary clothes. *(s)* coveralls, all-in-one.

10 **protrude** *(v)* extend above or beyond a surface (stick out). *(s)* poke out, jut, project. *(ant)* withdraw.

'Wales is the **catalyst**[1] for your Instinct, cariad. Instinct is only truly **awakened**[2] for the first time when in Wales, where the gold was mined. We had no choice,' said Gladys.

Teary-eyed, Claire gave Gladys a long, hard hug; if Gladys had fibbed to her, it must have been with good reason.

'You don't have to go, cariad; **ultimately**[3], the decision is yours.' Gladys gently **prised**[4] Claire away from her as she spoke. 'But listen to your Instinct. What does it tell you?' She wiped a tear from Claire's cheek.

Claire couldn't speak; the lump at the back of her throat stopped her. She picked up her school coat and put it back on. She grabbed her backpack and **bade**[5] a more formal goodbye to Anwen. Glancing at Gladys one more time, and without saying another word, she followed Gwilym and the uniformed man through the door.

The chill and gloom **dismayed**[6] her, and this time, no **attractive**[7] pony waited to take them. Thankful for her coat, she zipped it up and trailed after the men, an obvious **unwillingness**[8] in her manner. The men moved swiftly past the house and around the back of a stone barn. She squeaked with sudden joy as a flash of white **bowled**[9] alongside her; she'd never been so pleased to see Jack at her feet as she was now.

'Jacky! Thank goodness! I thought you weren't coming,' she panted, struggling to keep up, wishing she'd tried harder in PE and eaten fewer sweets.

Beyond the barn stood another stone building, with four wooden doors on the front. Three remained closed, but one was divided horizontally into two, a catch **retaining**[10] the top in place. As Claire approached, a low whinny **preceded**[11] the **adorable**[12] pony who had brought her here,

---

1   **catalyst** *(n)* something or someone that causes an event to begin. *(s)* spur, spark. *(ant)* inhibitor.

2   **awaken** *(v)* rouse into existence or activity. *(s)* wake, stir, arouse, evoke, kindle, stimulate. *(ant)* lull.

3   **ultimately** *(adv)* in the end. *(s)* finally, basically, fundamentally, eventually, conclusively. *(ant)* immediately.

4   **prise** *(v)* use force to pull or move apart. *(s)* wrench, lever, yank, tug, heave, haul. *(ant)* push, clamp.

5   **bid** *(v)* say a greeting or farewell (past tense: *bade*). *(s)* wish, utter.

6   **dismay** *(v)* cause to feel upset, concerned or distressed. *(s)* dishearten, dispirit, perturb. *(ant)* encourage.

7   **attractive** *(adj)* appealing or pleasing (nice-looking). *(s)* alluring, charming, desirable. *(ant)* repellent, ugly.

8   **unwillingness** *(n)* a reluctance to do something. *(s)* disinclination, hesitation, trepidation. *(ant)* willingness.

9   **bowl** *(v)* move rapidly in a certain direction. *(s)* speed, hurtle, roll, career, careen, streak. *(ant)* flounder.

10   **retain** *(v)* keep or fix something in place. *(s)* hold, maintain, restrain. *(ant)* release, free.

11   **precede** *(v)* come before in order, position or time. *(s)* introduce, foreshadow, lead. *(ant)* follow, succeed.

12   **adorable** *(adj)* lovable and appealing. *(s)* gorgeous, sweet, delectable, endearing. *(ant)* detestable.

her head popping over the stable door. Claire took a **wary**[1] step back and stopped within an arm's length of her.

'What's her name? I've forgotten,' she called out to Gwilym, unsure whether to touch.

'Welsh Lady,' replied Gwilym, walking back towards the pony. The man in overalls stopped and waited.

As Gwilym approached, the pony whinnied a soft, gentle greeting. He rubbed the side of her nose with the back of his fingers.

'Stroke her; she's as gentle as a lamb,' he said.

Unsure, Claire touched her pinky-white **muzzle**[2], and as if sensing her **apprehension**[3], the pony **stilled**[4]. Only her **pert**[5] rust-coloured ears moved, facing fully forward. The unfamiliar smells **tantalised**[6] Claire's nose: crisp, clean air, fresh hay and straw, and the indescribable smell of a well-kept, beautifully groomed horse. The pony's neck shone, soft and sleek. Her nostrils **flared**[7] as she whinnied again, encouraging Claire to continue stroking. She studied the pony's **dusky**[8] eyes, round and gentle, dressed with long, **sweeping**[9] lashes and **flecked**[10] with tones of warm amber. Although unfamiliar with horses, Claire sensed her **wisdom**[11] and kindness.

Gwilym watched her, his expression softening momentarily. 'Claire, we must go. I'm sure you will meet her again.'

Claire hoped so as she stole one last stroke of Lady's **chestnut**[12] neck. **Loath**[13] to leave the stables, she sniffed the wonderful horsey aroma on her hands and followed the two men.

The quaint farmhouse was hidden in the bottom of a deep bowl-shaped valley, steep, tree-

---

1   **wary** *(adj)* cautious about a problem or danger. *(s)* cagey, guarded, circumspect, careful. *(ant)* unwary.

2   **muzzle** *(n)* nose and mouth of an animal. *(s)* snout, snozzle.

3   **apprehension** *(n)* fear that something bad may happen. *(s)* worry, unease, anxiety. *(ant)* confidence.

4   **still** *(v)* become quiet, silent or unmoving. *(s)* calm, quieten, subdue, silence. *(ant)* arouse, unsettle.

5   **pert** *(adj)* (of a body part) small and well shaped. *(s)* jaunty, neat, trim, perky, animated. *(ant)* limp, lifeless.

6   **tantalise** *(v)* excite or tease the senses. *(s)* entice, tempt, fascinate, lure, draw. *(ant)* gratify, satisfy.

7   **flare** *(v)* (of nostrils) spread or widen. *(s)* open, expand, dilate, broaden, splay, grow. *(ant)* contract.

8   **dusky** *(adj)* deep and darkish in colour. *(s)* shadowy, hazy. *(ant)* bright, clear, light.

9   **sweeping** *(adj)* extending in a continuous curve (curved and long). *(s)* wide, full, broad. *(ant)* narrow.

10   **flecked** *(adj)* marked with flecks of colour. *(s)* spotted, splashed, freckled, streaked. *(ant)* unmarked.

11   **wisdom** *(n)* the quality of having experience or good judgement. *(s)* intelligence, insight. *(ant)* foolishness.

12   **chestnut** *(adj)* deep reddish brown like the colour of a chestnut. *(s)* rusty, coppery.

13   **loath** *(adj)* unwilling or reluctant (not wanting to do something). *(s)* opposed, disinclined, averse. *(ant)* eager.

covered sides shielding it and its **inhabitants**[1] from the outside world. A three-hundred-and-sixty-degree armoured coat of almost-**impassable**[2] thick **flora**[3] and **vegetation**[4] surrounded them. Grateful to be wearing *her* coat, Claire **stooped**[5] to enter the dense, dark wood, leaving the farm behind. Pulling her sleeves down over her hands, she looked up the hill, but all she could see was an **everlasting**[6] **mesh**[7] of thick, threatening forest that rose above them as far as the eye could see.

'Don't lose sight of Owain,' Gwilym warned. 'Keep going.'

'I'll try,' she answered, **unconvinced**[8].

Thrusting branches from their faces, they took a narrow, winding pathway, a track so well camouflaged it seemed only visible to Owain, who led the way. Claire followed with Gwilym staying behind, sandwiching her safely between them. Jack **hared**[9] back and **forth**[10], criss-crossing the track, **glints**[11] of white darting and streaking, careering between the **pillars**[12] of packed trees.

How does he do that without bashing into a tree? she marvelled to herself.

His tail whirred in delight as he grunted and snorted, **mimicking**[13] a **piglet**[14] **grubbing**[15] and rummaging in the wet earth. It reassured Claire that he seemed **carefree**[16] and happy,

---

1 **inhabitant** *(n)* person or animal that occupies or lives in a space. *(s)* occupant, resident, incumbent. *(ant)* guest.

2 **impassable** *(adj)* impossible to travel along, over or through. *(s)* impenetrable, inaccessible. *(ant)* accessible.

3 **flora** *(n)* plants or vegetation. *(s)* botany, herbage.

4 **vegetation** *(n)* a collection of plants, flora and foliage (usually in the wild). *(s)* botany, herbage.

5 **stoop** *(v)* bend one's head or body forward and downwards into a hunch. *(s)* crouch, slouch. *(ant)* straighten.

6 **everlasting** *(adj)* lasting forever or a long time. *(s)* continuous, endless, ceaseless, perpetual. *(ant)* temporary.

7 **mesh** *(n)* an interlaced structure. *(s)* lattice, network, webbing, tangle.

8 **unconvinced** *(adj)* unsure that something is true or can be trusted. *(s)* dubious, disbelieving. *(ant)* convinced.

9 **hare** *(v)* run with great speed and agility. *(s)* race, bolt, gallop, hustle, scoot, hotfoot, fly, career. *(ant)* dawdle.

10 **forth** *(adv)* forward in direction (or time). *(s)* onwards, ahead, away, along, headlong. *(ant)* back.

11 **glint** *(n)* a small gleam or flash of light. *(s)* glimmer, shimmer, flicker, sparkle, glance, trace. *(ant)* dullness.

12 **pillar** *(n)* a tall vertical structure. *(s)* column, post, pole, tower.

13 **mimic** *(v)* resemble or imitate (copy or behave like). *(s)* mirror, impersonate, simulate. *(ant)* differ from.

14 **piglet** *(n)* a baby or young pig.

15 **grub** *(v)* poke or dig about in the soil (often in search of food). *(s)* unearth, rummage, forage. *(ant)* plant, bury.

16 **carefree** *(adj)* free from anxiety and responsibility. *(s)* nonchalant, blithe, jovial, breezy, jaunty. *(ant)* troubled.

snuffling[1] and **tearing**[2] through the **undergrowth**[3].

As they **proceeded**[4], the treacherous track narrowed, steepening sharply as she began to **haul**[5] herself up the wooded hill. A springy bed of shifting pine needles, fallen **boughs**[6] and broken branches made for an **unstable**[7], precarious floor. Not being able to see the sky above scared her, the **confines**[8] of the **oppressive**[9] **greenery**[10] **suffocating**[11] her.

Owain, the man in front, moved easily, **forging**[12] ahead, but Claire sweated, struggling to climb. Pausing for a second, she unzipped her coat. She pictured Ben at cross-country, running that **atrocious**[13] course. Which was worse? She was blindly following this man she didn't even know! She glanced behind at Gwilym, who followed her patiently, his breathing even and unhurried. Gripping her toes deeper into the bed of pine needles, she **bore down**[14] hard with her legs, pushing herself up. Her muscles ached and her legs trembled as she clambered higher up the slope. Crawling painfully upwards, she yearned to flop down, roll onto her back and cry.

Owain became increasingly difficult to see as Claire struggled to keep up with him, especially since he wore a smudged dull-green khaki jacket. The pine trees and shrubs **intertwined**[15], so much so that the **scant**[16] path became **imperceptible**[17]. In its place, fallen twisted trees and bushy branches blocked their way. She'd have crawled in never-ending circles if she wasn't

---

1   **snuffle** *(v)* make repeated sniffing and breathing sounds as though smelling at something. *(s)* snort, pant, sniff.

2   **tear** *(v)* move exceedingly quickly. *(s)* dash, sprint, race, hare, charge, streak, pelt, zip, rip. *(ant)* saunter, amble.

3   **undergrowth** *(n)* dense growth of plants, shrubs and vegetation. *(s)* scrub, underbrush.

4   **proceed** *(v)* move forward. *(s)* continue, advance, progress, journey, travel. *(ant)* cease, recede, retreat.

5   **haul** *(v)* drag or pull with force or effort. *(s)* tow, lug, heave, yank, wrench. *(ant)* push, shove.

6   **bough** *(n)* a main branch of a tree. *(s)* limb, spur, offshoot, fork, appendage.

7   **unstable** *(adj)* not firm or secure, likely to give way. *(s)* insecure, precarious, unsound, changeable. *(ant)* stable.

8   **confines** *(n)* restrictive boundaries and limits of the surrounding region. *(s)* borders, limitations, margins.

9   **oppressive** *(adj)* weighing heavily on the mind, spirits or mood. *(s)* overwhelming, overpowering. *(ant)* light.

10   **greenery** *(n)* growing plants, green foliage and vegetation.

11   **suffocate** *(v)* cause to feel trapped, oppressed and unable to breathe. *(s)* choke, stifle, smother. *(ant)* free.

12   **forge** *(v)* move forward with a gradual and steady pace. *(s)* advance, progress, proceed, march. *(ant)* stop, halt.

13   **atrocious** *(adj)* extremely unpleasant. *(s)* dreadful, appalling, terrible, vile, frightful, dire. *(ant)* wonderful.

14   **bear down** *(v)* push in a downwards direction (past tense: *bore down*). *(s)* push down, press down.

15   **intertwine** *(v)* twist something together. *(s)* entwine, interweave, link, knit, mesh. *(ant)* untwine.

16   **scant** *(adj)* barely sufficient or adequate. *(s)* meagre, negligible, limited, scarce, inadequate. *(ant)* extensive.

17   **imperceptible** *(adj)* so subtle or gradual as not to be perceived (noticed). *(s)* unnoticeable, faint. *(ant)* obvious.

following Owain. **Distressed**[1], she stopped to check behind her.

She couldn't see Gwilym or Jack at all, yet they'd been there a moment ago. She tried to stand up to get a better view of where she was, but the **terrain**[2] was too steep; she'd risk falling. 'Jack!' she shouted. 'Gwilym, where are you? I can't see you!' Panicking, she scrambled a bit further up, trying to turn herself around to see, but it was impossible; she'd have to keep climbing. There was a slight ledge jutting up ahead; if she made it there, she could rest for a second.

'Jack!' she shouted again.

'Keep moving, Claire; the **summit**[3] is near.' Gwilym's voice sounded distant and **muffled**[4]. She had no idea which direction it was coming from.

She didn't want to keep moving; she was tired of tripping over **booby-trap**[5] roots, being shredded by **brambles**[6] and stung by nettles. She was clueless as to how far they'd climbed, but it all felt **gruelling**[7], like she'd covered miles. She had no idea where Owain was now, or the summit of anything; she could see nothing but undergrowth and trees. She pulled at gnarled, thorny stems for support, holding on for dear life.

As the **gradient**[8] sharpened to what felt like **vertical**[9], she knew she must try to reach a better **vantage**[10] point and wait for Gwilym or Jack. Her arms begged for relief. Cross-country was a **cinch**[11] compared to this – she'd never moan again.

Exhausted[12], she dug deep, pushing hard, when suddenly something yanked at both her ankles, and the **pulpy**[13] earth fell away beneath her feet. She landed on her stomach, her chin hitting the

---

1   **distressed** *(adj)* suffering from extreme anxiety, pain or sorrow. *(s)* anguished, miserable. *(ant)* soothed.

2   **terrain** *(n)* a stretch of ground or its features. *(s)* area, land, environment, territory, setting, shape.

3   **summit** *(n)* the highest point. *(s)* peak, top, apex, brow. *(ant)* bottom, base.

4   **muffled** *(adj)* not loud due to being obstructed or muted in some way. *(s)* stifled, faint, soft. *(ant)* loud.

5   **booby trap** *(n)* a trap or device appearing to be innocent when not. *(s)* ambush, trip wire, snare.

6   **bramble** *(n)* a prickly, thorny shrub, especially a blackberry bush. *(s)* brier, burr, gorse.

7   **gruelling** *(adj)* extremely demanding and tiring. *(s)* exhausting, arduous, strenuous, harrowing. *(ant)* easy.

8   **gradient** *(n)* degree of steepness. *(s)* incline, pitch, angle, leaning.

9   **vertical** *(adj)* at right angles to a horizontal plane. *(s)* perpendicular, erect, upright, plumb. *(ant)* horizontal.

10   **vantage** *(n)* a position or place offering the best view. *(s)* viewpoint, angle, stance.

11   **cinch** *(n)* an easy task. *(s)* breeze, nothing, doddle, gift, snap, cakewalk. *(ant)* difficulty, nightmare, hardship.

12   **exhausted** *(adj)* extremely tired. *(s)* drained, shattered, fatigued, debilitated. *(ant)* refreshed, energised.

13   **pulpy** *(adj)* soft and mushy. *(s)* springy, spongy, pliable, cushiony, yielding. *(ant)* firm, rigid, unyielding.

earth with a thud. **Winded**[1], she lost her grip and began grabbing at roots and branches, her face in the dirt as she slid downwards, feet first, flat on her front.

Claire grasped wildly at spiky **foliage**[2], but it tore **relentlessly**[3] at her fingers as she **desperately**[4] **grappled**[5] to halt her increasing **momentum**[6]. Her body whacked against a spiny branch, which **mercilessly**[7] snapped back, whipping against her cheek. Slipping further, she **clutched**[8] at lower branches, clawing at their scratchy **bark**[9]. **Friction**[10] **seared**[11] her **smarting**[12] fingers. She was **hurtling**[13] along now, grabbing air, but then she managed to grasp a branch and **wedge**[14] her feet between two trees. Gasping, she slowed to a **chaotic**[15] stop on a slight plateau.

Dazed and disorientated, she blinked, spitting out dirt and pine needles. She had fallen a fair way. Everywhere hurt and her eyes stung. Shaking with **exertion**[16] and fear, she looked down for Gwilym, but all she saw was one of the boys from the station at Crewe. It was the stockier one, who'd sat next to her on the platform, and he was about to grab hold of her ankles – again.

Pedalling wild bicycle kicks at him, she tried to roll over, but her backpack was stuck fast, tangled around some branches. She managed to twist onto her side, but he was almost upon her. Frantically trying to release herself, she yanked at the straps, but to no **avail**[17]; she was **ensnared**[18].

---

1   **winded** *(adj)* having difficulty breathing due to exertion or a blow to the stomach. *(s)* breathless.

2   **foliage** *(n)* lots of plant leaves together (collectively). *(s)* greenery, vegetation, verdure, flora.

3   **relentlessly** *(adv)* in a relentless (persistent) way. *(s)* insistently, ceaselessly, harshly, inexorably. *(ant)* slackly.

4   **desperately** *(adv)* in a desperate (hopeless) way. *(s)* frantically, frenziedly, urgently. *(ant)* calmly, moderately.

5   **grapple** *(v)* engage in a struggle. *(s)* wrestle, fight, battle, tussle, scuffle. *(ant)* surrender.

6   **momentum** *(n)* the impetus (speed) gained by a moving object. *(s)* force, motion, thrust. *(ant)* inertia.

7   **mercilessly** *(adv)* in a way that shows no mercy or clemency (forgiveness). *(s)* cruelly, harshly. *(ant)* kindly.

8   **clutch** *(v)* grab or grasp something tightly. *(s)* hold, grip, seize, clench, grapple. *(ant)* release, let go.

9   **bark** *(n)* the tough outer protective sheath of woody trees and shrubs.

10   **friction** *(n)* resistance when two surfaces rub together. *(s)* scraping, chafing, rubbing, abrasion.

11   **sear** *(v)* scorch or burn the surface of with intense heat. *(s)* singe, char, blister, sizzle. *(ant)* cool, freeze.

12   **smarting** *(adj)* feeling sharp, stinging pain. *(s)* burning, hurting, throbbing, aching. *(ant)* soothed, eased.

13   **hurtle** *(v)* move at speed, typically in an uncontrolled way. *(s)* career, bolt, bowl, dash, careen. *(ant)* dawdle.

14   **wedge** *(v)* force between or into a narrow space. *(s)* lodge, jam, cram, push, thrust, fix, hold. *(ant)* dislodge.

15   **chaotic** *(adj)* in a state of confusion and disorder. *(s)* muddled, haywire, messy, untidy. *(ant)* orderly.

16   **exertion** *(n)* mental or physical effort. *(s)* action, toil, labour, hard work. *(ant)* ease, rest, inaction.

17   **avail** *(n)* benefit or use. *(s)* advantage, reward, purpose, gain, profit, help, boon, edge. *(ant)* uselessness.

18   **ensnare** *(v)* catch or seize as though in a trap. *(s)* capture, entangle, snare, trap, enmesh. *(ant)* release.

'Get off me! Get off me!' she yelled, **parrying**[1] with her feet, but he **deflected**[2] them easily. 'Jack! Gwilym!' she yelled.

'They won't hear you,' the boy hissed. 'My friend has distracted them.'

'Get off me!' she screamed as he managed to grab her by the arm. But his strength far **surpassed**[3] hers, and he **hoisted**[4] her to her feet, **liberating**[5] her backpack with **ease**[6].

'Get up and shut up,' he said, hauling her upright and pulling her through the dense foliage.

'You're hurting me,' she yelled. 'Let go of me!'

He ignored her **protests**[7], jerking her harder and dragging her mercilessly down the hill into a small **glade**[8].

'What do you want with me? Where are you taking me?' she asked, **writhing**[9] beneath his grasp.

'If you say one more word, I'm **gagging**[10] you.'

Claire briefly caught his eyes, and the **enmity**[11] they exuded **overwhelmed**[12] her. He reminded her of Josh Drane. She stopped struggling but his grip remained **unrelenting**[13].

They stood together silently in the clearing. The boy's head tilted, **surveying**[14] the immediate area; he seemed to be waiting, listening for something.

Terrified and exhausted, she tried to think. Earning Instinct, being knighted, was any of it **credible**[15]? She was a hostage. What would Ben do now? Probably fight his way out, but she

---

1 **parry** *(v)* ward (fight) off an attack with a countermove. *(s)* deflect, block, dodge, prevent. *(ant)* take, allow.

2 **deflect** *(v)* cause to deviate from a course. *(s)* repel, avert, divert, prevent, ward off.

3 **surpass** *(v)* be better or greater than. *(s)* beat, eclipse, exceed, overshadow, transcend. *(ant)* follow, fail.

4 **hoist** *(v)* raise or haul up. *(s)* lift, erect, heave, winch, elevate. *(ant)* lower, drop.

5 **liberate** *(v)* set free. *(s)* detach, release, unfetter, disengage, unhook. *(ant)* restrain, confine, limit, prevent.

6 **ease** *(n)* absence of difficulty or effort. *(s)* easiness, efficiency, nonchalance, simplicity. *(ant)* difficulty.

7 **protest** *(n)* an expression of disapproval, disagreement or objection. *(s)* complaint, fuss. *(ant)* approval.

8 **glade** *(n)* an open space in a forest or wooded area. *(s)* clearing, opening, gap, dell.

9 **writhe** *(v)* twist and turn, contort the body. *(s)* squirm, wriggle, struggle, thrash. *(ant)* still, relax.

10 **gag** *(v)* put a gag over or into someone's mouth to stop them speaking. *(s)* restrain, muzzle, tape.

11 **enmity** *(n)* a state or feeling of active hostility. *(s)* hate, animosity, rancour. *(ant)* friendship, amity, goodwill.

12 **overwhelm** *(v)* have a strong emotional effect. *(s)* overcome, shake, disturb, stagger. *(ant)* underwhelm.

13 **unrelenting** *(adj)* not relenting (giving in). *(s)* unyielding, inexorable, relentless, merciless. *(ant)* relenting.

14 **survey** *(v)* look closely at or examine. *(s)* study, inspect, analyse, assess, evaluate, consider. *(ant)* overlook.

15 **credible** *(adj)* able to be believed. *(s)* believable, convincing, plausible, realistic. *(ant)* unbelievable.

wasn't Ben, and she couldn't fight her way out of this.

Conjuring[1] up tears was easy; they were on the **brink**[2]. Her shoulder-shaking wasn't **contrived**[3] either, but **ironically**[4], both would **contribute**[5] now.

'Stop crying or you're gagged,' he hissed, shaking her.

'I need the toilet,' she whispered, tears filling her eyes.

'Tough,' he replied.

'You don't get it,' she said. 'I *really* need to go to the toilet, now.'

'And I said *tough*. Now shut it.'

'I'm about to poo my pants,' said Claire, surprised at how **glibly**[6] the **lurid**[7] lie had rolled off her tongue.

'What?' hissed the boy through **gnashing**[8] teeth.

'I'm going to **soil**[9] my pants if you don't let me **squat**[10] in a bush,' she said with an exaggerated sob, **relishing**[11] the **revulsion**[12] on his face as his predicament **dawned**[13] on him.

He stared at her as if an **odious**[14] **stench**[15] had already **pervaded**[16] his nostrils.

'Hold it in,' he barked, easing his grip slightly but not letting go.

'I can't,' she whispered, shaking her head and bending her knees in **feigned**[17] desperation.

---

1   **conjure** *(v)* make something appear unexpectedly or from nowhere. *(s)* summon, raise, rouse. *(ant)* dispel.

2   **brink** *(n)* the point at which something is about to happen. *(s)* verge, threshold, edge, precipice, brim.

3   **contrived** *(adj)* created by deliberate use of skill and pretence. *(s)* concocted, fabricated, devised. *(ant)* natural.

4   **ironically** *(adv)* in a paradoxical, unexpected or coincidental way. *(s)* paradoxically, unexpectedly, coincidentally.

5   **contribute** *(v)* give something to help. *(s)* assist, aid, influence, support, fortify. *(ant)* obstruct, detract, harm.

6   **glibly** *(adv)* in a glib (easy) manner. *(s)* fluently, neatly, persuasively, smoothly, slickly, casually. *(ant)* hesitantly.

7   **lurid** *(adj)* presented in a shocking or sensational way. *(s)* ghastly, exaggerated, vivid, revolting. *(ant)* pleasant.

8   **gnash** *(v)* (the teeth) grind together in anger. *(s)* clench, grit, grate, rub, rasp, groan, gnaw.

9   **soil** *(v)* make dirty. *(s)* foul, sully, muck, muddy, stain, spot. *(ant)* cleanse.

10   **squat** *(v)* crouch down with bent knees. *(s)* cower, bend, hunch, stoop, hunker. *(ant)* stand, straighten.

11   **relish** *(v)* enjoy greatly and savour. *(s)* admire, revel, like, appreciate, delight in. *(ant)* detest, dislike, loathe.

12   **revulsion** *(n)* dislike, loathing and disgust. *(s)* repulsion, repugnance, aversion, distaste. *(ant)* attraction, like.

13   **dawn** *(v)* become evident, be perceived or understood by the mind. *(s)* realise, strike, occur. *(ant)* obscure.

14   **odious** *(adj)* extremely unpleasant. *(s)* abominable, revolting, repulsive, offensive, abhorrent. *(ant)* delightful.

15   **stench** *(n)* a strong and horrid smell. *(s)* stink, reek, pong, malodour. *(ant)* perfume, fragrance.

16   **pervade** *(v)* spread throughout, be present and apparent. *(s)* permeate, infiltrate, encompass. *(ant)* evacuate.

17   **feigned** *(adj)* simulated or pretend. *(s)* affected, fake, bluffed, artificial, insincere. *(ant)* real, sincere.

'It's coming,' she added for **maximum**[1] effect.

The boy grimaced and pushed her away. 'Go over there.' He pointed to a **thicket**[2]. 'And be quick.'

Trembling, she yanked her backpack from her shoulders.

'Turn around, then; you can't watch me,' she said, praying he would obey.

'Hurry up,' he snapped with a look of disgust. Turning around, he took a couple of large steps away from her.

Claire ducked down behind the **clump**[3] of bushes and unzipped her bag, coughing at the same time to mask the noise. Thank goodness she'd picked up Jack's oversized lead from the trap's floor when Gwilym had thrown it down earlier. She folded it in two, leaving enough length to swing the large metal **clasp**[4] attached to the end. She knew the David and Goliath story, and she knew this was, quite literally, a long shot – but she had no choice. She'd never outrun this tall, strong **lout**[5], and, **albeit**[6] **crude**[7], it was her only weapon.

'Hurry up,' hissed the boy, still facing away from her.

As he spoke, she stood up and steadily swung the lead like a **lasso**[8] above her head. The very moment he turned around, startled by the odd noise it made, she let go. The heavy metal clasp flew on a perfect **trajectory**[9] and hit him clean in the middle of his forehead.

The boy's hand shot up to his head, and he stood for a couple of seconds, staring straight at her. She gulped, expecting him to **pounce**[10], but instead, he toppled sideways, like a **felled**[11] tree.

Throwing her backpack on, Claire turned and fled downhill, blindly pushing branches and leaves away from her face. So long as the gradient continued downwards, she might find the

---

1   **maximum** *(adj)* greatest. *(s)* full, supreme, utmost, top, largest. *(ant)* minimum, smallest.

2   **thicket** *(n)* a dense group of shrubs, trees or bushes. *(s)* copse, coppice, grove, wood, clump.

3   **clump** *(n)* a small group of trees or shrubs growing together. *(s)* cluster, mass, thicket, batch.

4   **clasp** *(n)* a device that fastens things together. *(s)* catch, clip, fastener, buckle.

5   **lout** *(n)* an aggressive, thuggish or uncouth boy or man. *(s)* thug, yob, brute, oaf, bully. *(ant)* sophisticate.

6   **albeit** *(con)* although. *(s)* though, notwithstanding, even though, while.

7   **crude** *(adj)* rudimentary (basic) or makeshift. *(s)* simple, rough, unsophisticated. *(ant)* sophisticated.

8   **lasso** *(n)* a rope with a noose at one end, used for catching animals. *(s)* loop, lariat, tether.

9   **trajectory** *(n)* the course followed by a moving projectile (missile). *(s)* route, flight, path, line.

10   **pounce** *(v)* spring forward to attack or seize. *(s)* tackle, ambush, swoop, strike, surge, dive, bound. *(ant)* recoil.

11   **felled** *(adj)* cut down or toppled. *(s)* chopped, floored, decked. *(ant)* raised, upright.

farmhouse again. Not risking any further **jeopardy**[1], she refrained from calling Jack or Gwilym. She knew restricting herself to a straight line was impossible without any **landmarks**[2], so she just ran and hoped for the best.

After several minutes of skidding, tripping and stumbling, she needed to recover her breath, so she hid beneath a low tangle of bushes. She hadn't realised how noisy her movements had been until she stopped. Her **parched**[3] mouth and lips were almost stuck together. Taking a **slug**[4] of water from the bottle in her rucksack, she stopped herself from **draining**[5] it. There wasn't much left; she'd need to **ration**[6] it. Trying to quieten her breaths, convinced her short **reprieve**[7] would soon be over, she listened for the boy. She wasn't wrong. The snaps and cracks of trodden undergrowth came towards her, growing steadily quicker and louder. Curling herself down into a ball, she was sure he would hear her pounding heart.

What would he do with her now? A loud crack to her right signalled the inevitable: he was upon her. A flash of movement in her **peripheral**[8] vision **affirmed**[9] her fears. She closed her eyes tightly shut and waited; then something cold prodded her cheek. She opened her eyes and screamed.

'Jack! Jack! It's you!' Claire yelled, grabbing the little dog to her chest. He was covered in mud and trying to lick her face. He jumped away, leaping and turning tight circles. She had followed him once today, and she had no **qualms**[10] about following him now.

'Where to, boy?' she said, jumping to her feet.

There was no sign of the boy, Owain or Gwilym as she followed Jack back through the maze of forest and undergrowth, **ascending**[11] relentlessly to what she hoped was the **apex**[12].

---

1   **jeopardy** *(n)* danger of harm, loss or failure. *(s)* risk, threat, trouble, peril, hazard, difficulty. *(ant)* safety.

2   **landmark** *(n)* an object or feature of a landscape that is seen or recognisable. *(s)* marker, sign, pointer.

3   **parched** *(adj)* dried up from sun exposure or lack of water. *(s)* dehydrated, shrivelled. *(ant)* hydrated.

4   **slug** *(n)* a drink of something taken in a large swig or draught. *(s)* gulp, glug, glassful, mouthful, hit. *(ant)* sip.

5   **drain** *(v)* drink the entire contents of something. *(s)* empty, finish, consume, deplete. *(ant)* fill, replenish.

6   **ration** *(v)* allow only a fixed amount of something. *(s)* limit, restrict, control, save, keep. *(ant)* lavish.

7   **reprieve** *(n)* a cancellation or postponement (delay) of punishment. *(s)* pardon, abatement. *(ant)* continuation.

8   **peripheral** *(adj)* relating to or situated on the periphery (edge). *(s)* fringe, outer, bordering. *(ant)* central.

9   **affirm** *(v)* confirm or uphold. *(s)* sustain, proclaim, assert, guarantee, declare, support, verify. *(ant)* deny, reject.

10   **qualm** *(n)* a feeling of doubt or unease. *(s)* misgiving, foreboding, trepidation, apprehension. *(ant)* confidence.

11   **ascend** *(v)* go up or climb up. *(s)* mount, scale, rise. *(ant)* descend, drop.

12   **apex** *(n)* the top or highest part of something, especially one forming a point. *(s)* summit, peak. *(ant)* base.

After a while of constant climbing, Claire's finger touched a lip of rock. A ledge protruded outwards, and she hooked both hands over the top. She felt the ground with the flats of her hands. *Grass?* she thought. *Grass!*

'Jack, wait. Stay there, boy,' she ordered.

Mustering every muscle, she gave one final, mighty haul, let out a loud grunt and hoisted herself over the jutting ledge, rolling onto her side and flat onto her back in the grass.

'Yes!' she shouted. 'I did it!'

Claire gasped, every cell in her body screaming for oxygen. She stretched out starfish-shaped and started laughing, looking up at the clouds. She'd really made it.

Jack followed, **unceremoniously**[1] leaping over the ledge easily and **plastering**[2] her **filthy**[3] face with **soggy**[4] kisses.

'Thanks, Jack,' she laughed, pushing him away.

Completely drained and exhausted, she didn't want to move. The clouds floated above, rolling back and forth in **soporific**[5] waves. She could have dozed off right there in the dirt, but she forced herself to roll over and edge her way back to the ledge, peering over the side.

'Wow, did I climb up that?' Claire marvelled at herself.

From here she could witness the **sheer**[6] drop she'd climbed. Crawling closer to the edge, she realised in awe that its **rim**[7] formed the **circumference**[8] of a huge circle, its massive **diameter**[9] stretching further than the eye could **discern**[10]. A **crater**[11], like a **dormant**[12] volcano, full of thick, overgrown bushes and trees. Up on the rim, in stark contrast, the tiny patch of grass she lay on

---

1   **unceremoniously** *(adv)* done without ceremony (nicely). *(s)* casually, easily, inelegantly. *(ant)* formally.

2   **plaster** *(v)* coat or cover something with a substance. *(s)* daub, spread, smear. *(ant)* uncover.

3   **filthy** *(adj)* very dirty. *(s)* grimy, mucky, muddy, grubby, soiled, messy. *(ant)* clean, neat, pristine, sterile.

4   **soggy** *(adj)* wet or soft. *(s)* damp, moist, squelchy, sodden, mushy, pulpy. *(ant)* dry, arid, hard, dehydrated.

5   **soporific** *(adj)* inducing drowsiness or sleep. *(s)* sedative, hypnotic, calming, tranquilising. *(ant)* invigorating.

6   **sheer** *(adj)* so steep as to be perpendicular or nearly so. *(s)* vertical, precipitous, sharp. *(ant)* gentle, moderate.

7   **rim** *(n)* the upper or outer edge of an object. *(s)* border, lip, perimeter, circumference. *(ant)* centre.

8   **circumference** *(n)* the curved line that forms the boundary of a circle. *(s)* edge, border. *(ant)* middle.

9   **diameter** *(n)* a straight line passing through the centre of a circle (or a sphere). *(s)* width, span, breadth.

10   **discern** *(v)* see or recognise. *(s)* perceive, observe, fathom, detect, spot. *(ant)* miss, overlook, disregard.

11   **crater** *(n)* a cavity or hole in a surface, a large bowl-shaped cavity in the ground. *(s)* hollow, pit. *(ant)* mound.

12   **dormant** *(adj)* temporarily inactive. *(s)* sleeping, resting, quiet, latent, idle, inert, quiescent. *(ant)* active.

quickly disappeared into a **sparse**[1] **wilderness**[2]. Huge piles of **rubble**[3], rocks and soil streaked the landscape with a mixture of red and orange, and there were several reddish-green-tinged lakes. A faint **metallic**[4] smell wafted in the air.

Dizzied by the **magnitude**[5], like a baby crawling **in reverse**[6], she backed away from the edge. Then suddenly Jack's loud barks caught her attention. She was still on all fours when she turned to see Gwilym striding towards her, Jack at his heels. Shocked, and now clear of the edge, she jumped to her feet.

'How come you left me?' Claire shouted. 'What happened to you and the other **bloke**[7] I was supposed to be following? Some **lad**[8] dragged me down the hill; he could have killed me!' she yelled even louder, pointing an **accusing**[9] finger. 'Who was that boy, anyway?'

'But he didn't kill you, did he?' replied Gwilym calmly. 'That boy is a Mal-Instinctive; he was on one of the motorbikes. How did you escape him?'

Still angry, Claire thought about the **vulgar**[10] excuse with which she'd **outwitted**[11] the boy, but embarrassed, she **desisted**[12] from divulging the full details to Gwilym.

'I threw Jack's lead at him,' she answered **flatly**[13].

Only as she spoke did the enormity of what she'd done hit her. 'It hit him on his forehead,' she mumbled, looking at Gwilym's **impassive**[14] face watching hers.

'I didn't think I'd get away from him,' she cried, covering her face with her hands in horror at the memory of it.

---

1   **sparse** *(adj)* thinly dispersed or scattered about. *(s)* scarce, scant, light, bare, scrubby. *(ant)* dense, thick.

2   **wilderness** *(n)* wild or uncultivated land. *(s)* wasteland, wilds, outback. *(ant)* city, metropolis.

3   **rubble** *(n)* waste or rough fragments of stone, brick or concrete. *(s)* debris, wreckage, ruins.

4   **metallic** *(adj)* relating to or resembling something metal. *(s)* metal-like. *(ant)* non-metallic.

5   **magnitude** *(n)* the large size or extent of something. *(s)* enormity, scale, degree, level. *(ant)* smallness.

6   **in reverse** *(adv)* backwards. *(s)* rearwards. *(ant)* forward.

7   **bloke** *(n)* an informal word for a man. *(s)* chap, guy, lad, fellow, fella, dude. *(ant)* woman.

8   **lad** *(n)* an informal word for a young male or boy. *(s)* guy, kid, youth, juvenile. *(ant)* lass, girl.

9   **accusing** *(adj)* reproachful (blaming someone). *(s)* alleging, indicting, condemning. *(ant)* absolving.

10 **vulgar** *(adj)* lacking sophistication or good taste. *(s)* tasteless, gross, crude, offensive, improper. *(ant)* decent.

11 **outwit** *(v)* deceive by greater ingenuity. *(s)* outsmart, outmanoeuvre, outfox, defeat, beat. *(ant)* lose.

12 **desist** *(v)* stop doing something. *(s)* cease, abstain, refrain, halt, discontinue, end, quit. *(ant)* continue.

13 **flatly** *(adv)* in a flat (lifeless) manner. *(s)* unenthusiastically, blandly, dully. *(ant)* animatedly, brightly.

14 **impassive** *(adj)* not feeling or showing emotion. *(s)* inexpressive, unrevealing, expressionless. *(ant)* expressive.

'Clearly, you did,' replied Gwilym.

She looked up at him. '*Clearly,* I had no choice,' she **retorted**[1], with more than a hint of sarcasm[2] in her voice.

'Today has been *all* your choice, Claire,' replied Gwilym softly as an unusual sound cut through the air; a low whining noise, increasing in pitch and volume by the second. A blast of wind whipped up, blowing Claire's hair everywhere. Pushing strands from her eyes and mouth, she turned towards the noise.

Her mouth dropped open and her eyes widened. On a flat area, **roughly**[3] a hundred metres away, stood a massive bright yellow helicopter. Big, **bold**[4] letters on the side spelled 'RAF'.

'What the heck?' she shouted as its blades continued to pick up speed.

'Claire, this way, we must leave quickly; they will hear the helicopter, and there may be more of them,' shouted Gwilym, running towards the aircraft, beckoning above the **din**[5].

'Wow! I've always wanted to go in a helicopter,' she yelled, her words completely lost in the noise.

Jack ran alongside her, barking.

Gwilym **donned**[6] a helmet identical to that of the other pilot, who she could now see was Owain. Jack leaped in with ease, as if he was used to helicopter travel. To think she'd been stressed about him travelling on a tram! The terrier seemed perfectly at home as Gwilym helped Claire in and strapped her into a safety harness.

'Put this headset on, Claire. Owain and I can talk to you from up front. Jack will stay safe on board; it's a short journey,' instructed Gwilym.

'OK,' Claire nodded seriously.

Her stomach flipped with excitement and apprehension. The **gyrating**[7] blades caused so

---

1   **retort** *(v)* say something in answer to a remark. *(s)* reply, snap, counter, retaliate, riposte, bite back.

2   **sarcasm** *(n)* the use of irony (opposite) to mock or convey dislike. *(s)* derision, scorn, disdain. *(ant)* flattery.

3   **roughly** *(adv)* in an approximate (rough) way. *(s)* more or less, about, around, generally. *(ant)* exactly.

4   **bold** *(adj)* (of colour, design or shape) having a clear appearance. *(s)* strong, vivid, striking. *(ant)* indistinct.

5   **din** *(n)* a loud, irritating and prolonged noise. *(s)* uproar, racket, commotion, hubbub. *(ant)* silence.

6   **don** *(v)* put on or get dressed in. *(s)* throw on, slip on, change into. *(ant)* take off, remove.

7   **gyrate** *(v)* move rapidly in a circle or spiral. *(s)* rotate, revolve, spin, whirl, twirl, turn.

much noise and **turbulent**[1] wind they **resorted**[2] to **rudimentary**[3] sign language until her headset connected.

Gwilym closed the doors and took his seat next to Owain. Jack's 'safe place' was on her lap, one strap from her harness looped across him. As the helicopter lifted off the ground, she squealed with delight, gripping Jack so hard he **squirmed**[4].

'Are you all right back there, Claire?' Owain's voice crackled into the earpiece of her headset.

'I'm great! It's fun! Jack's fine too!' she yelled into her microphone.

'Claire, speak normally; there's no need to shout,' Gwilym said as his co-pilot shook his head and pointed to his ears.

'I can't believe you're a pilot, Gwilym,' marvelled Claire, watching him handle the helicopter's controls. 'I thought you were a farmer,' she said.

'Owain and I are Knights Hawk, Claire. We once rode the best horses; now we pilot the best aircraft – and can still ride horses if called for. Our modes of transport are more sophisticated and **varied**[5] today, by **necessity**[6],' replied Gwilym.

'Wow, what *is* this place?' she asked, looking out at the scenery as they ascended. 'It's like another planet!'

'It's a disused copper mine. You've climbed out of a man-made crater. It's a **barren**[7] **environment**[8] up top, but by using clever means to help **cultivate**[9] the grass and trees inside the crater, it provides an excellent **haven**[10] for the farm at the bottom of it.'

'A copper mine? That's crazy; it looks like a **quarry**[11], but on Mars,' she exclaimed.

---

1   **turbulent** *(adj)* (of air or water) moving unsteadily. *(s)* unstable, tempestuous, blustery. *(ant)* settled, still.

2   **resort** *(v)* adopt a course of action to resolve a difficult situation. *(s)* employ, apply, use, affect, try.

3   **rudimentary** *(adj)* involving basic principles or forms. *(s)* elementary, fundamental, simple. *(ant)* complex.

4   **squirm** *(v)* wriggle or twist the body. *(s)* writhe, fidget, wiggle, shift, skew, struggle. *(ant)* relax.

5   **varied** *(adj)* incorporating different types or elements. *(s)* various, diverse, assorted. *(ant)* samey, identical.

6   **necessity** *(n)* the state or fact of being required. *(s)* prerequisite, obligation, need, requirement. *(ant)* option.

7   **barren** *(adj)* (of land) producing little or no vegetation. *(s)* arid, austere, bare, bleak, deserted. *(ant)* productive.

8   **environment** *(n)* the area surrounding a place or thing. *(s)* setting, location, situation, surroundings, terrain.

9   **cultivate** *(v)* prepare and use (land) for crops or gardening. *(s)* sow, plant, grow, tend, nurture. *(ant)* neglect.

10   **haven** *(n)* a place of safety or refuge. *(s)* sanctuary, shelter, asylum, cover, harbour. *(ant)* hell hole, war zone.

11   **quarry** *(n)* a deep pit from which stone or other materials are extracted. *(s)* mine, excavation, shaft.

The house where she had drunk tea with Gladys was completely **undetectable**[1], **screened**[2] by an impassable **mass**[3] of green and brown.

'Where are we going?' asked Claire, trying not to shout.

'To a museum,' replied Gwilym.

---

1   **undetectable** *(adj)* unable to be detected, seen or noticed. *(s)* invisible, unnoticeable, unseen. *(ant)* obvious.

2   **screen** *(v)* hide with a screen or something forming a screen. *(s)* conceal, cover, shield, shelter. *(ant)* reveal.

3   **mass** *(n)* a large body of matter with no definite shape. *(s)* amount, quantity, area, accumulation. *(ant)* bit.

6. Above and Below the City

'The gem must be protected. It rests in a museum in Manchester. There's a plot **afoot**[1] to steal it,' **declared**[2] Gwilym over the headset.

Rebecca's school trip is to a museum, realised Claire.

Despite the headset, the engine vibration and spinning **rotor**[3] blades roared above Gwilym's voice. 'The Mal-Instinctives who stole the gem from Llywelyn want it back. We cannot allow that.'

'What would happen?' Claire asked from the back, but Gwilym didn't answer. 'How's Rebecca involved in this?' asked Claire, the thrill of the flight **dwindling**[4] at the **prospect**[5] of what Gwilym might say next.

'Mal-Instinctives have lured Rebecca into their web, preying on her weakness and **vulnerability**[6]. We brought you to Wales to initiate your Instinct, but also to ensure they didn't take you.'

'Take me?' she spluttered.

'The Mal-Instinctives have your sister. They are **sceptical**[7] of your Instinct, and we encourage their **misconception**[8]. Their uncertainty of you increases your safety. Although they will

---

1   **afoot** *(adj)* in preparation or progress. *(s)* stirring, brewing, around, existent, circulating.

2   **declare** *(v)* say in a serious and clear manner. *(s)* proclaim, announce, state, assert, affirm. *(ant)* withhold.

3   **rotor** *(n)* a rotary part of a machine (part that turns). *(s)* blade, propeller, turbine. *(ant)* stator.

4   **dwindle** *(v)* become smaller. *(s)* decrease, decline, abate, fade, diminish, reduce, disappear. *(ant)* increase.

5   **prospect** *(n)* a future or anticipated event. *(s)* thought, vision, idea, contemplation.

6   **vulnerability** *(n)* the state of being exposed to possible harm. *(s)* weakness, susceptibility. *(ant)* invulnerability.

7   **sceptical** *(adj)* not easily convinced, having doubts. *(s)* dubious, cynical, uncertain, questioning. *(ant)* certain.

8   **misconception** *(n)* an incorrect view or opinion. *(s)* mistake, misunderstanding, error, delusion. *(ant)* accuracy.

surreptitiously[1] watch all Cadwalladers, good Instinct is not always obvious to them.'

'Watch us how? How can you be so sure I can do anything at all?' asked Claire.

'I'm not sure,' he replied. 'Success is not about being the best, but about *trying* your best.'

Gwilym's words resonated with her; a warm **sensation**[2] **permeated**[3] her chest – a prickle of **pride**[4]. When she had escaped from that boy and climbed that **insurmountable**[5] **mammoth**[6] hill, success had astonished and **inspired**[7] her. For the first time in her life, she felt **liberated**[8] and not like the unfit kid nobody picked for their team.

Claire squinted through the helicopter's small, scratched window. The city lights beneath blinked and twinkled, distant and **picturesque**[9]; no dust and **grime**[10] up here. The glittering display reminded her of a Christmas scene.

She scoured the extensive **skyline**[11] for landmarks yet, as far as this window would permit, recognised none. None, that is, until they began to fly lower. Gradually, looming closer, she could make out a huge, **expansive**[12] rectangular structure. Its metal corners **artfully**[13] smoothed and **proportioned**[14] into wide, **elegant**[15] curves. Multiple **tubular**[16] supports **layered**[17] the top,

---

1   **surreptitiously** *(adv)* in a surreptitious (secret) way. *(s)* furtively, slyly, covertly. *(ant)* overtly, openly.

2   **sensation** *(n)* a physical feeling or perception. *(s)* sense, impression, awareness.

3   **permeate** *(v)* pass or spread throughout something. *(s)* pervade, enter, fill, flood, penetrate. *(ant)* evacuate.

4   **pride** *(n)* a feeling of satisfaction. *(s)* enjoyment, pleasure, fulfilment, gratification, joy. *(ant)* shame.

5   **insurmountable** *(adj)* too great to overcome. *(s)* invincible, impossible, unbeatable. *(ant)* easy, surmountable.

6   **mammoth** *(adj)* extremely large. *(s)* huge, colossal, stupendous, monumental, gargantuan. *(ant)* tiny.

7   **inspire** *(v)* fill with the desire to do or feel something. *(s)* motivate, encourage, enthuse. *(ant)* discourage.

8   **liberated** *(adj)* free from convention or usual ideas. *(s)* untied, released, unfettered. *(ant)* shackled, confined.

9   **picturesque** *(adj)* visually attractive. *(s)* quaint, charming, delightful, scenic, pleasing. *(ant)* unattractive.

10   **grime** *(n)* dirt that is ingrained (stuck) on the surface of something. *(s)* filth, muck, stain. *(ant)* cleanliness.

11   **skyline** *(n)* an outline of buildings and land defined against the sky. *(s)* horizon, distance, vista, silhouette.

12   **expansive** *(adj)* covering a wide area in terms of space or scope. *(s)* extensive, broad, sweeping. *(ant)* narrow.

13   **artfully** *(adv)* in an artful (creative) way. *(s)* tastefully, cleverly, elegantly, stylishly. *(ant)* tastelessly.

14   **proportioned** *(adj)* having dimensions or shapes that work well together. *(s)* balanced. *(ant)* unbalanced.

15   **elegant** *(adj)* possessing grace or simple beauty. *(s)* well designed, tasteful, stylish, refined. *(ant)* inelegant.

16   **tubular** *(adj)* made from a tube or tubes. *(s)* cylindrical, tube-like.

17   **layer** *(v)* arrange in a layer or layers, to make a layer of. *(s)* overlay, deposit, build.

bent and **bonded**[1], an intricate **amalgamation**[2] of white and grey **girders**[3]. She strained to see more. The rectangle's vast **base**[4] shone a **vivid**[5], fresh green, **edged**[6] with red. The lower they flew, the greener it glowed.

'Wow!' she slapped her hand to her mouth; her eyes ogled the scene. 'It can't be!' she exclaimed.

She could just make out what **bordered**[7] the red areas: some sort of **banner**[8] with letters written on plastic panels. Large white capital letters printed onto the back of **upturned**[9] seats. They spelled out one word in capitals: 'UNITED'. As the helicopter **hovered**[10] above, **pirouetting**[11] in a neat, **agile**[12] circle, then gently touching down, she clearly saw the name 'MANCHESTER'. The helicopter had landed in the centre circle of the pitch at Manchester United's football ground – Old Trafford.

'I don't believe it! I don't believe this!' she shouted at Jack. 'Wait until I tell Pete and my dad!' she yelled. 'They just won't believe it!'

Exchanging[13] a warm glance in response to Claire's reaction, the pilots shared a short-lived look of sentimentality before shutting off the engines and jumping out. Jack leaped out as the two men climbed into the back. They threw down their helmets and peeled off their flying suits to reveal normal clothes. Replacing their boots with trainers, they passed as two ordinary men from Manchester.

'I can't believe it! We've landed on the pitch at Old Trafford. How come you're allowed to do that?' she **babbled**[14], waving her arms **ecstatically**[15].

---

1   **bonded** (adj) (of a thing) fixed to another or each other. (s) fused, welded, joined, connected. (ant) split.

2   **amalgamation** (n) a mixture or unification. (s) combination, fusion, blend, merger. (ant) separation.

3   **girder** (n) a strong beam used for building. (s) rafter, strut, joist, lintel, bar, crossbeam.

4   **base** (n) the lowest part or edge of something. (s) bottom, foot, foundation. (ant) top.

5   **vivid** (adj) (of a colour) intensely deep or bright. (s) vibrant, glowing, radiant, rich, brilliant. (ant) dull, muted.

6   **edged** (adj) having an outside edge or boundary. (s) framed, trimmed, outlined.

7   **border** (v) form an edge along something. (s) surround, bound, fringe, hem, outline, enclose, flank.

8   **banner** (n) something bearing a slogan, advertisement or design. (s) sign, placard, standard, board, notice.

9   **upturned** (adj) turned upwards or upside down. (s) overturned, tipped over, upended. (ant) righted.

10   **hover** (v) remain in one place in the air. (s) hang, float, drift. (ant) descend, ascend.

11   **pirouette** (v) perform a pirouette. (s) twirl, whirl, spin, rotate, turn, circle.

12   **agile** (adj) able to move easily and quickly. (s) nimble, spry, responsive, swift, lithe, lively. (ant) sluggish, stiff.

13   **exchange** (v) give whilst receiving something else in return. (s) trade, reciprocate, share, swap.

14   **babble** (v) talk rapidly and continuously. (s) blather, jabber, prattle, gabble, blether, chatter. (ant) enunciate.

15   **ecstatically** (adv) in an ecstatic (overjoyed) manner. (s) delightedly, crazily, elatedly, jubilantly. (ant) miserably.

'We have loyal **comrades**[1], Claire. Helicopters fly in **frequently**[2] here; we won't stand out,' answered Gwilym. 'We are also welcome at the other **prominent**[3] ground, in the city's east, but today this location is more **convenient**[4].'

'Come now, hurry.' Gwilym **motioned**[5], striding across the pitch with Owain.

Chasing after the men with Jack by her side, Claire wished she could have had a moment to take a photo for Pete and her dad.

No way will they believe me, she thought. *I can't wait to tell Ben too, even though he's a City fan.*

Dumbfounded[6] by her surroundings, she followed the men through the players' tunnel, into a spacious rectangular room. Rows of lockers lined the walls, simple, plain benches beneath. The floor was tiled, and a faint **whiff**[7] of **chlorine**[8] reminded her of school swimming lessons.

'Claire, this way.' Owain held open a narrow door that led into a dark tunnel. He flicked on a torch so bright it **dazzled**[9] Claire, lighting their way. Jack raced off ahead, nose glued to the ground. Owain led the way, and Gwilym stayed behind her.

As speedily as they'd entered the short tunnel, they exited through another door, into a **vacant**[10] car park. The magnificently lit stadium towered **palatially**[11] behind them. They hadn't seen a **soul**[12].

In the distance, on the car park's far side, Claire noticed a flashing blue light. Both men appeared **unperturbed**[13] as a police car approached.

Claire thought they were about to be **arrested**[14].

---

1   **comrade** *(n)* a colleague or a friend. *(s)* associate, partner, co-worker, ally, companion, buddy. *(ant)* enemy, foe.

2   **frequently** *(adv)* in a frequent (regular) way. *(s)* often, customarily, habitually. *(ant)* seldom, infrequently.

3   **prominent** *(adj)* important or famous. *(s)* eminent, notable, major, renowned, known. *(ant)* obscure, unknown.

4   **convenient** *(adj)* fitting in suitably well with one's needs. *(s)* appropriate, handy, nearby. *(ant)* inconvenient.

5   **motion** *(v)* direct with a movement of the hand or head. *(s)* gesture, wave, signal, indicate, beckon.

6   **dumbfound** *(v)* greatly astonish. *(s)* stagger, startle, amaze, flabbergast, confound, stupefy. *(ant)* underwhelm.

7   **whiff** *(n)* a smell that is only smelled briefly or faintly. *(s)* trace, hint, sign, suggestion. *(ant)* saturation.

8   **chlorine** *(n)* a toxic, irritant chemical or pale green gas, used as a disinfectant in water.

9   **dazzle** *(v)* (of a light) blind temporarily. *(s)* daze, overwhelm, stun.

10   **vacant** *(adj)* (of a place) not occupied. *(s)* bare, deserted, empty, clear, unfilled, unoccupied. *(ant)* occupied.

11   **palatially** *(adv)* in a way that resembles a palace (splendid and large). *(s)* grandly, impressively. *(ant)* austerely.

12   **soul** *(n)* an individual person (human being). *(s)* body, being, creature, mortal.

13   **unperturbed** *(adj)* not anxious or concerned. *(s)* untroubled, unworried, calm, cool. *(ant)* perturbed.

14   **arrest** *(v)* seize and take into custody (jail). *(s)* apprehend, detain. *(ant)* release.

The car screeched to a halt just centimetres from them. Owain yanked open the passenger door and jumped into the front. Gwilym **ushered**[1] Claire into the back, and Jack hopped in after them.

'Seat belt, Claire,' said Gwilym.

The **caustic**[2] smoke of **scorched**[3] tyres and black **telltale**[4] tracks left the only clues they had been there as they hurtled towards the city centre, lights and **sirens**[5] blazing.

'Sir,' said the young female driver, 'we have cleared the entrance and lit the tunnel through to the room for you. Our **estimated**[6] time of arrival is ten minutes,' she said, **running**[7] a red traffic light. Claire thought she looked roughly Rebecca's age, yet she drove like a racing driver.

'Claire, listen carefully.' Gwilym's tone was now more serious than before. 'Once in the museum, stay close to me. Owain will be inside too, as will our fellow knights Evans and his wife. Your help with the Rebecca situation will be **invaluable**[8] to us. Felicity, our driver, will guard the tunnels for us.'

The young driver looked in her rear-view mirror and gave Claire a brief nod before fixing her **concentration**[9] back on the road as she sped along at frightening speeds.

'What tunnel?' asked Claire, clutching the edge of the seat as they squealed around an **appallingly**[10] tight corner. Wedged between Gwilym's feet, Jack couldn't move.

'Our way in and out,' replied Gwilym **matter-of-factly**[11].

In half the normal time it would have taken to reach the city centre, the police car skidded to a halt outside a **classic**[12] **Georgian**[13] building.

---

1   **usher** *(v)* show, escort or guide someone somewhere. *(s)* accompany, shepherd, conduct, lead. *(ant)* follow.

2   **caustic** *(adj)* able to corrode, burn or cause harm. *(s)* corrosive, acidic, alkaline, mordant. *(ant)* harmless.

3   **scorched** *(adj)* burned with flame or heat. *(s)* singed, charred, blackened, branded, seared. *(ant)* cool, frozen.

4   **telltale** *(adj)* suggesting or betraying something. *(s)* revealing, indicative, meaningful. *(ant)* uninformative.

5   **siren** *(n)* a device that makes a loud warning sound. *(s)* alarm, alert, signal, bell, horn.

6   **estimated** *(adj)* roughly calculated. *(s)* approximate, general, guessed, vague. *(ant)* precise, exact.

7   **run** *(v)* fail to stop at something. *(s)* jump, ignore. *(ant)* stop for, heed.

8   **invaluable** *(adj)* extremely useful. *(s)* indispensable, crucial, irreplaceable, vital, important. *(ant)* worthless.

9   **concentration** *(n)* the act of focusing all attention. *(s)* application, awareness, attentiveness. *(ant)* inattention.

10   **appallingly** *(adv)* to an appalling (shocking or horrifying) degree. *(s)* atrociously, outrageously. *(ant)* appealingly.

11   **matter-of-factly** *(adv)* in a practical and unemotional manner. *(s)* straightforwardly, sensibly. *(ant)* emotionally.

12   **classic** *(adj)* very typical of its kind. *(s)* archetypal, quintessential, timeless, traditional. *(ant)* atypical.

13   **Georgian** *(adj)* (relating to British architecture) of the Georgian period (George V and George VI, 1910–52).

'This way, sir.' Felicity jumped out of the car. 'Around to the side, please.'

Efficiently[1] Felicity directed them to an unremarkable wooden door, its blue paint flaked and peeled. She pulled out a rusty key from her pocket and turned it in the lock.

She waved them forward into a tight **holding area**[2]; a square wooden **landing**[3] stood at the top of a steep **flight**[4] of stairs upon which they now stood, squished together in single file. An eerie, echoing slam **emanated**[5] from the bottom of the staircase just as Felicity, with a final, unpleasant clunk, turned and locked the door behind them, **unsettling**[6] Claire.

What if all this is a trap? Claire thought, panic rising in her. *What if these men are the bad ones in all of this, and it's me they're really after?* Choosing to dismiss the chilling thought, but still feeling uneasy, she thought of Ben instead.

'I'll lead the way, sir,' said Felicity, squeezing past them. She held the same type of torch Owain had used. 'Jack, go in front,' she ordered.

Obediently[7] he **scuttled**[8] past them down the steps, his tail waving in the air, Felicity after him. Hesitating, Claire followed Owain with tentative steps; she **detested**[9] small spaces. Gwilym stayed so close behind she felt his warm breath on the back of her neck. Not sure if she should be comforted or panicked by this **encroachment**[10], she tiptoed on.

The steps **pitched**[11] down steeply, and the temperature **plummeted**[12] to the chill of a fridge. At the foot of the stairs, Felicity stopped at another door, similar to the last, and **inserted**[13] the same key into the lock. It was so rusted and **corroded**[14] she struggled to twist the key in it. She

---

1   **efficiently** *(adv)* done in an efficient (able) way. *(s)* capably, deftly, professionally, proficiently. *(ant)* inefficiently.

2   **holding area** *(n)* an area where a person or thing can wait. *(s)* waiting area, assembly point.

3   **landing** *(n)* area at the top of or on a staircase. *(s)* hallway, corridor, hall, platform.

4   **flight** *(n)* a series of steps between floors or levels. *(s)* staircase, stairs.

5   **emanate** *(v)* come or spread out from. *(s)* arise, derive, issue, emerge, rise, proceed. *(ant)* absorb, withdraw.

6   **unsettle** *(v)* cause to feel anxious. *(s)* bother, upset, disturb, worry, perturb, unnerve. *(ant)* appease, soothe.

7   **obediently** *(adv)* in a compliant or submissive way. *(s)* dutifully, biddably, deferentially. *(ant)* disobediently.

8   **scuttle** *(v)* run or scamper hurriedly or furtively (secretly). *(s)* dart, dash, rush, bustle, scurry. *(ant)* saunter.

9   **detest** *(v)* dislike intensely. *(s)* abhor, despise, loathe, hate, abominate. *(ant)* love, adore.

10   **encroachment** *(n)* an intrusion or gradual advance beyond usual limits. *(s)* invasion, impingement. *(ant)* retreat.

11   **pitch** *(v)* slope. *(s)* incline, slant, descend, ascend, dip, tilt. *(ant)* straighten, level.

12   **plummet** *(v)* fall or drop straight down at high speed. *(s)* dive, tumble, crash, decrease. *(ant)* climb, rise.

13   **insert** *(v)* put something into something else. *(s)* push, place, fit. *(ant)* remove, withdraw, extract.

14   **corroded** *(adj)* eaten or worn away. *(s)* rusty, decomposed, crumbly, flaky, decayed. *(ant)* preserved.

jiggled it **laterally**[1] with small movements back and forth, encouraging it to open, yet, **resisting**[2] her **endeavours**[3], it wouldn't budge. Owain stepped forward to assist, when Claire, surprising herself, interrupted.

'Let me try; I might be able to do it.' She held out her hand to Felicity for the key.

Owain squashed up against the wall, allowing her to squeeze by as Felicity passed her the key. Claire slowly fed the key into the keyhole and tried the lock – but it stuck **fast**[4]. She tried again, jiggling it **randomly**[5] as a rash of embarrassment flushed her cheeks.

Focusing[6], and with her ear close to the lock, she held the key still. **Sensitively**[7] she moved it a millimetre to the left, then back to the centre, then a tad to the right, trying to feel the **mechanism**[8]. She **lingered**[9] and pulled back the metal key slightly, with such **delicacy**[10], until it balanced and clicked. It **yielded**[11] so **marginally**[12] she feared it didn't fit at all. **Willing**[13] the rusty key to turn, she **minutely**[14] adjusted her hold again; then it gently gave way and **rotated**[15] **freely**[16], and the door unlocked. She pushed the door, its **discoloured**[17], stiff **hinges**[18] creaking **laboriously**[19] open. She'd done it! She'd opened the door!

She turned around to look at Gwilym with pride. 'Well done,' he said, almost breaking into a

---

1   **laterally** *(adv)* in a lateral (sideways) manner. *(s)* sideways, crosswise, edgewise, horizontally. *(ant)* vertically.

2   **resist** *(v)* withstand, combat or counter an action or effect. *(s)* refuse, defy, refrain from. *(ant)* succumb to.

3   **endeavour** *(n)* an attempt or effort. *(s)* aim, bid, striving, struggle, exertion, undertaking. *(ant)* idleness.

4   **fast** *(adj)* firmly fixed, secured or attached. *(s)* immovable, set, sound, tight, jammed, stuck. *(ant)* loose, wobbly.

5   **randomly** *(adv)* in a random (irregular) way. *(s)* aimlessly, haphazardly, erratically. *(ant)* systematically.

6   **focus** *(v)* pay attention to or concentrate on. *(s)* look, direct, fix, centre, aim, rivet. *(ant)* ignore.

7   **sensitively** *(adv)* in a sensitive (gentle) way. *(s)* subtly, delicately, carefully, precisely, finely. *(ant)* clumsily.

8   **mechanism** *(n)* a system of parts working together in a machine, tool or apparatus. *(s)* device, contraption.

9   **linger** *(v)* take or stay longer than necessary due to reluctance. *(s)* delay, dawdle, dither, dally. *(ant)* rush.

10   **delicacy** *(n)* fineness, intricacy or precision. *(s)* skill, care, deftness, dexterity. *(ant)* ineptness, awkwardness.

11   **yield** *(v)* give way to pressure, arguments or demands. *(s)* cede, succumb, surrender, capitulate. *(ant)* resist.

12   **marginally** *(adv)* in a marginal (slight) way. *(s)* minutely, minimally, somewhat, insignificantly. *(ant)* substantially.

13   **will** *(v)* want something to happen. *(s)* long, wish, desire, yearn, pray.

14   **minutely** *(adv)* with minute amounts or great attention to detail. *(s)* carefully, painstakingly. *(ant)* carelessly.

15   **rotate** *(v)* move in a circle. *(s)* turn, revolve, spin, swivel, pivot.

16   **freely** *(adv)* without interference or restriction. *(s)* effortlessly, easily, willingly, readily. *(ant)* arduously.

17   **discoloured** *(adj)* changed to a less attractive colour. *(s)* stained, faded, tarnished, marked. *(ant)* shiny, clean.

18   **hinge** *(n)* a movable joint or mechanism that a gate or door is hung upon. *(s)* link, pivot.

19   **laboriously** *(adv)* in a laborious (difficult) way. *(s)* arduously, painstakingly, painfully, onerously. *(ant)* easily.

smile. With that, Felicity and Owain moved swiftly back in front, and before she knew it, she was following them into a **dimly**[1] lit corridor.

Cold, windowless grey metal doors lined the corridor's walls. Their feet fell in thumping, dull echoes, which sounded deafening in the stark space around them. A waft of **disinfectant**[2] and stale food hung in the air. Claire recognised the doors as the entrances to prison cells – she'd seen similar ones on TV. Felicity took out another bunch of keys and opened one of the thick, weighty barriers. It creaked open, like a **predictable**[3] **introduction**[4] to a horror movie, and they all stepped into the cell behind her.

Appalled[5] at the cell's **paltry**[6] size and emptiness, Claire **recoiled**[7] at the metal toilet and thin, hard bench. The smell reminded her of lifts in the flats where her friend lived. A brown blanket lay folded on the bench, a thin grey pillow on top. She shivered, spooked by the cell's **claustrophobic**[8] starkness.

Felicity knelt and reached under the bench, feeling for something against the wall. She stood up and waited. Nothing happened initially, not for a few seconds; then slowly the **grim**[9] bed lifted and retracted smoothly, slotting **flush**[10] and unseen into the wall. It **unmasked**[11] an opening – a dark, **uninviting**[12], **poky**[13] hole.

'I'll wait here, sir,' said Felicity. 'I'll ensure all the cells are clear and your exits are not **impeded**[14].'

As she spoke, it struck Claire how pretty Felicity's features were.

'This tunnel leads directly from this police station to the museum where the Gwalch Gem

---

1   **dimly** *(adv)* with only faint light. *(s)* murkily, vaguely, darkly, gloomily, dingily, flatly. *(ant)* brightly, clearly.

2   **disinfectant** *(n)* a chemical liquid that destroys bacteria. *(s)* germicide, cleanser, antiseptic, sanitiser, purifier.

3   **predictable** *(adj)* able to be predicted. *(s)* unsurprising, expected, unoriginal. *(ant)* unexpected, original.

4   **introduction** *(n)* a preliminary or opening section. *(s)* prelude, beginning, prologue. *(ant)* conclusion.

5   **appalled** *(adj)* greatly dismayed or shocked. *(s)* horrified, disgusted, sickened, outraged. *(ant)* charmed.

6   **paltry** *(adj)* very small. *(s)* meagre, worthless, measly, trifling, insignificant. *(ant)* substantial, considerable.

7   **recoil** *(v)* suddenly spring or flinch back in horror or disgust. *(s)* withdraw, retreat, dodge. *(ant)* confront.

8   **claustrophobic** *(adj)* inducing claustrophobia (fear of enclosed spaces). *(s)* suffocating, stifling. *(ant)* open.

9   **grim** *(adj)* unattractive or forbidding. *(s)* dreadful, ghastly, ugly, uninviting, dingy. *(ant)* attractive, inviting.

10   **flush** *(adj)* so as to be level or even with another surface. *(s)* flatly, smoothly. *(ant)* unevenly, irregularly.

11   **unmask** *(v)* expose the true character of or truth about. *(s)* reveal, unveil, uncover, bare. *(ant)* hide, conceal.

12   **uninviting** *(adj)* not attractive or appealing. *(s)* bleak, unpleasant, repellent, distasteful. *(ant)* attractive.

13   **poky** *(adj)* (of a place) uncomfortably small and cramped. *(s)* tiny, restricted, tight, boxy. *(ant)* spacious.

14   **impede** *(v)* delay or prevent by obstructing. *(s)* handicap, block, hamper, hinder, bar. *(ant)* facilitate, clear.

bracelet rests,' said Gwilym to Claire, kneeling in the earth, about to crawl into the space.

Jack rushed past him as he spoke to lead the way, his **mischievous**[1] terrier instincts taking over as he darted into the giant **burrow**[2]. Owain waited behind Claire this time, but she froze at the entrance. Staring into metres of darkness, she swallowed as a feeling of rising **nausea**[3] threatened her throat. Kneeling at the precarious entrance, her palms pressed down into the tunnel's damp earth. She pulled back **violently**[4], as though touching a naked flame.

'I'm not going in there,' she said, shaking her head. 'No way.'

The prospect of **slithering**[5] into this unknown **lair**[6], too low to stand, **petrified**[7] her.

Jack was nowhere to be seen, and Gwilym's short-lived **outline**[8] was quickly fading away in the distance.

She stayed there, rigid, stuck for what seemed like an **eternity**[9], Owain waiting behind, neither **cajoling**[10] nor forcing her. The tunnel stank, **musty**[11] and wet, like the school's **stagnant**[12] gardening shed. Visions from a terrifying **potholing**[13] **documentary**[14] she'd seen flashed **vividly**[15] into her head: curious, daring people who **voluntarily**[16] sandwiched themselves between slime-dripping rocks, with torches on their heads, navigating suffocating spaces.

---

1   **mischievous** *(adj)* having a fondness for playfully causing trouble. *(s)* naughty, impish. *(ant)* well behaved.

2   **burrow** *(n)* a hole or tunnel dug by a small animal as a dwelling. *(s)* den, lair, hideaway, sett.

3   **nausea** *(n)* a feeling of sickness. *(s)* queasiness, biliousness, revulsion. *(ant)* wellness.

4   **violently** *(adv)* in a violent (strong) manner. *(s)* intensely, powerfully, forcefully, vigorously. *(ant)* gently.

5   **slither** *(v)* move over a surface with a twisting or oscillating motion. *(s)* crawl, slide, glide, slip, wriggle.

6   **lair** *(n)* a place where a wild animal lives, secret hideaway. *(s)* den, warren, hole, hideout.

7   **petrify** *(v)* make so frightened as to be unable to move. *(s)* terrify, scare, horrify, appal. *(ant)* reassure.

8   **outline** *(n)* the contours of an object. *(s)* silhouette, shape, form, figure, profile.

9   **eternity** *(n)* infinite or unending time. *(s)* perpetuity, forever, endlessness, aeon. *(ant)* instant, jiffy.

10   **cajole** *(v)* persuade to do something by sustained coaxing. *(s)* entice, tempt, urge, bribe. *(ant)* compel, force.

11   **musty** *(adj)* having a stale, mouldy, or damp and dank smell. *(s)* stuffy, fusty, rank, fetid. *(ant)* fresh.

12   **stagnant** *(adj)* having no air flow or current. *(s)* stale, still, dirty, stuffy, foul. *(ant)* fresh, flowing.

13   **potholing** *(n)* the exploration of underground caves as a hobby. *(s)* caving.

14   **documentary** *(n)* a factual report or programme. *(s)* factual film, biopic.

15   **vividly** *(adv)* in a vivid (strong and clear) way. *(s)* distinctly, lively, lucidly, plainly, acutely. *(ant)* vaguely.

16   **voluntarily** *(adv)* of one's own free will or choice. *(s)* willingly, happily, gladly, readily. *(ant)* involuntarily.

'I won't do it,' she said again, her **fertile**[1] imagination **arousing**[2] more **horrific**[3] scenarios[4]. 'I'm not going in.'

Fighting the urge to faint, she flopped down and **pleaded**[5] **pitifully**[6] up at Owain.

'I can't do it,' she whispered.

The knight's face remained **expressionless**[7]. 'You will have to wait here, then,' he said, not moving.

She peered into the dark hole again.

If I don't go in after Gwilym and Jack, what will happen? she asked herself. *Will I ruin everything?*

She looked up at Owain again, but he said nothing.

Terrified, envisaging beetles and bugs, she placed her hands back in the dirt. **Steeling**[8] herself, inch by inch, her **determination**[9] and **conscience**[10] **motivating**[11] her on, she crawled into the space. Owain shone his bright torch, lighting her way.

At least I can see now, she thought, then immediately recoiled.

Incapacitated[12] with revulsion, she pictured a bed of stinging insects in the dirt beneath her. Forcing herself forward, sweating with terror, she crawled on, **straggling**[13] behind Gwilym and Jack, trying not to touch anything alive with her hands and yelping each time she thought she did.

'Keep going. Keep going,' she chanted, **coaxing**[14] herself **grudgingly**[15] forward. 'How long is

---

1   **fertile** *(adj)* (of the mind) having new and inventive ideas. *(s)* imaginative, creative. *(ant)* unimaginative.

2   **arouse** *(v)* evoke a feeling, emotion or response. *(s)* stimulate, provoke, awaken, stir, rouse. *(ant)* dampen.

3   **horrific** *(adj)* causing horror. *(s)* ghastly, horrendous, appalling, dreadful, sickening, gruesome. *(ant)* appealing.

4   **scenario** *(n)* a possible sequence of events. *(s)* situation, state, development, consequence.

5   **plead** *(v)* make an emotional appeal. *(s)* beg, beseech, implore, supplicate, request. *(ant)* offer.

6   **pitifully** *(adv)* in a pitiful (pathetic) manner. *(s)* miserably, wretchedly, sadly, woefully. *(ant)* admirably.

7   **expressionless** *(adj)* not conveying any emotion on the face. *(s)* unresponsive, deadpan. *(ant)* expressive.

8   **steel** *(v)* mentally prepare for something difficult. *(s)* strengthen, toughen, fortify, brace. *(ant)* weaken.

9   **determination** *(n)* the quality of being determined. *(s)* willpower, resolve, fortitude, grit. *(ant)* weakness.

10   **conscience** *(n)* one's internal moral sense of right and wrong. *(s)* ethics, integrity, morality. *(ant)* immorality.

11   **motivate** *(v)* provide or prompt with a reason for action. *(s)* inspire, encourage, persuade. *(ant)* demotivate.

12   **incapacitate** *(v)* prevent from functioning normally. *(s)* debilitate, weaken, disable, undermine. *(ant)* enable.

13   **straggle** *(v)* move slowly and remain some distance behind. *(s)* lag, trail, drop back. *(ant)* hasten, hurry.

14   **coax** *(v)* persuade gently to do something. *(s)* cajole, entice, tempt, lure, urge, inveigle. *(ant)* force, compel.

15   **grudgingly** *(adv)* in a grudging (reluctant) manner. *(s)* unwillingly, resentfully, loathingly. *(ant)* willingly.

this tunnel? Please. I hate this. How long is it?' she asked Owain, panic rising further as dirt and dust fell down into her eyes and mouth.

'We are nearly there; it is short,' replied Owain.

'Calm, Claire, calm,' she told herself, **gagging**[1] on a mouthful of dirt.

Up ahead, Gwilym was waiting for her. She increased her crawling speed, **placated**[2] at seeing him and at a glimpse of Jack's **deliriously**[3] happy tail. In front of Gwilym, she could see a handleless wooden **hatch**[4] blocking their way.

'Jack, back!' Gwilym ordered.

The knight, restricted by the tunnel's size, squared his **bulk**[5] against the wood and **shouldered**[6] the **barricade**[7], pushing it inwards, enabling his fingers to curl around its edge. Grappling for a better **purchase**[8], he finally managed to **lever**[9] it out of the way. Claire almost **butted**[10] Gwilym out through the opening as she pushed forward, gasping for air. She shot out, landing face down on yet another dirty floor.

The tunnel had opened into a dark, **austere**[11] room, now partially lit by Owain's torch. He found an old-fashioned light switch on the wall, and a **muted**[12] yellow light glowed softly, partly **illuminating**[13] their features.

Shelves stuffed with antiquities – **conserved**[14] **articles**[15] of all shapes and sizes – surrounded them, covered in a thick layer of dust, seemingly untouched for years. Claire knelt, spitting

---

1   **gag** *(v)* retch or choke. *(s)* heave, suffocate, stifle, hyperventilate. *(ant)* breathe, swallow.

2   **placate** *(v)* make less angry or hostile. *(s)* pacify, soothe, calm, appease, mollify. *(ant)* enrage, incense.

3   **deliriously** *(adv)* in a delirious (excited) manner. *(s)* madly, frantically, wildly, ecstatically. *(ant)* dejectedly.

4   **hatch** *(n)* a small opening for access in a floor, wall or roof. *(s)* flap, entrance, doorway, access.

5   **bulk** *(n)* the mass, size or substance of something large. *(s)* immensity, volume. *(ant)* tininess, insignificance.

6   **shoulder** *(v)* push out of the way with a shoulder. *(s)* jostle, bulldoze, thrust, force, shove. *(ant)* pull, wrench.

7   **barricade** *(n)* a barrier erected to prevent or delay entry. *(s)* blockade, obstacle, obstruction. *(ant)* opening.

8   **purchase** *(n)* a firm contact or grip. *(s)* grasp, hold, clasp, leverage, foothold. *(ant)* release.

9   **lever** *(v)* move with concerted physical effort. *(s)* force, wrench, ease, push, prise.

10   **butt** *(v)* strike against something with the head. *(s)* headbutt, bump, ram, thrust, shove.

11   **austere** *(adj)* having a plain appearance. *(s)* severe, simple, basic, sombre, unadorned. *(ant)* fussy, ornate.

12   **muted** *(adj)* reduced in strength or intensity. *(s)* soft, dim, subdued, dull. *(ant)* bright, light, garish.

13   **illuminate** *(v)* light up. *(s)* brighten, lighten, irradiate, illume. *(ant)* darken, dim.

14   **conserved** *(adj)* preserved from harm or destruction. *(s)* safeguarded, protected. *(ant)* destroyed, ruined.

15   **article** *(n)* an item or object. *(s)* piece, thing, entity, commodity, artefact, thingamajig, stuff.

out and blinking away dirt. A covering of filth **speckled**[1] Jack's coat. Sneezing and snuffling, he shook the grime off in the way only dogs can, twisting and shaking in opposite directions from nose to tail, **coating**[2] Claire in the **process**[3]. She laughed as she brushed it from her sleeves, and was **overcome**[4] by an urge to hug him, so she held him close, kissing his dirty nose.

Standing up slowly, she absorbed her new surroundings. Yesterday she wouldn't have **entertained**[5] that smothering hole of a tunnel; she would have refused point-blank. *I can do this*, she thought, staring steadfastly at the two men and Jack, **bracing**[6] herself for whatever came next.

---

1   **speckle** *(v)* mark with lots of small spots or patches of colour. *(s)* stipple, spatter, dapple, mottle.

2   **coat** *(v)* cover with a layer of something. *(s)* overlay, paint, smother, cake, smear, plaster, varnish. *(ant)* strip.

3   **process** *(n)* a series of actions taken to achieve an outcome. *(s)* course, method, proceeding.

4   **overcome** *(v)* overwhelm or move emotionally. *(s)* grip, seize, affect, disturb. *(ant)* underwhelm.

5   **entertain** *(v)* give any attention or consideration to. *(s)* countenance, contemplate, ponder. *(ant)* reject, spurn.

6   **brace** *(v)* prepare for something difficult or unpleasant. *(s)* steel, prime, fortify, steady, ready. *(ant)* weaken.

7. The Race for the Cutter

Upstairs in the stuffy cinema, Rebecca Cadwallader was oblivious to her sister's timely arrival in the **basement**[1] beneath her. In fact, Rebecca Cadwallader was becoming oblivious to anything.

'Sir, Rebecca's not well,' Josh Drane called to his teacher, interrupting the film. His **bogus**[2] act of caring and **civil**[3] behaviour deserved an award.

'What's the matter, Drane?' replied Mr Hollie, looking dubiously at his pupil.

'Dunno, sir. She's acting funny and she's hot. She says she's gonna faint. I don't think she's putting it on,' replied Drane slimily.

The powdered drug he'd **administered**[4] to Rebecca's drink would keep her feeling unwell, though not so ill as to pressure the teacher to cancel the trip. Rebecca would **comply**[5] with Drane and, better still, afterwards remember nothing.

'Rebecca, how are you? What's wrong?' whispered Mr Hollie, approaching her seat.

The other pupils **craned**[6] their necks to look as whispers rapidly spread around the hushed cinema. Clearly, they needed little excuse to distract them from the educational film – they had no interest in following it.

'I feel funny, sir. A bit weird and boiling hot. I want to lie down.'

---

1 **basement** *(n)* the floor of a building that is below ground level. *(s)* cellar, vault, crypt. *(ant)* attic.

2 **bogus** *(adj)* not true or genuine. *(s)* fake, spurious, false, counterfeit, phoney, sham, mock. *(ant)* authentic.

3 **civil** *(adj)* polite and courteous. *(s)* respectful, well mannered, considerate, obliging. *(ant)* rude.

4 **administer** *(v)* dispense (give out) or apply. *(s)* deliver, issue, deal, distribute. *(ant)* withhold, deny.

5 **comply** *(v)* obey a wish or command. *(s)* abide by, observe, conform, yield, respect, submit. *(ant)* disobey.

6 **crane** *(v)* stretch one's body or neck to see something. *(s)* outstretch, extend, stick out. *(ant)* retract, shrink.

Drane watched the teacher study the telltale **sheen**[1] of sweat on Rebecca's **wan**[2] face as she **slurred**[3] her words.

Mr Hollie sniffed, then sighed. 'This is all I need,' he said, tutting.

'Mmm, she's sober,' he muttered to himself. 'I can't detect any trace of **alcohol**[4].'

'Drane, stay here with Rebecca and Miss Malik. I'll be right back. I'm going to ask Mr Evans for help. She needs to lie down somewhere.'

'Course, sir,' replied Drane, his face portraying a picture of concern.

Mr Hollie turned with an irritated groan towards his assistant.

'Miss Malik, Rebecca Cadwallader isn't feeling well. Stay with her and **supervise**[5] the class while I **confer**[6] with Mr Evans, the museum's curator,' he demanded imperiously.

Not waiting for her answer, he hurried out.

Outside the cinema door, he almost rammed into the curator. 'Oh, good, Mr Evans,' he blurted.

'Is everything all right, Mr Hollie?' **queried**[7] Mr Evans. 'The film has a while to run yet.'

'One of my pupils is unwell. Could she lie down somewhere? Hopefully, it won't be for long,' said the teacher. 'I'm sure there's no real **malady**[8], but it is rather hot and stuffy in there,' he added in a **pompous**[9] manner.

'Oh dear, I am sorry. We have an office with a **reclining**[10] chair. She can rest there with my wife, if that helps,' replied Mr Evans.

'Yes, please. Thank you, and sorry for the **inconvenience**[11],' replied the teacher.

Mr Evans spoke into a **clunky**[12] walkie-talkie radio, requesting his wife be asked to come to

---

1   **sheen** *(n)* a soft lustre (shine or gloss) on a surface. *(s)* polish, burnish, gleam, glaze. *(ant)* dullness.

2   **wan** *(adj)* pale-faced and giving the impression of illness or exhaustion. *(s)* pallid, ashen, drawn. *(ant)* glowing.

3   **slur** *(v)* speak unclearly so that the sounds merge. *(s)* mumble, garble, mispronounce, blend. *(ant)* enunciate.

4   **alcohol** *(n)* a liquid that intoxicates (makes drunk). *(s)* booze, liquor, hooch, drink, inebriant.

5   **supervise** *(v)* watch over and control. *(s)* oversee, govern, manage, direct, handle, organise. *(ant)* neglect.

6   **confer** *(v)* discuss or exchange opinions. *(s)* talk, deliberate, converse, advise, convene.

7   **query** *(v)* question. *(s)* enquire, ask, probe, grill, quiz, interrogate. *(ant)* answer.

8   **malady** *(n)* an ailment or disease. *(s)* sickness, illness, disorder, malaise, condition, affliction. *(ant)* wellness.

9   **pompous** *(adj)* self-important or affectedly grand. *(s)* pretentious, exaggerated, vain, grandiose. *(ant)* modest.

10   **reclining** *(adj)* (of a seat) able to move the back into a sloping position. *(s)* tilting.

11   **inconvenience** *(n)* a cause of difficulty or trouble. *(s)* nuisance, hassle, bother, aggravation. *(ant)* convenience.

12   **clunky** *(adj)* heavy and old-fashioned. *(s)* solid, bulky, unwieldy, outdated. *(ant)* light, modern.

the cinema urgently. Within a minute or so, a crook-backed lady shuffled into sight. She had **frizzy**[1] grey hair, rounded shoulders and what could only be described as a **drab**[2] and **meek**[3] **demeanour**[4]. Her large, hooked nose supported thick-lensed glasses that **magnified**[5] her watery and **bloodshot**[6] eyes.

Mr Evans spoke for her.

'This is my wife, Marjorie. She will help with your pupil. Shall we move her to the office?' He gestured.

'Yes. That would be most helpful. Thank you for **accommodating**[7] her,' replied Mr Hollie. 'No need to cancel anything unless she **deteriorates**[8]; let's not worry her parents yet.'

The teacher and his wife supported Rebecca under each arm as they helped her from the cinema. Drane emerged and stared straight at the curator Evans, a challenge in his eyes. He knew Evans sensed his true identity but was **positive**[9] the old man wouldn't dare act against him single-handedly. However, he didn't much care; he was ready. Drane never **underestimated**[10] any Instinctive, knowing too well that appearances could **deceive**[11], but his **confidence**[12] in their **prodigious**[13] plan prevailed. His master would soon arrive to **reclaim**[14] the bracelet that held the Gwalch Gem; the bracelet would soon be theirs again.

*

Before Drane had arrived at his museum, Robert Evans had unlocked the furthest side room in the basement, clearing the entrance and exit tunnels Gwilym Cadwaladr would need. Having

---

1   **frizzy** *(adj)* formed of lots of small, tight curls. *(s)* crimped, wiry, kinked, fuzzy. *(ant)* straight, smooth, sleek.

2   **drab** *(adj)* lacking brightness, style or interest. *(s)* dreary, dull, plain, dowdy, lacklustre, flat. *(ant)* bright.

3   **meek** *(adj)* easily imposed on. *(s)* submissive, quiet, gentle, timid, compliant, humble, weak. *(ant)* assertive.

4   **demeanour** *(n)* outward bearing or behaviour. *(s)* appearance, attitude, disposition, air, character, conduct.

5   **magnify** *(v)* make to appear larger. *(s)* boost, enhance, enlarge, increase, exaggerate. *(ant)* decrease, lessen.

6   **bloodshot** *(adj)* (of the eyes) tinged with blood, typically because of tiredness. *(s)* red, inflamed, pink.

7   **accommodate** *(v)* help or assist. *(s)* aid, oblige, support, be of service. *(ant)* disoblige, hinder, prevent, impede.

8   **deteriorate** *(v)* become progressively worse. *(s)* decay, decline, degenerate, weaken. *(ant)* improve.

9   **positive** *(adj)* without doubt. *(s)* satisfied, certain, persuaded, sure, convinced, confident. *(ant)* uncertain.

10   **underestimate** *(v)* regard someone as less capable than they really are. *(s)* undervalue, misjudge. *(ant)* overestimate.

11   **deceive** *(v)* give the wrong impression. *(s)* mislead, hoodwink, dupe, delude, trick. *(ant)* be honest.

12   **confidence** *(n)* a feeling of self-assurance and belief in oneself. *(s)* certainty, faith, trust. *(ant)* uncertainty.

13   **prodigious** *(adj)* remarkably or impressively great. *(s)* extraordinary, exceptional, impressive. *(ant)* average.

14   **reclaim** *(v)* take or get something back. *(s)* retrieve, regain, recover, repossess. *(ant)* forfeit, lose.

checked his two resident security guards were at their **relevant**[1] stations, he knew all was now in place.

The museum's alarm worked from an old-fashioned security room situated on the first floor. One overweight, unfit guard sat swinging in a **swivel**[2] chair. **Employed**[3] to monitor the museum's CCTV screens, he stuffed his face with crisps and watched videos on his phone instead. **Periodically**[4] he **cast**[5] an **indifferent**[6] glimpse at the **grainy**[7] screens. If someone **tampered**[8] with an exhibition case, an alarm **triggered**[9] on his **console**[10]. Now and then, **overzealous**[11] youngsters accidentally set them off, but serious **incidents**[12] were **hitherto**[13] unheard of.

The guard's partner, trying to look important, patrolled around the exhibition hall and surrounding areas. The two guards sometimes swapped places to **stave off**[14] the boredom. Still, none of this mattered. The guards were **utterly**[15] powerless to protect the gem; their presence was **solely**[16] for show. The Knights Hawk had engineered the glass that housed the gem, creating an **impenetrable**[17] fort. The only **device**[18] **capable**[19] of breaking into the **invincible**[20] glass was the Cutter.

1 **relevant** *(adj)* relating to what is being done or considered. *(s)* pertinent, appropriate. *(ant)* irrelevant.

2 **swivel** *(n)* a device joining two parts such that one or both can rotate freely.

3 **employ** *(v)* give work to and pay. *(s)* retain, engage, use, hire, place. *(ant)* dismiss, sack, fire.

4 **periodically** *(adv)* from time to time, now and then. *(s)* occasionally, sometimes, sporadically. *(ant)* frequently.

5 **cast** *(v)* direct one's eyes or a look at something. *(s)* throw, turn, shoot, dart, glance, level.

6 **indifferent** *(adj)* having no interest. *(s)* casual, apathetic, uninterested, unconcerned. *(ant)* concerned.

7 **grainy** *(adj)* (of an image) not sharp or clear. *(s)* fuzzy, vague, indistinct, blurry. *(ant)* sharp, clear, distinct.

8 **tamper** *(v)* mess around or meddle with. *(s)* interfere, tinker, disturb, alter, intrude. *(ant)* leave alone.

9 **trigger** *(v)* cause something to function or set off. *(s)* start, activate, spark, initiate, fire. *(ant)* halt.

10 **console** *(n)* a panel containing controls for electronic equipment. *(s)* desk, board.

11 **overzealous** *(adj)* too zealous (keen). *(s)* enthusiastic, eager, spirited, intense. *(ant)* apathetic, uninterested.

12 **incident** *(n)* an instance of something happening. *(s)* event, occurrence, experience, case, episode, occasion.

13 **hitherto** *(adv)* until this point. *(s)* previously, formerly, beforehand, yet, before, thus far. *(ant)* henceforth.

14 **stave off** *(v)* delay or prevent something. *(s)* stop, avert, inhibit, hinder, thwart. *(ant)* embrace, encourage.

15 **utterly** *(adv)* to an extreme degree. *(s)* absolutely, completely, totally, entirely. *(ant)* somewhat, partly.

16 **solely** *(adv)* involving nothing or no one else. *(s)* only, simply, merely, exclusively, just. *(ant)* not only.

17 **impenetrable** *(adj)* impossible to pass through or enter. *(s)* dense, solid, impermeable, thick. *(ant)* penetrable.

18 **device** *(n)* a thing made or adapted for a specific purpose. *(s)* tool, mechanism, apparatus, gadget.

19 **capable** *(adj)* able to do something. *(s)* competent, proficient, adequate, apt, effective. *(ant)* incapable.

20 **invincible** *(adj)* too powerful to be defeated or overcome. *(s)* indestructible, unbeatable. *(ant)* vulnerable.

Mr Evans observed **judiciously**[1] as Drane followed the adults and the sick girl into the office. Reluctant to let Drane out of his sight, he tore himself away and headed straight for the basement. There remained one more task to perform to **safeguard**[2] the gem's future. Hurrying, he didn't notice two boys exit the cinema and walk nonchalantly in different directions. Nor did he spot the suited man who moved unseen amongst the glass **cabinets**[3].

⋆

The man who had just entered the museum unseen had easily avoided being caught on CCTV. Fully aware of the guards' **insignificance**[4], he **predicted**[5] the real security would arrive in the form of the Knights Hawk. **Specifically**[6] when and how they would show themselves was unknown, but his **band**[7] of young Mal-Instinctives were in place, and the girl was taken care of. Today he would take back **ownership**[8] of the Gwalch Gem bracelet. The man paused, calculating his every move. He watched Evans cross the exhibition hall and leave by a narrow door that he knew led down to the basement. He waited a few seconds, then followed.

As he opened the door, he glanced over his shoulder, checking no one **undesirable**[9] saw him. He didn't see the black cat that darted through the door at the very moment of his backward look. The two youths who had left the cinema **sauntered**[10] among the cabinets, pretending to enjoy their contents. They, too, waited awhile and then, one at a time, crossed the hall, following their leader through the door and down the steps into the basement.

The **lean**[11], suited man **lurked**[12], **shadowing**[13] Evans. Far enough behind not to be seen,

---

1   **judiciously** *(adv)* in a judicious (careful) way. *(s)* wisely, sensibly, cautiously, prudently. *(ant)* foolishly.

2   **safeguard** *(v)* protect from damage or harm. *(s)* shield, defend, maintain, preserve, uphold. *(ant)* endanger.

3   **cabinet** *(n)* a unit for storing or displaying articles. *(s)* case, cupboard, dresser, closet, chest, locker, container.

4   **insignificance** *(n)* lack of importance for consideration. *(s)* triviality, irrelevance. *(ant)* significance.

5   **predict** *(v)* say or guess that something will happen in the future. *(s)* foresee, forecast, expect, anticipate.

6   **specifically** *(adv)* in a specific (clear and exact) way. *(s)* precisely, particularly, categorically. *(ant)* vaguely.

7   **band** *(n)* a group of people who share common purposes. *(s)* gang, crew, posse, team, league. *(ant)* lone wolf.

8   **ownership** *(n)* the right, state or act of possessing something. *(s)* possession, control, proprietorship.

9   **undesirable** *(adj)* not wanted. *(s)* displeasing, unwelcome, uninvited, disagreeable. *(ant)* desirable, wanted.

10   **saunter** *(v)* walk in a slow and relaxed manner. *(s)* stroll, amble, wander, mosey, dawdle. *(ant)* hurry, hasten.

11   **lean** *(adj)* thin, especially healthily so. *(s)* slender, slim, wiry, sinewy, trim, bony, angular. *(ant)* stout, fat.

12   **lurk** *(v)* be or remain hidden, hang about. *(s)* prowl, loiter, skulk, creep, steal, slink. *(ant)* appear, materialise.

13   **shadow** *(v)* follow and observe closely and secretly. *(s)* tail, trail, track, pursue, stalk. *(ant)* guide, lead.

he **pursued**[1] his **quarry**[2] as it **scurried**[3] deeper into the basement. The old man Evans would lead him to the Cutter; without it he would never shatter the showcase that **masqueraded**[4] as **standard**[5] glass. He must **acquire**[6] the Cutter, the **fragment**[7] the Knights Hawk had **harvested**[8] from the Gwalch Gem itself when they had **seized**[9] it back from him, all those years ago.

In a similar way that a diamond is needed to cut another diamond, the knights had created a glass that could be cut solely by a piece of the gem itself. **Consequently**[10], it alone would permit entry into that case. Here lay the gem's **infallible**[11] security. The impenetrable glass, the Cutter and the Knights Hawk **guaranteed**[12] the gem's safety.

*

Beyond the foot of the stairs, the **hostile**[13] basement twisted into a cold, airless collection of corridors that quickly narrowed into tight passageways. They led off to **myriad**[14] side rooms and **complex**[15] tunnels as **antiquated**[16] lamps flickered, **scarcely**[17] lighting the way. **Undeterred**[18], Evans knew the layout far too well to fear it. He made his way **ably**[19] along the dim route until he reached the room from which Gwilym Cadwaladr was due to emerge. He stopped in front of the closed door and listened before tapping lightly. After a slight delay came the faintest of coded

---

1   **pursue** *(v)* chase or follow. *(s)* hunt, trail, track, tail, shadow, hound, seek, trace, stalk. *(ant)* guide, lead.

2   **quarry** *(n)* an animal pursued by a hunter or predator for food. *(s)* prey, game, victim, target, kill. *(ant)* hunter.

3   **scurry** *(v)* move quickly with short, hurried steps. *(s)* dash, dart, scamper, scuttle, hasten. *(ant)* saunter, amble.

4   **masquerade** *(v)* make a false and deceptive show of pretence. *(s)* impersonate, pose, imitate.

5   **standard** *(adj)* normal or average. *(s)* typical, ordinary, regular, usual, basic, everyday. *(ant)* unusual, special.

6   **acquire** *(v)* obtain (get) or buy something. *(s)* secure, gain, attain, take, achieve, receive. *(ant)* lose, relinquish.

7   **fragment** *(n)* a part broken or detached from a whole. *(s)* piece, scrap, portion, bit, sliver, chip. *(ant)* whole.

8   **harvest** *(v)* collect or obtain something for future use. *(s)* gather, pick, reap, garner.

9   **seize** *(v)* forcibly take possession of. *(s)* capture, abduct, hijack, grab, grasp. *(ant)* relinquish, give, return.

10   **consequently** *(adv)* as a result. *(s)* so, therefore, thus, subsequently, accordingly.

11   **infallible** *(adj)* always effective, never failing. *(s)* dependable, fail-safe, unerring, flawless, sound. *(ant)* fallible.

12   **guarantee** *(v)* provide a formal assurance, ensure safety or outcome. *(s)* secure, promise. *(ant)* undermine.

13   **hostile** *(adj)* unwelcoming or showing opposition. *(s)* harsh, adverse, unfavourable, unpleasant. *(ant)* friendly.

14   **myriad** *(adj)* extremely great in number. *(s)* many, numerous, untold, multiple, countless, endless. *(ant)* few.

15   **complex** *(adj)* having many different and connected parts. *(s)* complicated, intricate. *(ant)* simple, clear.

16   **antiquated** *(adj)* old-fashioned or outdated. *(s)* ancient, archaic, obsolete, outmoded. *(ant)* modern.

17   **scarcely** *(adv)* only just, almost not. *(s)* hardly, barely, slightly. *(ant)* generously, greatly, sufficiently.

18   **undeterred** *(adj)* carrying on despite setbacks (not put off). *(s)* undaunted, resolute. *(ant)* deterred.

19   **ably** *(adv)* in an able manner. *(s)* competently, capably, well, adeptly, adroitly, easily. *(ant)* incompetently.

responses. He turned the handle and nudged the door **ajar**[1]. Glancing back over his shoulder, checking the immediate **vicinity**[2], he opened the door and entered the room.

'Glad you are here, sir, and Owain too,' said Evans, bowing his head in respect at the knights. 'I must report the boy Drane has the sister.' Abruptly he quietened – he had spotted Claire.

'Thank you, Evans.' Gwilym stepped in, **curtailing**[3] further conversation. 'Please brief me outside before we proceed,' he added, heading for the door, allowing Evans no opportunity to comment.

Shocked, Claire **instantly**[4] recognised Evans as the **creepy**[5] man from the train that morning. What on earth was he doing here? It felt an age ago, yet it had only happened that morning. Why had he been on that train, and how had he beaten the helicopter and reached the museum before them? Wary of him earlier, she felt her unease **tangibly**[6] now, but as the two men re-entered, she knew her questions must wait.

'Owain, stay down in the basement and cover the **key**[7] areas. Evans will go in the opposite direction.' Gwilym spoke in urgent bursts. 'The Master will come with Mal-Instinctives. I must go to the gem. Claire, this way,' he said **curtly**[8], heading back into the corridor. 'Owain, take Jack with you,' he ordered.

*

Within earshot, but **secreted**[9] away in the shadows, the suited man blended in unnoticed as he observed the knights, missing nothing and **evaluating**[10] everything. As Owain left with Jack, the hidden man nodded an **affirming**[11] signal back to his two waiting boys to **tail**[12] the knight. The suited man stood silent and still. He watched and listened as Gwilym turned back towards the waiting curator.

---

1   **ajar** *(adj)* slightly open. *(s)* agape, unclosed, cracked, unfastened. *(ant)* closed, shut.

2   **vicinity** *(n)* surrounding or nearby areas. *(s)* proximity, propinquity, locale. *(ant)* distance.

3   **curtail** *(v)* impose a restriction on. *(s)* restrain, curb, limit, inhibit, halt. *(ant)* develop, extend, increase.

4   **instantly** *(adv)* at once, immediately. *(s)* instantaneously, straight away, promptly. *(ant)* gradually, eventually.

5   **creepy** *(adj)* causing a feeling of unease, wariness or fear. *(s)* weird, eerie, sinister, spooky. *(ant)* pleasant.

6   **tangibly** *(adv)* in a real, clear and definite way. *(s)* evidently, noticeably, palpably. *(ant)* intangibly.

7   **key** *(adj)* of crucial importance. *(s)* critical, main, central, significant, vital, essential. *(ant)* unimportant.

8   **curtly** *(adj)* in a curt (abrupt) manner. *(s)* bluntly, brusquely, tersely, harshly, shortly, gruffly. *(ant)* gently.

9   **secreted** *(adj)* hidden. *(s)* concealed, veiled, shrouded, stowed, disguised. *(ant)* displayed, revealed.

10   **evaluate** *(v)* form an idea of. *(s)* assess, judge, appraise, gauge, estimate, calculate, check. *(ant)* misjudge.

11   **affirming** *(adj)* supporting or stating firmly. *(s)* confirming, encouraging, verifying. *(ant)* negating, nullifying.

12   **tail** *(v)* follow and observe, often in secret. *(s)* track, shadow, trail, stalk, pursue, chase. *(ant)* lead, guide.

'Evans, you know what to do. Go to the Cutter now. Protect it with your life.'

'Yes, sir,' Evans replied, then moved to leave.

'Claire, this way,' said Gwilym.

From the shadows, the suited man smiled to himself. He watched them all leave and then turned to pursue Evans, who he now knew would lead him directly to what he needed.

✳

Owain's wide stride covered **ample**[1] ground as he followed Gwilym's orders. As he headed in the opposite direction to Evans, his supercharged torch lit the basement in wide, sweeping arcs. He navigated the **labyrinth**[2] of passageways and side rooms, only one of which held the Cutter, but the Knights Hawk had **branded**[3] it to memory. So far, he'd found no sign of Mal-Instinct as he swept his light around each musty chamber. He investigated every **nook**[4] and **cranny**[5], every twist and turn, and there seemed nothing **untoward**[6]. Then, suddenly, Jack froze, **rooted**[7] to the spot. His **hackles**[8] up, he gurgled an **ominous**[9], low growl. Owain stopped dead, shrinking back for cover in a dusty **recess**[10] covered in **cobwebs**[11].

'What is it, boy?' he whispered.

Jack's growl deepened. His ears pricked forward, and his **scruffy**[12] body stiffened, ready to pounce. That was when Owain took the first kick. Fast, **furious**[13] and expertly **executed**[14], it knocked him clean off his feet. Stunned, he rolled onto all fours, deflecting part of a second

---

1   **ample** *(adj)* enough or more than enough. *(s)* plentiful, abundant, generous. *(ant)* insufficient, meagre.

2   **labyrinth** *(n)* a complicated network of passages. *(s)* maze, warren, tangle, web, jumble, muddle.

3   **brand** *(v)* mark indelibly (in a permanent way). *(s)* stamp, imprint, tattoo, burn, scar.

4   **nook** *(n)* a corner or recess, often providing security or seclusion. *(s)* alcove, niche, cranny. *(ant)* protrusion.

5   **cranny** *(n)* a little, narrow space or opening. *(s)* gap, niche, crevice, crack, cleft, split. *(ant)* closure.

6   **untoward** *(adj)* unanticipated, inappropriate or inconvenient. *(s)* troublesome, problematic. *(ant)* pleasant.

7   **rooted** *(adj)* caused to stand immobile through curiosity, fear or amazement. *(s)* planted, fixed, riveted.

8   **hackles** *(n)* erectile (upright) hairs on an animal's back, risen when it is alarmed. *(s)* spike, spine, bristle.

9   **ominous** *(adj)* indicating imminent misfortune. *(s)* threatening, warning. *(ant)* unthreatening, auspicious.

10   **recess** *(n)* a small corner or hollow place, usually in a wall. *(s)* alcove, indentation, bay, niche. *(ant)* protrusion.

11   **cobweb** *(n)* a spider's web, especially when unoccupied, typically old and dusty. *(s)* gossamer.

12   **scruffy** *(adj)* untidy or dirty. *(s)* bedraggled, messy, unkempt, dishevelled, ratty, tatty, grubby. *(ant)* tidy, neat.

13   **furious** *(adj)* extremely angry, violent or energetic. *(s)* ferocious, vehement, fierce, feverish. *(ant)* calm, mild.

14   **execute** *(v)* put order, plan or action into effect, carry out. *(s)* perform, implement, achieve. *(ant)* fail.

kick; then he **vaulted**[1] up onto his feet, ducking the third completely.

Akin to a **samurai's**[2] blade, his **reflexes**[3] were **honed**[4] as his attackers struck again. The two boys were trained **combatants**[5] and, although still young, fought **viciously**[6]. Owain instantly **identified**[7] them as Mal-Instinctives. One boy **posed**[8] no problem; two would be troublesome.

They came at him relentlessly, whirling and kicking, throwing **steely**[9] punches and kicks with lightning-quick moves. They were martial artists, **acrobatic**[10] and **systematic**[11], but then so was Owain. A Knight Hawk, he'd had centuries to acquire these Eastern **techniques**[12] and had been taught by **classical**[13] tutors. He parried and dodged more than he attacked, **tactically**[14] wanting to tire them out, then finish them. The Knights Hawk would not **condemn**[15] **needlessly**[16]; they captured and **reasoned**[17], but if all else failed, then they would kill.

With ease, the larger boy leaped towards him, spinning a **phenomenal**[18] three-hundred-and-sixty-degree turn in the air. He kicked high, towards Owain's face, his foot **connecting**[19] precisely. Owain took the cruel blow to his chin and stumbled. The other boy grabbed him from behind, **wrestling**[20] him to the floor. The back of Owain's head hit the ground with a sickening smack.

---

1   **vault** *(v)* leap or spring by supporting or propelling oneself with one's hands. *(s)* jump, bound.

2   **samurai** *(n)* a member of a powerful military order in Japan. *(s)* warrior, swordsman, knight.

3   **reflex** *(n)* a reaction done without conscious thought. *(s)* impulse, response.

4   **hone** *(v)* refine, sharpen or perfect over time. *(s)* improve, enhance, polish, practise, drill. *(ant)* impair.

5   **combatant** *(n)* someone engaged in fighting. *(s)* pugilist, soldier, warrior. *(ant)* ally, peacemaker.

6   **viciously** *(adv)* in a vicious (cruel or violent) manner. *(s)* brutally, savagely, ferociously, brutishly. *(ant)* gently.

7   **identify** *(v)* indicate or establish identity. *(s)* recognise, distinguish, detect, determine, spot. *(ant)* mistake.

8   **pose** *(v)* present or be. *(s)* constitute, cause, create, set, establish.

9   **steely** *(adj)* coldly determined. *(s)* ruthless, hard, strong, tough, unyielding, resolute. *(ant)* soft, irresolute.

10   **acrobatic** *(adj)* adept (skilled) at gymnastic feats. *(s)* lithe, supple, flexible, athletic. *(ant)* stiff, unfit.

11   **systematic** *(adj)* acting according to a plan or system. *(s)* methodical, organised, efficient. *(ant)* disorganised.

12   **technique** *(n)* a way of carrying out a task. *(s)* method, approach, system, skill, modus operandi.

13   **classical** *(adj)* representing a long-established, proven style. *(s)* traditional, orthodox. *(ant)* new, novel.

14   **tactically** *(adv)* in a tactical (planned) manner. *(s)* strategically, deliberately, intentionally. *(ant)* accidentally.

15   **condemn** *(v)* punish, or sentence to death. *(s)* doom, convict. *(ant)* absolve, pardon, acquit, exonerate.

16   **needlessly** *(adv)* done in a needless (unnecessary) way. *(s)* avoidably, pointlessly. *(ant)* necessarily.

17   **reason** *(v)* persuade with rational (sensible) argument. *(s)* talk around, convince, influence. *(ant)* dissuade.

18   **phenomenal** *(adj)* exceptionally good. *(s)* remarkable, impressive, prodigious, outstanding. *(ant)* ordinary.

19   **connect** *(v)* (of a blow) accurately hit the intended target. *(s)* impact, strike, collide, meet, clash. *(ant)* miss.

20   **wrestle** *(v)* force or fight by grappling (tussling). *(s)* struggle, brawl, battle, scuffle, scramble.

They had him, or so it seemed, but perhaps their **misplaced**[1] **conceit**[2] caused them to drop their guard. Jack, waiting, sprang from the shadows. The boy who was now **straddling**[3] Owain's chest lifted his fist to punch again as the terrier's teeth sank into his upper thigh. Jack had always prided himself on his canine **accuracy**[4], and rarely missed. When a Jack Russell locks its jaw onto its prey, it doesn't let go. The youth rolled back, **wailing**[5] as Jack's head shook **aggressively**[6] against the boy's skin. Seemingly distracted by his **accomplice's**[7] howling, the other boy's grip on Owain loosened. It was enough; Owain took him down with a stunning blow. The boy would be **unconscious**[8] for some time.

'Jack, leave!' commanded Owain, grabbing the other bleeding youth and yanking him to his feet.

Jack immediately let go of the boy. Owain dragged the wailing youth into a side room, where he bound and gagged him, using the boy's own belt and socks. Blood **oozed**[9] through his trousers, but he'd live. It took more than that to kill a Mal-Instinctive.

Owain deftly **secured**[10] the other boy in the same manner and sprinted away down the corridor. Stealth was not an option now, and speed was **crucial**[11]. These boys were mere foot soldiers; the Master would be present. He had to find Evans, and the Cutter, right now.

*

On the opposite side of the **murky**[12] basement, slinking through the dark, the **statuesque**[13], suited man tailed Robert Evans. For him, the Mal-Master, following the little old knight was easy, and

---

1   **misplaced** *(adj)* (of feelings) directed inappropriately. *(s)* misdirected, erroneous. *(ant)* appropriate.

2   **conceit** *(n)* excessive pride. *(s)* self-importance, big-headiness, vanity, smugness, arrogance. *(ant)* modesty.

3   **straddle** *(v)* spread the legs wide apart (either side of something). *(s)* bestride, span, sprawl.

4   **accuracy** *(n)* correctness or precision. *(s)* certainty, skill, exactness, exactitude, mastery. *(ant)* inaccuracy.

5   **wail** *(v)* make a prolonged, high-pitched sound. *(s)* bawl, yowl, cry, scream, moan, screech. *(ant)* laugh, giggle.

6   **aggressively** *(adv)* done in an aggressive (forceful) way. *(s)* violently, belligerently, vigorously. *(ant)* gently.

7   **accomplice** *(n)* a person who helps another commit a crime. *(s)* co-conspirator, collaborator, abettor.

8   **unconscious** *(adj)* not awake or aware of one's environment. *(s)* asleep, comatose. *(ant)* conscious.

9   **ooze** *(v)* gently flow, trickle or seep. *(s)* bleed, exude, emerge, leak, creep, drip, leach, issue. *(ant)* gush, pour.

10   **secure** *(v)* fix, attach or fasten firmly. *(s)* position, tighten, lock, bind, tie, safeguard. *(ant)* unfasten, release.

11   **crucial** *(adj)* of absolute (complete) importance. *(s)* critical, vital, key, essential, fundamental. *(ant)* trivial.

12   **murky** *(adj)* gloomy and dark. *(s)* dim, shadowy, sombre, dreary, dingy, obscured. *(ant)* bright, light, clear.

13   **statuesque** *(adj)* tall and attractive with fine posture (pose). *(s)* good-looking, well formed. *(ant)* short, ugly.

Evans would lead him to the Cutter. He was **unruffled**[1] that Evans had sensed him following and **plunged**[2] the passageways into darkness; that wouldn't stop him. **On the contrary**[3], he revelled in the smell of the **beleaguered**[4] knight's fear.

Reaching a crossroads in the passageway, the panting knight turned a sharp right, then stopped abruptly. The Master smiled to himself. *Show me the door, old knight. Show me the door.* The Master waited, listening. He must move cautiously **lest**[5] he scare Evans off; Evans must **disclose**[6] the Cutter to him.

The Master detected no movement from Evans. A thrill shot through him; the Cutter must be close. He must remain patient. Dozens of doors lined the passageway. Which one would Evans enter?

'Patience, Dewi,' he told himself. 'Patience.'

Without warning, a dazzling flash of emerald light filled the shadows, its **luminescence**[7] so astoundingly bright it momentarily blinded the Master.

Blinking furiously, the Master swooped around the corner in time to hear one of the side-room doors slamming shut. He dived at the door, forcing it open to reveal complete darkness. Only a single second passed between lifting his night-vision **monocular**[8] to his eye and finding the light switch, but to his **chagrin**[9], Evans was nowhere to be seen.

Evans had simply vanished. Still, the Master didn't care about Evans. He didn't care what magic the knight had conjured to escape, because he could sense the Cutter's presence in this room. Whichever secret tunnel Evans had disappeared into as a **ploy**[10] to **divert**[11] him did not matter. The Master sensed the Cutter's proximity, and it was calling to him.

---

1   **unruffled** *(adj)* not agitated or disturbed. *(s)* unperturbed, tranquil, relaxed, composed, calm. *(ant)* flustered.

2   **plunge** *(v)* suddenly bring into a specified condition or state. *(s)* thrust, force, throw.

3   **on the contrary** *(adv)* just the opposite (in meaning, nature or direction). *(s)* far from it, conversely.

4   **beleaguered** *(adj)* put in a difficult situation. *(s)* besieged, harassed, plagued, tormented. *(ant)* assisted.

5   **lest** *(con)* with the intention of preventing or to avoid the risk of. *(s)* in case, for fear that.

6   **disclose** *(v)* make known. *(s)* show, reveal, uncover, unveil, divulge, impart, tell. *(ant)* hide, conceal, secrete.

7   **luminescence** *(n)* the release of light by a substance. *(s)* radiance, brightness, glare. *(ant)* darkness.

8   **monocular** *(n)* an optical instrument used to view distant objects with one eye.

9   **chagrin** *(n)* annoyance or distress. *(s)* disappointment, exasperation, displeasure, irritation. *(ant)* delight, joy.

10   **ploy** *(n)* a cunning (clever, shrewd) plan or action. *(s)* trick, manoeuvre, strategy, ruse, tactic.

11   **divert** *(v)* cause a change of course or direction. *(s)* distract, avert, deter, redirect, dissuade. *(ant)* focus.

The side room's time-worn shelves were lined with labelled objects and **obsolete**[1] **exhibits**[2] from upstairs, **painstakingly**[3] **categorised**[4] by type. The Master raised his hands to chest height and **inclined**[5] his palms outwards, gliding them **languidly**[6] towards specific **ornaments**[7]. Closing his eyes, he hummed as they **levitated**[8] up and down the protruding ledges, **assiduously**[9] seeking his prized goal, his single target.

Detecting the slightest **sensory**[10] **disturbance**[11] at his fingertips, he paused; his humming **ceased**[12]. He didn't move, focusing on one object. Calmly opening his **serpentine**[13] eyes, he looked closely at what appeared to be a disregarded **trinket**[14] placed at the back of the **burgeoning**[15] shelf.

He stepped in closer, sniffing at it and snorting like a pig discovering the rarest of **truffles**[16]. It was a **petite**[17] fairy **figurine**[18] holding a bow, a **quiver**[19] of arrows perched sweetly on her back. He picked it up and blew away a layer of dust. A thin grin **distorted**[20] his mouth as he **plucked**[21] out a **fragile**[22] arrow from her quiver. He held it up to his eyes, twirling it around in smug

---

1   **obsolete** *(adj)* no longer produced or used. *(s)* old, outdated, superseded, ancient. *(ant)* modern, current.

2   **exhibit** *(n)* an object or collection on public display. *(s)* item, piece, article, specimen, sample.

3   **painstakingly** *(adv)* done in a painstaking (careful) way. *(s)* thoroughly, diligently, meticulously. *(ant)* carelessly.

4   **categorise** *(v)* place in a certain grade, rate, class or group. *(s)* classify, sort, catalogue, label. *(ant)* disorganise.

5   **incline** *(v)* slightly bend or turn forward, downwards or towards. *(s)* skew, tilt, aim, tip. *(ant)* flatten.

6   **languidly** *(adv)* in a languid (relaxed) manner. *(s)* unhurriedly, lazily, slowly, unenergetically. *(ant)* vigorously.

7   **ornament** *(n)* a small, decorative object. *(s)* trinket, knick-knack, adornment, figurine, bauble.

8   **levitate** *(v)* rise and hover in the air. *(s)* float, ascend, drift up, fly up. *(ant)* sink, lower, descend, drop.

9   **assiduously** *(adv)* in an assiduous (tireless) way. *(s)* diligently, intently, carefully, persistently. *(ant)* casually.

10   **sensory** *(adj)* relating to sensation or physical senses. *(s)* perceptible, palpable. *(ant)* imperceptible.

11   **disturbance** *(n)* an interruption. *(s)* interference, distraction, intrusion, tremor. *(ant)* calm, stillness.

12   **cease** *(v)* stop, end or finish. *(s)* conclude, terminate, halt, pause, quit, discontinue. *(ant)* start, continue.

13   **serpentine** *(adj)* of or like a serpent or snake. *(s)* snake-like, cunning, sly, shrewd. *(ant)* honest, stupid.

14   **trinket** *(n)* a small ornament or item of jewellery. *(s)* knick-knack, bauble, charm, trifle.

15   **burgeoning** *(adj)* growing or expanding rapidly. *(s)* flourishing, swelling, proliferating. *(ant)* dwindling.

16   **truffle** *(n)* a strong-smelling, rare underground fungus found with pigs and dogs. *(s)* earthnut.

17   **petite** *(adj)* attractively small and dainty. *(s)* slight, elfin, delicate, diminutive, little, tiny. *(ant)* large, bulky.

18   **figurine** *(n)* a statuette (small statue or sculpture). *(s)* ornament, figure, model, effigy, representation.

19   **quiver** *(n)* an archer's case for holding arrows.

20   **distort** *(v)* pull or twist out of shape. *(s)* bend, contort, deform, disfigure, alter, warp. *(ant)* straighten.

21   **pluck** *(v)* take hold of and quickly remove from. *(s)* pick, pull, tug, grasp, extract, tweak, yank. *(ant)* insert.

22   **fragile** *(adj)* easily broken or damaged. *(s)* delicate, flimsy, brittle, breakable, weak. *(ant)* sturdy, robust.

ceremony, savouring the moment. There, on the end, **unpolished**[1] and barely visible, was the fragment of Gwalch Gem. This fragment, the Cutter, could cut the otherwise-impenetrable glass before those **incompetent**[2] security guards would notice a thing. Dropping the figurine onto the floor, he laid his **trophy**[3] **protectively**[4] into a tiny metal box and placed it into his breast pocket.

The Master then returned to the job in hand. Had his boys dealt with Owain, or would his knightly skills have overcome them? Either way, Evans, wherever he had disappeared to, would know he was likely to have found the Cutter, their **sacred**[5] tool, and would alert the Knights Hawk. He knew he must act quickly, and fled back into the maze of passageways, heading towards the stairs that would take him up into the exhibition hall and to the case that held the Gwalch Gem bracelet.

✦

Seconds later, Owain reached the room, missing the Master by a heartbeat. Flinging open the door and sweeping the dusty space with his torch, his heart plunged – he was too late. The fairy figurine lay shattered on the ground, and he knew checking the quiver would be **futile**[6] – the arrow wouldn't be there. Now the Master had the Cutter, Owain thought of nothing but protecting the Gwalch Gem bracelet. He spun around and raced back towards the stairs, fast on the heels of the Master.

---

1   **unpolished** *(adj)* not having a polished (buffed or shined) surface. *(s)* matt, flat, dull, lacklustre. *(ant)* polished.

2   **incompetent** *(adj)* lacking the skills. *(s)* unable, inept, useless, amateurish, bungling. *(ant)* able, competent.

3   **trophy** *(n)* an object regarded as a prize. *(s)* medal, cup, award, crown, title, booty, souvenir.

4   **protectively** *(adv)* in a protective manner. *(s)* possessively, tenderly, gently, affectionately. *(ant)* aggressively.

5   **sacred** *(adj)* regarded with respect and reverence (admiration). *(s)* venerable, protected. *(ant)* profane.

6   **futile** *(adj)* useless and pointless. *(s)* fruitless, vain, unsuccessful, ineffective, ineffectual, wasted. *(ant)* useful.

8. A Knight's Tale

Upstairs in the museum's office, Rebecca lay dribbling onto the cushion of a tatty chair. Josh Drane perched on its arm, seeming to nurse her so **convincingly**[1] that Mr Hollie had left them with the curator's wife and rushed back to check on his class in the cinema. In the **cramped**[2] office, a **composed**[3] and **collected**[4] Marjorie Evans carefully observed Drane. She was always a patient woman, and her demeanour remained **unflappable**[5] and reticent. Playing cat and mouse, they waited, poised and silent. **Opposing**[6] Instinctives knew the threat of each other's presence.

The drugged girl's **palpable**[7] **trepidation**[8] filled the **inadequate**[9] space. Rebecca lay **incapable**[10] now, the **dose**[11] of chemicals **asserting**[12] their **comprehensive**[13] control. She would listen only to Drane and, once recovered, would remember nothing.

Outside the office, in the exhibition hall, the boy who had sneaked from the back of the

---

1 **convincingly** *(adv)* in a way that convinces. *(s)* persuasively, believably, realistically. *(ant)* unconvincingly.

2 **cramped** *(adj)* uncomfortably small or restricted. *(s)* confined, tight, poky, limited. *(ant)* spacious, capacious.

3 **composed** *(adj)* having one's feelings under control. *(s)* serene, cool, calm, collected, poised. *(ant)* flustered.

4 **collected** *(adj)* calm and self-controlled. *(s)* composed, placid, together, unruffled, sanguine. *(ant)* agitated.

5 **unflappable** *(adj)* calm in a crisis. *(s)* composed, unflustered, imperturbable, unexcitable. *(ant)* flappable.

6 **opposing** *(adj)* in competition or conflict with. *(s)* rival, combatant, opposite, hostile. *(ant)* allied, agreeable.

7 **palpable** *(adj)* so intense as to seem almost tangible (real). *(s)* obvious, profound, substantial. *(ant)* intangible.

8 **trepidation** *(n)* anxiety or fear about what may happen. *(s)* dread, foreboding, apprehension. *(ant)* assurance.

9 **inadequate** *(adj)* lacking the required (needed) quantity or quality. *(s)* insufficient, deficient. *(ant)* adequate.

10 **incapable** *(adj)* unable to achieve or do something. *(s)* powerless, helpless, incapacitated. *(ant)* capable.

11 **dose** *(n)* a measured quantity of something. *(s)* draught, dosage, portion, amount.

12 **assert** *(v)* work, behave or speak in a confident and forceful manner. *(s)* press, claim, establish. *(ant)* retract.

13 **comprehensive** *(adj)* wide-ranging, of a large scope. *(s)* complete, full, all-inclusive, total. *(ant)* limited.

cinema line earlier **loitered**[1] amongst the glass cases. Surreptitiously checking the time, he feigned interest in the exhibits, **imitating**[2] an ordinary, interested student and not the **planted**[3] **decoy**[4] and Mal-Instinctive that he was.

He watched the second hand sweep twice around the museum's giant clock face. Then, using his full body weight, he shoved a glass exhibit case as **forcibly**[5] as he could, continuing to rock it back and forth.

Upstairs in the security centre, the **flabby**[6] guard, Dave, visibly choked as the alarm rang out.

'Come in, Bert, come in,' he spluttered into his walkie-talkie, spraying a shower of crisps from his mouth. Wiping his mouth on his sleeve, he **heaved**[7] himself up to his feet. 'What is it, mate?' Bert's voice crackled over the radio.

'Number one five eight, the alarm's going off. I can see a lad rocking the case,' replied the guard, spattering crisps again. 'I'll meet you there.'

He brushed crumbs off his **portly**[8] stomach, puffed out his chest and donned his guard's cap. Case 158 was an awfully long walk from the security room. Normally, he'd **gripe**[9] at the prospect of unwelcome exercise, but right now, he didn't mind at all. So excited at his chance to play the hero, he broke from his **dallying**[10] into a wobbly trot. As he **waddled**[11] off to help Bert with the boy, his fleshy **paunch**[12] of a belly sloshed from side to side, like an overfilled beach ball.

*

---

1   **loiter** *(v)* wait around without apparent purpose. *(s)* linger, lurk, skulk, dawdle, tarry, dally. *(ant)* rush, scurry.

2   **imitate** *(v)* pretend to be. *(s)* impersonate, copy, mimic, emulate, resemble, replicate. *(ant)* differ from.

3   **plant** *(v)* place someone in a group to act as a spy. *(s)* establish, infiltrate, insert, embed.

4   **decoy** *(n)* something used to mislead or lure into a trap. *(s)* distraction, smokescreen, bait. *(ant)* repellent.

5   **forcibly** *(adv)* in a forcible manner. *(s)* forcefully, strenuously, mightily, roughly, bodily. *(ant)* weakly, gently.

6   **flabby** *(adj)* (of the body) loose and fleshy. *(s)* unfit, unfirm, soft, sagging, flaccid. *(ant)* firm, fit, athletic.

7   **heave** *(v)* lift or haul with huge effort. *(s)* raise, hoist, manoeuvre, elevate, heft, drag. *(ant)* drop, flop.

8   **portly** *(adj)* large, fat or overweight. *(s)* round, corpulent, chubby, tubby, heavy. *(ant)* slim, slender, skinny.

9   **gripe** *(v)* whinge or complain in a persistent, irritating way. *(s)* moan, protest, grumble, object. *(ant)* praise.

10   **dallying** *(n)* slow action or movement. *(s)* dilly-dallying, dawdling, lingering, loitering, delay. *(ant)* haste, rush.

11   **waddle** *(v)* walk with a clumsy swaying motion. *(s)* toddle, wobble, totter, sway. *(ant)* stride, glide.

12   **paunch** *(n)* a large, rotund (round) or protruding belly. *(s)* potbelly, gut, spare tyre, midriff. *(ant)* plane.

At the opposite end of the exhibition hall, away from the guards, a gap in the door cracked open, and Gwilym peeked through. Using the **kerfuffle**[1] between the boy and the guards to his **advantage**[2], he beckoned Claire to follow him up the last few steps into the hall. He closed the door behind them, and they darted for cover, scrabbling between towering wooden shelves stuffed with **volumes**[3] of **antique**[4] books, which lined one wall of the hall. Scanning the area, Gwilym quickly **evaluated**[5]; across the hall, he saw the cinema door was still closed, and according to Evans, Drane held the girl. He put a finger to his lips and signalled to Claire to remain still.

His Instinct warned him that the footsteps he heard approaching behind him from the basement belonged to neither Owain nor Evans. This presence, **merely**[6] feet away, **forewarned**[7] him of a Mal-Instinctive he had not **encountered**[8] for many years.

'Dewi,' he whispered.

'What?' asked Claire, seeing the look on Gwilym's face. 'What is it?'

'It is Dewi, Llywelyn's brother.'

'Where?' said Claire, her eyes darting everywhere.

'Behind us. If he has the Cutter, then we are too late,' said Gwilym.

'The Cutter?' asked Claire, remembering what Gwilym had said to Evans just minutes before.

'I must go back,' he said in a low, urgent whisper.

'Why?' she asked.

'I have no time to explain. Your sister is in the office. Drane is Dewi's second in command, and his Mal-Instinct may be powerful. You must now face him alone,' he said, pointing across the hall.

'But how can I help Rebecca without you?' she asked, but he had already turned away.

As he moved to the door, Claire shrank into the shadow of the bookshelf and watched him go.

*

---

1   **kerfuffle** *(n)* a disturbance or fuss. *(s)* commotion, hubbub, tumult, melee, rumpus, ruckus. *(ant)* tranquillity.

2   **advantage** *(n)* the opportunity to gain or benefit from something. *(s)* good, improvement, use, profit. *(ant)* disadvantage.

3   **volume** *(n)* a book forming part of a work or series. *(s)* tome, publication, digest, album, edition.

4   **antique** *(adj)* belonging to former times. *(s)* old, collectable, vintage, historic. *(ant)* new.

5   **evaluate** *(v)* form an idea of. *(s)* assess, judge, work out, calculate, rate, gauge, weigh up. *(ant)* misjudge.

6   **merely** *(adv)* only, just and nothing more. *(s)* barely, simply, slightly, purely, solely.

7   **forewarn** *(v)* inform of a future danger or problem. *(s)* warn, caution, alert, prime, prewarn, advise.

8   **encounter** *(v)* meet unexpectedly. *(s)* face, confront, run into, come across. *(ant)* avoid.

Bracing himself, Gwilym jerked open the basement door. The steep steps revealed unexpected emptiness, the threatening presence nowhere to be seen. Only a familiar **lone**[1] white **bundle**[2] sat at the bottom of the steps.

'Jack,' said Gwilym. 'Go with Claire now,' he commanded, running down the steps towards him. 'Go!'

Jack **scaled**[3] the steep steps two at a time, his claws struggling for purchase on the slippery surface. He quickly reached the top, but in his haste, Gwilym had descended into the basement and let the door shut behind him, leaving Jack **stranded**[4] on the top step.

Jack pushed his nose repeatedly at the door, but it wouldn't yield. Standing on his hind legs, his frantic paws scratched hard at the paint. He panted as he sprang up and down, trying to reach the handle, knocking it with his front paws. The **tenacious**[5] Jack Russell refused to submit and bounced and sprang until, eventually, **persistence**[6] paid off, and he struck the handle inch-perfect. Levering the handle in precisely the right spot, he dipped it enough to release the catch, and it gave way. A couple of centimetres opening offered enough for Jack's impatient nose to push through, making room for his slim shoulders. The dog's determination succeeded, and he wriggled the rest of his body through the limited space and sped towards Claire.

*

Beneath, in the basement, Gwilym edged deeper into the dim, airless passages. Drops of **fetid**[7] moisture dripped from the **mouldy**[8] ceiling, splashing his **stony**[9] face. He flicked them away with the back of his hand, pausing to **assess**[10] his next steps. If he moved **prematurely**[11], he would risk an **ambush**[12]. Regardless of the door that had been between them, the Master had sensed him,

---

1   **lone** *(adj)* having no companions (company). *(s)* individual, solitary, single, alone, solo. *(ant)* accompanied.

2   **bundle** *(n)* a collection of things, often wrapped or tied together. *(s)* package, pile, parcel, pack, bunch.

3   **scale** *(v)* climb up or over (something steep). *(s)* ascend, mount, clamber, clear, scrabble. *(ant)* descend.

4   **stranded** *(adj)* left without the means (capability) to leave. *(s)* trapped, stuck, marooned. *(ant)* rescued.

5   **tenacious** *(adj)* not giving up. *(s)* stubborn, persistent, determined, dogged, resolute. *(ant)* irresolute.

6   **persistence** *(n)* the act of continuing despite difficulty. *(s)* tenacity, perseverance, resolve. *(ant)* feebleness.

7   **fetid** *(adj)* smelling extremely unpleasant. *(s)* stinking, putrid, rotten, rank, fusty, malodorous. *(ant)* fresh.

8   **mouldy** *(adj)* covered with a fungal growth (mould) that causes decay. *(s)* rotten, festering. *(ant)* fresh, new.

9   **stony** *(adj)* not having or showing feeling or sympathy. *(s)* flinty, unyielding, hard, tough. *(ant)* compassionate.

10   **assess** *(v)* evaluate or estimate. *(s)* consider, determine, work out, judge, gauge. *(ant)* misjudge, presume.

11   **prematurely** *(adv)* in a premature (early) way, too soon. *(s)* hastily, rashly, impulsively. *(ant)* belatedly.

12   **ambush** *(n)* a surprise attack. *(s)* assault, trap, ensnarement, deception, trick, ambuscade.

yet not attacked. This meant one thing: if Dewi ran from him, he did so with purpose. Dewi fought a fearless and **malicious**[1] fight; he would never portray **cowardice**[2]. Gwilym knew him far too well for that. Llywelyn's brother never **exhibited**[3] weak or **craven**[4] behaviour. So why did he turn from him? Why not **confront**[5] Gwilym there on the steps? He **deduced**[6] it must **relate**[7] to the Cutter – and he must find it now.

∗

In the maze of the basement's outer depths, Owain sprinted from the **ransacked**[8] side room. With the Cutter gone and Evans not there, he had arrived too late. He **bolted**[9] along the **subterranean**[10] passages, ducking the low ceilings and sliding on damp, earthy floors. Whoever had stolen the Cutter, and Owain feared he knew, would move so quickly they would be difficult to **intercept**[11]. As he ran towards the basement steps, he gave no thought to Gwilym, Claire or Evans; his **priority**[12] centred **purely**[13] on saving the Cutter.

∗

Meanwhile, as Gwilym crept deeper into the **bowels**[14] of the sombre basement, he knew Dewi still lurked in its oppressive depths. As he hunted Llywelyn's brother, images of him filled his mind: Dewi, who had so betrayed the prince centuries before, stealing his wife and causing the death of his beloved hound, Gelert; the brother who had stolen the Gwalch Gem bracelet,

---

1 **malicious** *(adj)* having malice, intending harm. *(s)* malevolent, spiteful, mean, cruel, wicked. *(ant)* kind.

2 **cowardice** *(n)* lack of bravery or valour. *(s)* weakness, fear, spinelessness, timidity, cravenness. *(ant)* courage.

3 **exhibit** *(v)* manifest (show) clearly, put on. *(s)* demonstrate, reveal, display, present. *(ant)* hide, conceal.

4 **craven** *(adj)* completely lacking in courage. *(s)* cowardly, gutless, spineless, lily-livered. *(ant)* brave, bold.

5 **confront** *(v)* come face to face with a hostility, challenge or opposition. *(s)* brave, tackle, meet. *(ant)* avoid.

6 **deduce** *(v)* reach a conclusion (realisation) by thinking and reasoning. *(s)* infer, conclude, judge.

7 **relate** *(v)* be connected to or associated with. *(s)* link, concern, pertain, associate. *(ant)* dissociate.

8 **ransacked** *(adj)* searched, with items stolen or damaged. *(s)* looted, plundered.

9 **bolt** *(v)* move or run away suddenly, sometimes to escape. *(s)* sprint, dash, scarper, skedaddle. *(ant)* linger.

10 **subterranean** *(adj)* beneath the earth's surface. *(s)* underground, deep, buried. *(ant)* above ground, surface.

11 **intercept** *(v)* obstruct to prevent from continuing. *(s)* stop, interrupt, block, catch, divert. *(ant)* help, allow.

12 **priority** *(n)* the most important thing or consideration. *(s)* main concern, urgency, primacy. *(ant)* triviality.

13 **purely** *(adv)* entirely and exclusively, completely and totally. *(s)* wholly, solely, only, simply, just. *(ant)* partly.

14 **bowels** *(n)* the depths, the deepest part. *(s)* core, belly, heart, interior, middle. *(ant)* peak, summit.

plundering[1] it for his own greedy gain, leaving the prince heartbroken and **desolate**[2]; Dewi, the Master of the Mal-Instinctives.

Anger burned his throat in a **bitter**[3] stream of **bile**[4]. Struggling to swallow, he pictured the evil horrors **committed**[5] by Dewi while he had possessed the bracelet. He checked himself, forcing the **grievous**[6] past from his mind. Anger and **resentment**[7] would serve only to **hinder**[8] and weaken him against his arch-enemy, and that he could ill afford.

But this **overpowering**[9] **passion**[10] allowed the Master his way in.

Suddenly something pulled at Gwilym's insides; a **crucifying**[11] clench gripped him. A torture so **potent**[12], so life-**sapping**[13], he fell stricken to his knees. Clutching his head in an **unworldly**[14] agony, an unpleasant, thick, metallic taste seeped onto his tongue.

Stumbling, weakened, he rose, turning fearlessly, expecting to face his **foe**[15] – but saw no one. Again another searing pain floored him. **Blundering**[16] about and disorientated, he staggered and leaned against a **tacky**[17], wet wall, blood now trickling from his mouth.

Wheeling[18] around in torment, Gwilym **sagged**[19] to the ground, agonised. Only by drawing from his deepest strength did he manage to drag himself upright, but then another expert blow

---

1   **plunder** *(v)* steal goods from, often using force. *(s)* rob, raid, pillage, ransack, fleece, loot. *(ant)* give, gift.

2   **desolate** *(adj)* very unhappy, melancholy, gloomy or lonely. *(s)* forlorn, inconsolable. *(ant)* happy.

3   **bitter** *(adj)* tasting sharp or bad, or angry or resentful due to hurt or injustice. *(s)* sour, indignant. *(ant)* sweet.

4   **bile** *(n)* anger and bitterness, or a digestive fluid. *(s)* irritability, vitriol, sourness, wrath. *(ant)* contentment.

5   **commit** *(v)* carry out. *(s)* act, perpetrate, perform, execute, cause, complete, enact. *(ant)* abstain, fail.

6   **grievous** *(adj)* (of something bad) dreadful. *(s)* sad, grave, dire, heinous, painful, shameful. *(ant)* good, venial.

7   **resentment** *(n)* a feeling of indignation (anger) at unfair treatment. *(s)* hatred, bitterness. *(ant)* satisfaction.

8   **hinder** *(v)* make difficult, hamper, obstruct or slow down. *(s)* delay, inhibit, thwart, impede. *(ant)* help.

9   **overpowering** *(adj)* very strong or intense. *(s)* overwhelming, dominating, consuming. *(ant)* mild.

10   **passion** *(n)* a strong and difficult-to-control emotion. *(s)* fervour, anger, rage, fury, wrath. *(ant)* indifference.

11   **crucifying** *(v)* causing pain, suffering and anguish. *(s)* torturous, tormenting, agonising, racking. *(ant)* soothing.

12   **potent** *(adj)* having huge effect, influence, vigour (strength) or power. *(s)* forceful, mighty. *(ant)* weak.

13   **sap** *(v)* gradually weaken, erode, destroy or deplete power. *(s)* drain, debilitate, reduce. *(ant)* bolster.

14   **unworldly** *(adj)* not seemingly of this planet. *(s)* strange, alien, unearthly, other-worldly. *(ant)* worldly, normal.

15   **foe** *(n)* an enemy, nemesis or opponent. *(s)* antagonist, rival, opposition. *(ant)* friend, ally, comrade.

16   **blunder** *(v)* stumble around. *(s)* stagger, lurch, misstep, flounder. *(ant)* glide, breeze.

17   **tacky** *(adj)* slightly damp or sticky. *(s)* wet, adhesive, gummy, messy, viscous. *(ant)* dry, clean, fresh.

18   **wheel** *(v)* turn around rapidly to face another way. *(s)* veer, circle, swivel, rotate, sweep, swing.

19   **sag** *(v)* slump, sink, subside or bulge downwards under pressure or lack of strength. *(s)* droop, drop. *(ant)* rise.

landed, flooring him again. Reeling, he lay stunned, searching for this supreme **assailant**[1]. Yet the passage where he lay in agony presented no **physical**[2] **opponent**[3]. No tangible Master fought this fight. No one stood before him. The **deplorable**[4] **demon**[5] was **afflicting**[6] him **internally**[7]. Dewi was attacking him from the inside, and his **brutally**[8] **effective**[9] methods had broken him. Thoughts of the gem, and Claire alone upstairs, desperately filled his mind as he **spiralled**[10] into **oblivion**[11].

*

Just seconds away, Owain raced on, heading for the stairs that led to the exhibition hall. He must stop the glass case being cut. The bracelet must not be lost again; he had lived with that **calamity**[12] before. Sprinting, he skidded around a slippery, sharp corner, staggering to maintain his balance. The flickering wall lamps finally failed, plunging the passage into darkness. Fumbling for his torch, he slowed, spotting a **listless**[13], humped shape lying on the ground. An outline of a person, not moving, one far too still.

'Gwilym?' he whispered. 'Gwilym!' he cried in **anguish**[14], sinking to his knees.

Shocked and feeling for a heartbeat, he scanned Gwilym for injuries; a **cursory**[15] inspection revealed nothing obvious. A few **superficial**[16] **grazes**[17] should not trouble such a knight, but then what **plagued**[18] Gwilym so?

---

1 **assailant** *(n)* a person who physically harms or attacks another. *(s)* assaulter, aggressor, opponent. *(ant)* ally.

2 **physical** *(adj)* composed of matter. *(s)* bodily, corporeal, real, tangible, solid, palpable. *(ant)* immaterial.

3 **opponent** *(n)* somebody who is in conflict or disagreement with another. *(s)* antagonist, adversary. *(ant)* ally.

4 **deplorable** *(adj)* completely unacceptable. *(s)* awful, disgraceful, wretched, unpardonable. *(ant)* admirable.

5 **demon** *(n)* a cruel, evil person. *(s)* devil, fiend, monster, ogre, beast. *(ant)* hero, god, angel.

6 **afflict** *(v)* cause pain or trouble to and affect adversely. *(s)* bother, distress, ail, vex, plague. *(ant)* aid.

7 **internally** *(adv)* on the inside of the body. *(s)* inwardly, centrally. *(ant)* externally, outwardly.

8 **brutally** *(adv)* in a brutal (cruel) way. *(s)* viciously, violently, ferociously, inhumanely. *(ant)* humanely, kindly.

9 **effective** *(adj)* producing a desired or intended result. *(s)* successful, effectual. *(ant)* ineffective, ineffectual.

10 **spiral** *(v)* fall continuously. *(s)* plummet, plunge, descend, swirl, decline, worsen. *(ant)* rise, ascend.

11 **oblivion** *(n)* the state of being unaware or unconscious. *(s)* obscurity, nothingness. *(ant)* consciousness.

12 **calamity** *(n)* a disastrous event. *(s)* catastrophe, tragedy, blight, distress, misery, blow. *(ant)* blessing.

13 **listless** *(adj)* lacking enthusiasm, interest or energy. *(s)* lifeless, lethargic, limp. *(ant)* active, alert, alive, awake.

14 **anguish** *(n)* severe mental or physical pain. *(s)* suffering, agony, torment, torture. *(ant)* happiness, joy.

15 **cursory** *(adj)* hasty and without detail. *(s)* superficial, half-hearted, perfunctory. *(ant)* thorough, detailed.

16 **superficial** *(adj)* on or of the surface, not deep or serious. *(s)* shallow, insignificant. *(ant)* deep, substantive.

17 **graze** *(n)* a slight injury to the skin. *(s)* scratch, scrape, abrasion, lesion.

18 **plague** *(v)* cause continual distress to. *(s)* afflict, torture, torment, beleaguer, harass. *(ant)* soothe, support.

'Gwilym?' he pleaded. 'What is it? What afflicts you? Gwilym, speak!' Owain shook his friend gently. 'Gwilym?'

'Dewi,' **wheezed**[1] Gwilym, struggling to open his eyes. 'He is …' But the **venerable**[2] knight could say no more.

Owain held Gwilym in desperation, knowing the Master had **hijacked**[3] the Cutter and defeated the strongest of knights. In **turmoil**[4], he knew he must leave this noble knight, his friend, to an unknown **destiny**[5] in order to save the Cutter.

Then a wild howl escaped his own throat. **Racked**[6] with pain, **immobilised**[7] in twisting agony, he, too, collapsed, writhing beside his friend. Dewi's strength had grown throughout his years of longing to **repossess**[8] the bracelet. Never had these knights encountered this **abhorrent**[9], maybe **lethal**[10], tactic, clawing and ripping at their very core.

Owain **succumbed**[11] quickly. Powerless, he touched his fellow knight one last time. 'Gwilym, you are stronger than this **tyrant**[12]. You are **mightier**[13] than he. Gwilym, please, please …' **beseeched**[14] Owain as his voice fell away to nothing, his body broken.

---

1   **wheeze** *(v)* making a whistling or rattling sound in the chest. *(s)* gasp, rasp, cough, whisper.

2   **venerable** *(adj)* respected because of character, wisdom or achievements. *(s)* esteemed. *(ant)* disreputable.

3   **hijack** *(v)* steal or take over. *(s)* seize, commandeer, capture, appropriate, kidnap, nick. *(ant)* give, bestow.

4   **turmoil** *(n)* a state of confusion, disturbance or uncertainty. *(s)* tumult, commotion, disorder. *(ant)* order.

5   **destiny** *(n)* unknown future state or events. *(s)* fate, fortune, doom, circumstance. *(ant)* past.

6   **rack** *(v)* cause extreme pain. *(s)* beset, agonise, torment, torture, harrow, crucify. *(ant)* comfort, relieve.

7   **immobilise** *(v)* prevent from operating or moving as normal. *(s)* stop, disable, paralyse, cripple. *(ant)* mobilise.

8   **repossess** *(v)* seize back, recover or regain possession of something. *(s)* retake, reclaim, recapture. *(ant)* lose.

9   **abhorrent** *(adj)* causing disgust and loathing. *(s)* repugnant, hateful, loathsome, despicable. *(ant)* agreeable.

10   **lethal** *(adj)* able to cause death, hugely harmful or destructive. *(s)* deadly, fatal, mortal. *(ant)* life-giving.

11   **succumb** *(v)* give in or give way. *(s)* yield, submit, surrender, buckle, accede, capitulate. *(ant)* withstand.

12   **tyrant** *(n)* a cruel and oppressive ruler. *(s)* dictator, bully, tormentor, persecutor.

13   **mighty** *(adj)* strong and powerful. *(s)* great, fierce, hardy, vast, tough. *(ant)* weak.

14   **beseech** *(v)* ask someone urgently or fervently. *(s)* implore, beg, request, entreat, plead, supplicate. *(ant)* offer.

9. Hearing Things

As Claire glanced back at the basement's closed door, she stifled a cough, spluttering as her heart **pummelled**[1] her chest, as if its rhythm was thrown **askew**[2]. Gwilym had pursued the Master, **abandoning**[3] her to **fend for herself**[4].

So far, unable to move, she'd achieved nothing. Anxiety gnawed her stomach, twisting the emptiness as weakness **consumed**[5] her. She trembled, unable to **assemble**[6] her thoughts.

What had Gwilym said? She tried to remember. **Detached**[7] from reality, she envisaged knights **toiling**[8] in suffocating mines, **sacrificing**[9] everything to find the magical Welsh gold. She pictured Rebecca, her mum and dad, Jayne's warm smile and Ben beaming at his winner's medals. Their images **waltzed**[10] in **frivolous**[11] **merriment**[12], dizzying her head. Then, reality kicked back in, and cruel, salty tears washed the images clear away, blurring her vision as they did.

This morning she'd been Claire Cadwallader, a schoolgirl. What had she become? Some knight's 'niece' with 'Instinct', capable of remarkable feats? She didn't know, and she didn't believe

---

1   **pummel** *(v)* strike at repeatedly with the fists. *(s)* beat, thrash, cudgel, mash, bash, pound, batter.

2   **askew** *(adv)* at an angle, out of the usual position, wrong. *(s)* awry, aslant, askance, out of true. *(ant)* straight.

3   **abandon** *(v)* leave alone or behind. *(s)* desert, discard, jettison, forsake, ditch, dump. *(ant)* accompany, keep.

4   **fend for oneself** *(v)* look after oneself without help. *(s)* hold one's own, manage alone. *(ant)* be cared for.

5   **consume** *(v)* strongly affect or overwhelm with a feeling. *(s)* dominate, overpower, control. *(ant)* abandon.

6   **assemble** *(v)* collect or gather together in one place. *(s)* marshal, summon, muster, rally. *(ant)* disband, scatter.

7   **detached** *(adj)* disengaged or removed. *(s)* separate, disconnected, isolated, dissociated. *(ant)* connected.

8   **toil** *(v)* work incessantly (non-stop) or extremely hard. *(s)* labour, slog, strive, slave. *(ant)* laze, idle, relax.

9   **sacrifice** *(v)* give up something for the sake of others. *(s)* surrender, forgo, forfeit, cede. *(ant)* keep, obtain.

10   **waltz** *(v)* dance a waltz (a type of ballroom dance). *(s)* swirl, whirl, spin, twirl.

11   **frivolous** *(adj)* light-hearted and not serious. *(s)* giddy, merry, playful, frolicsome. *(ant)* serious, sensible.

12   **merriment** *(n)* fun, gaiety and high spirits. *(s)* cheer, joy, hilarity, revelry, jollity. *(ant)* misery, depression.

it, and now she faced an unknown, imminent test – alone.

Managing to take tiny steps, she ducked amongst the exhibits, avoiding being seen by the two security guards at the other end of the hall. One guard held a boy she recognised from Rebecca's year. There was no sign of the rest of Rebecca's class.

She dropped onto all fours and **inched**[1] **prudently**[2] forward, zigzagging around cabinets and stands, her knees gathering a collection of dusty grit as she crawled across the wide hall towards the office that held her sister. Reaching the other side, she rested against the wall between two shelves, steeling herself to move further along to the office.

Eventually, she broke cover and crawled up close to the office door, her heart beating in her throat. **Paling**[3], she froze after her shoulder banged hard against the door frame.

'Ow!' She'd bitten her lip so hard it bled. Licking the blood away, she awaited discovery but, thank goodness, none came. Her **knotted**[4] shoulders **slackened**[5] in relief as a long, silent sigh escaped her lungs.

Stalling[6], consumed by fear and **indecision**[7], she bit her nails and **vacantly**[8] regarded some ugly vases in a nearby case. She crouched half-upright and turned to face the door that stood between her and Rebecca. **Teetering**[9], she reached for the handle but, unable to bring herself to turn it, retreated. She leaned back against the wall, **frustrated**[10] and annoyed, and sank down onto her backside. As she landed, she accidentally whipped her head sideways, catching her temple on the doorframe with a thud. It hurt.

'Ouch!' she yelped, rubbing the **sizeable**[11] lump that **instantaneously**[12] popped up. Curling

---

1   **inch** *(v)* move along carefully and slowly. *(s)* ease, budge, edge, shuffle, creep, crawl. *(ant)* rush, leap.

2   **prudently** *(adv)* in a prudent (careful) way. *(s)* sensibly, cautiously, wisely. *(ant)* imprudently, recklessly.

3   **pale** *(v)* lose colour in the face due to shock or fear. *(s)* whiten, blanch, blench. *(ant)* colour, blush, redden.

4   **knotted** *(adj)* (of a muscle) tense and hard. *(s)* tight, bunched, snarled, coiled. *(ant)* loose, relaxed.

5   **slacken** *(v)* become slack (loose). *(s)* ease, release, relax, weaken, relent, soften. *(ant)* tighten, strengthen.

6   **stall** *(v)* delay or divert to put off or gain more time. *(s)* hesitate, dither, equivocate, halt. *(ant)* advance, hurry.

7   **indecision** *(n)* the inability to decide quickly. *(s)* indecisiveness, hesitancy, uncertainty. *(ant)* decisiveness.

8   **vacantly** *(adv)* in an uninterested or inexpressive way. *(s)* blankly, indifferently. *(ant)* animatedly, interestedly.

9   **teeter** *(v)* be unable to decide between things or actions. *(s)* waver, vacillate, falter, see-saw. *(ant)* decide.

10   **frustrated** *(adj)* feeling upset at lack of success. *(s)* annoyed, exasperated, discouraged. *(ant)* encouraged.

11   **sizeable** *(adj)* quite large. *(s)* substantial, considerable, significant. *(ant)* small, insignificant, minor.

12   **instantaneously** *(adv)* in an instantaneous (sudden) way. *(s)* instantly, immediately, rapidly. *(ant)* gradually.

into a ball, she rested her cheek against the wooden frame, tears brimming as she **massaged**[1] the sore lump.

∗

Below, in the basement, in the haze of his thoughts, Gwilym caught sight of the tall, **slender**[2] beauty **tenderly**[3] cradling her baby. A low, misty sun tinted her skin the hue of pale gold. She beamed in wonder towards her loving prince – proud, **devoted**[4] parents of an **heir**[5] born to become a wise and fair ruler. Her shimmering blonde **tresses**[6] tumbled to her waist, casually **tousled**[7]; they floated like feathers, **caressing**[8] the folds of her **ivory**[9] **robe**[10]. An image of a doting mother and loving wife. A vision of enduring union, which cruelly faded away.

Gwilym blinked; his reluctant, heavy lids fought to open. He **dredged**[11] his fogged brain, scouring for another glimpse of the woman whose **tenuous**[12] image had entered his mind. He prised his eyelids apart, forcing them to focus. When they finally **cooperated**[13], he lifted his head, but the image of the **divine**[14] **incantation**[15] had melted away. The vision that had been there, the **mirage**[16], was gone.

'Owain?' he whispered. 'Owain?' he tried again.

Gwilym blinked and saw his friend and fellow knight lying beside him. Pushing the ground

---

1   **massage** *(v)* knead or rub with the hands. *(s)* palpate, manipulate, work, press, caress, stroke.

2   **slender** *(adj)* slim and graceful. *(s)* lean, willowy, trim, lithe, svelte. *(ant)* big, chubby, firm, heavy, plump, fat.

3   **tenderly** *(adv)* in a tender (caring) manner. *(s)* lovingly, affectionately, fondly, kindly. *(ant)* unkindly, harshly.

4   **devoted** *(adj)* very loving or loyal. *(s)* faithful, true, caring, affectionate, committed, dedicated. *(ant)* disloyal.

5   **heir** *(n)* someone who will succeed another and inherit rank, property or title. *(s)* successor. *(ant)* predecessor.

6   **tress** *(n)* a long lock (a strand) of hair. *(s)* curl, ringlet, wisp, length.

7   **tousled** *(adj)* made untidy but in an attractive way. *(s)* messy, disarrayed, ruffled, dishevelled. *(ant)* tidy.

8   **caress** *(v)* touch gently. *(s)* stroke, brush, skim, glance, embrace, graze. *(ant)* beat, hit, strike.

9   **ivory** *(adj)* creamy white like ivory (tusk of an elephant). *(s)* off-white, creamy, blonde.

10   **robe** *(n)* a formal and grand long dress. *(s)* gown, frock, costume, garb, garment.

11   **dredge** *(v)* search deeply. *(s)* explore, delve, probe, comb, scrutinise. *(ant)* overlook.

12   **tenuous** *(adj)* (of a situation or concept) weak or slight. *(s)* vague, flimsy, hazy, sketchy. *(ant)* substantial.

13   **cooperate** *(v)* comply with a request or requirement. *(s)* agree, oblige, assist. *(ant)* disagree, hinder, impede.

14   **divine** *(adj)* incredibly pleasing. *(s)* delightful, beautiful, ravishing, exquisite, dazzling. *(ant)* unsatisfactory.

15   **incantation** *(n)* the conjuration (conjuring) of a magical being or effect. *(s)* spell, enchantment.

16   **mirage** *(n)* an optical illusion, unrealistic hope or wish. *(s)* vision, hallucination, delusion, fantasy. *(ant)* reality.

for support, Gwilym **feebly**[1] **laboured**[2] to his knees. Too weak to stand, he leaned, crumpled, against the wall, **disabled**[3]. Slowly, very slowly, the fog in his brain lifted enough for him to think more clearly. **Mercifully**[4], the beginnings of strength seeped into his beleaguered body.

'Owain, Owain, you must try,' he urged in a sudden **blaze**[5] of **clarity**[6]. 'He has not the **might**[7] for the two of us. He cannot **overthrow**[8] us if we join together; he cannot win.'

Gwilym realised the Master's aggressive force had been **diluted**[9] significantly between the two knights; his strength, sliced in half, was **inferior**[10]. One-on-one, the traitorous brother, Dewi, was hugely **competent**[11], yet he could not **smite**[12] both knights together. **Combined**[13], Gwilym was certain Owain and he could prevail.

'Owain, picture a victory, a shield, a defence no force can **foil**[14],' he **implored**[15]. 'You are a Knight Hawk, a **warrior**[16]. **Quell**[17] your emotion and fight,' he encouraged, desperately trying to **revive**[18] his friend. 'Together we can **thwart**[19] this dark Master. His evil cannot **penetrate**[20] our minds if we **unite**[21]. Please, Owain, please hear me.'

A faint frown rippled across Owain's forehead as he stirred, moaning.

---

1   **feebly** *(adv)* in a feeble (weak) manner. *(s)* unsteadily, fraily, shakily, delicately. *(ant)* robustly, ably.

2   **labour** *(v)* move with difficulty. *(s)* struggle, toil, strive, strain. *(ant)* ease.

3   **disabled** *(adj)* rendered (put) out of action. *(s)* incapacitated, debilitated, immobilised, crippled. *(ant)* enabled.

4   **mercifully** *(adv)* fortunately. *(s)* thankfully, luckily, happily. *(ant)* unfortunately.

5   **blaze** *(n)* an obvious outburst of something. *(s)* burst, eruption, flood, surge, effusion. *(ant)* slump, ebb.

6   **clarity** *(n)* the quality of being clear or intelligible. *(s)* sharpness, lucidity. *(ant)* obscurity.

7   **might** *(n)* strength, force or power. *(s)* capacity, valour, potency, powerfulness, influence. *(ant)* weakness.

8   **overthrow** *(v)* put an end to, dispose of. *(s)* beat, topple, conquer, defeat, destroy, overpower. *(ant)* lose to.

9   **dilute** *(v)* make weaker in force. *(s)* diminish, reduce, attenuate, temper, mitigate. *(ant)* strengthen.

10   **inferior** *(adj)* lower in ability or quality. *(s)* lesser, subordinate, poorer, substandard. *(ant)* superior.

11   **competent** *(adj)* capable, able and efficient (good at something). *(s)* proficient, adept. *(ant)* incompetent.

12   **smite** *(v)* conquer or defeat. *(s)* beat, destroy, overthrow, kill, quash, crush. *(ant)* lose to.

13   **combined** *(adj)* merged or joined, united for a common purpose. *(s)* unified, consolidated. *(ant)* separate.

14   **foil** *(v)* prevent something from succeeding. *(s)* stop, frustrate, thwart, counter, oppose. *(ant)* assist, aid, abet.

15   **implore** *(v)* plead or beg desperately. *(s)* beseech, pray, entreat, appeal. *(ant)* offer.

16   **warrior** *(n)* a brave or experienced fighter. *(s)* combatant, soldier, knight, defender, guardian. *(ant)* pacifist.

17   **quell** *(v)* suppress (put an end to) and silence. *(s)* subdue, quash, crush, repress, control. *(ant)* incite, intensify.

18   **revive** *(v)* restore to consciousness, life or strength. *(s)* revitalise, reinvigorate, stimulate. *(ant)* torpefy.

19   **thwart** *(v)* successfully oppose. *(s)* foil, counter, ruin, stop, impede, defeat, overpower. *(ant)* aid, facilitate.

20   **penetrate** *(v)* go through or break into. *(s)* enter, invade, infiltrate, breach, overrun, access. *(ant)* exit.

21   **unite** *(v)* bring together to form a whole or for a common purpose. *(s)* join, unify, combine, bond. *(ant)* divide.

'Owain, he is using our minds to **inflict**[1] terror on our bodies. He has **insufficient**[2] strength for two. Join with me; build a wall; we can shut him out,' begged Gwilym, squeezing his friend's hand.

Owain stirred. A distant hint of recognition flitted across his face as he tried to focus on Gwilym.

'Concentrate, Owain. **Reject**[3] the corruption. Grasp the reality. Go towards the virtuous,' urged Gwilym, all the while fighting his own internal agony.

Owain blinked twice, as if signalling he understood. The **staunch**[4] friends communicated, **channelling**[5] their thoughts, their energy **forging**[6] into one impenetrable barrier.

As they lay in the basement's **dank**[7] filth, their **monstrous**[8] **ordeal**[9] gradually **subsided**[10].

'Claire,' said Gwilym. 'If he cannot defeat us, he will go straight for the bracelet and Claire. Nothing will stand between Dewi and the bracelet.'

✳

Upstairs, in the exhibition hall, Claire's cheek numbed as she pressed it harder against the frame of the office door. Lonely and frustrated, her head still hurting, she rubbed her tears with her sleeve. Hearing a **peculiar**[11] **jabbering**[12] sound from within the office, she stiffened. She pushed her ear to the door. A babble of **unintelligible**[13] words emanated from the room. Straining to hear, she pulled away, baffled by the unusual tone. *Are they arguing?* she thought, puzzled by the

---

1   **inflict** *(v)* cause or impose pain or suffering. *(s)* enforce, wreak, exact, perpetrate, force. *(ant)* relieve, remit.

2   **insufficient** *(adj)* not enough. *(s)* inadequate, deficient, scarce, unsatisfactory. *(ant)* sufficient, adequate.

3   **reject** *(v)* refuse to agree or comply with (obey). *(s)* decline, spurn, disallow, deny. *(ant)* accept, allow.

4   **staunch** *(adj)* loyal and committed. *(s)* stalwart, faithful, devoted, steadfast, reliable. *(ant)* unreliable, disloyal.

5   **channel** *(v)* direct towards a specific outcome, end or object. *(s)* transmit, convey, focus, guide. *(ant)* diverge.

6   **forge** *(v)* form or create with effort. *(s)* generate, develop, organise, establish, shape. *(ant)* demolish, destroy.

7   **dank** *(adj)* cold and damp. *(s)* musty, humid, clammy, unaired, moist, fusty, soggy, wet. *(ant)* warm, dry.

8   **monstrous** *(adj)* completely evil or wrong. *(s)* grotesque, cruel, hideous, ghastly, horrendous. *(ant)* delightful.

9   **ordeal** *(n)* a prolonged and horrid experience. *(s)* test, trial, tribulation, trauma, affliction, nightmare. *(ant)* joy.

10   **subside** *(v)* become less severe or intense. *(s)* diminish, ease, abate, calm, lull, relent. *(ant)* increase.

11   **peculiar** *(adj)* different from normal or usual. *(s)* unusual, odd, bizarre, uncanny, queer, abnormal. *(ant)* normal.

12   **jabbering** *(n)* quick and incomprehensible speech. *(s)* prattling, babbling, gabbling, rambling. *(ant)* articulation.

13   **unintelligible** *(adj)* impossible to understand. *(s)* incomprehensible, unfathomable. *(ant)* intelligible, clear.

cacophony[1] of voices, a muddled **ruckus**[2], **unfathomable**[3], making no sense at all.

Then a boy's familiar voice pierced her ears like a poisoned dart. With dread, she recognised it as Drane's. But it was when she recognised her sister's **inarticulate**[4] rubbish, the slurred, stuttering words, that Claire's blood froze. What had Drane done to her? She **seethed**[5] with anger.

A woman's soft voice **mingled**[6] with Drane's, difficult to hear, kind and **mature**[7]; but overpowered, it became lost in the **altercation**[8]. *Is that the curator's wife Gwilym mentioned?* she thought, pressing her ear even flatter against the door. Concentrating hard, she tried to **decipher**[9] their conversation, but it was a futile effort – she'd have to go in.

Standing up straight, she looked at the door. 'Open it, Claire,' she mouthed, trying to **persuade**[10] herself.

The voices were loud in there now, all **clamouring**[11] to be heard. Drane's **distinctive**[12] **drone**[13] sickened her. Mrs Evans's voice drifted above Rebecca's; she seemed to be soothing her sister. That was when Claire realised they weren't arguing; there was no **dispute**[14]. They weren't disagreeing or **deliberating**[15]; they were thinking. She didn't hear their voices talking from inside, she heard their thoughts.

Her nerves crackled to her fingertips. She didn't dare turn the handle, afraid to move lest she no longer heard them. The hairs on her forearms rose, standing **erect**[16] on her skin. Could she

---

1   **cacophony** *(n)* an unpleasantly harsh mix of sounds. *(s)* din, racket, discord, loudness, noise. *(ant)* harmony.

2   **ruckus** *(n)* a commotion (noisy disturbance). *(s)* ruction, tumult, racket, uproar, turmoil. *(ant)* peace.

3   **unfathomable** *(adj)* not capable of being understood. *(s)* indecipherable, inscrutable. *(ant)* fathomable, clear.

4   **inarticulate** *(adj)* (of words) not clearly pronounced or expressed. *(s)* unintelligible. *(ant)* articulate, eloquent.

5   **seethe** *(v)* be filled with intense but unexpressed (not shown) anger. *(s)* simmer, fume, smoulder. *(ant)* calm.

6   **mingle** *(v)* mix together. *(s)* blend, merge, unite, join, intermingle, fuse, combine, amalgamate. *(ant)* separate.

7   **mature** *(adj)* fully grown or old. *(s)* senior, adult, middle-aged, elderly. *(ant)* young, immature.

8   **altercation** *(n)* an audible (can be heard) argument. *(s)* quarrel, disagreement. *(ant)* agreement.

9   **decipher** *(v)* succeed in understanding or identifying something. *(s)* decode, decrypt. *(ant)* cipher.

10   **persuade** *(v)* induce to do something by asking or reasoning. *(s)* coax, motivate, cajole. *(ant)* dissuade.

11   **clamour** *(v)* shout or utter loud cries or calls. *(s)* shriek, yell, bawl, scream, roar. *(ant)* whisper.

12   **distinctive** *(adj)* standing out because of a specific characteristic. *(s)* distinguishing, individual. *(ant)* common.

13   **drone** *(n)* dull or monotonous speech. *(s)* murmur, monotone, mumble. *(ant)* lilt.

14   **dispute** *(n)* a disagreement or argument. *(s)* debate, altercation, controversy, clash. *(ant)* agreement, accord.

15   **deliberate** *(v)* engage in careful consideration. *(s)* think, consider, debate, contemplate, ponder. *(ant)* decide.

16   **erect** *(adj)* straight or rigidly upright. *(s)* vertical, perpendicular, plumb, stiff. *(ant)* horizontal, prone, prostrate.

really hear what these people thought? Was she reading their minds? Tossing the thought aside as a preposterous notion, she readied herself again.

She was forcing herself to open the door, but then she stopped. Alarmed, she now understood Rebecca's jumbled nonsense. She knew her **cocky**[1] sister well enough to recognise when something was very wrong. Whilst briefing Gwilym in the basement, Evans had said Rebecca was ill, but Claire realised Drane must have done something to her. She could definitely hear Rebecca's thoughts **surging**[2] back and forth, dipping in and out of **lucidity**[3]. Would Rebecca even recognise her if she entered the room?

She leaned closer, decoding the words; they **ebbed**[4] and **flowed**[5] in unclear, **oscillating**[6] echoes. **Riveted**[7], she heard 'the Master' and 'any minute'. Had the woman muttered 'cutting'? Straining to **interpret**[8] Drane's words in particular, she steadied her thoughts to help block out the others.

'Focus, Claire, focus,' she encouraged herself. 'Listen for the rat.'

She pictured Drane's **verminous**[9] face, **immersing**[10] herself in his thoughts, determined to hear his plotting and **scheming**[11]. Reeling at what she heard, she stepped away, **aghast**[12]. Finally, she grasped the handle and turned it.

*

Behind her, across the hall and out of view, Claire didn't see the Master emerge from the basement. He paused, his handsome **profile**[13] now harsh and **twitching**[14] as he took slow, measured breaths. His hungry eyes skimmed the exhibition cases, flashing with greed. He swallowed, tasting

---

1   **cocky** *(adj)* cheeky or overly bold, conceited or overconfident. *(s)* arrogant, smug, brash. *(ant)* modest.

2   **surge** *(v)* increase suddenly and with more power. *(s)* outpour, rise, gush, heave, course. *(ant)* decline, ebb.

3   **lucidity** *(n)* clarity (clearness) of expression. *(s)* intelligibility, articulacy, logic. *(ant)* ambiguity.

4   **ebb** *(v)* (of a quality or emotion) gradually lessen. *(s)* decrease, diminish, dwindle, wane. *(ant)* flow, increase.

5   **flow** *(v)* proceed or produce continuously and effortlessly. *(s)* arise, ensue, continue. *(ant)* ebb, trickle.

6   **oscillating** *(adj)* varying (changing), swinging back and forth. *(s)* vacillating, alternating, undulating.

7   **riveted** *(adj)* completely engrossed so unable to move. *(s)* fascinated, enthralled, mesmerised. *(ant)* bored.

8   **interpret** *(v)* understand the meaning of. *(s)* construe, untangle, comprehend, decipher. *(ant)* misinterpret.

9   **verminous** *(adj)* resembling vermin (wild animals believed by some to cause harm). *(s)* rat-like, ratty.

10   **immerse** *(v)* involve oneself deeply in. *(s)* absorb, engross, engage, occupy, steep. *(ant)* withdraw, remove.

11   **scheming** *(n)* the activity of making devious (underhand, dishonest) plans. *(s)* plotting, conspiring, conniving.

12   **aghast** *(adj)* shocked or horrified. *(s)* thunderstruck, astounded, stunned, appalled. *(ant)* unaffected.

13   **profile** *(n)* a side view or outline, especially of the face. *(s)* contour, shape, form, silhouette.

14   **twitch** *(v)* jerk, tremble or quiver lightly and involuntarily (without will). *(s)* spasm, convulse.

success. He would **dispose of**[1] the girl Claire if required to. How **robust**[2] was her Instinct? Would she be a problem?

After his fight with the two knights, his powers were **depleted**[3], but not so weak he couldn't crush a meddling girl if called for. Looking **complacently**[4] at the metal box in his palm, his coal-black eyes flared as he relived the power that would soon be his again, after so long without it. As he **lamented**[5] those wilderness years, he bristled with anticipation. Success was so close; its flavour sweetened his tongue. Savouring the taste, he regained his strength and eyed Claire.

*

Unaware the Master watched her, Claire realised she had never known true fear before. Shaking and sweaty, her **pulse**[6] drummed, and her arm behaved like it belonged to someone else. Although petrified at the thought of Drane, she pushed open the door. **Adrenaline**[7] flooded her bloodstream, **dilating**[8] her pupils into round black saucers.

'Rebecca!' she yelled. 'What has he done to you?' Turning to Drane, she shouted, 'What have you done to my sister?' Her questions were **rhetorical**[9]; she wanted no lies from him.

Claire stood watching Rebecca's distant eyes trying to focus. Rebecca said nothing, eyeing Claire as she might an **indistinct**[10] stranger. She glistened with sweat, an **ashen**[11] **pallor**[12] deadening her skin. A thin string of saliva dribbled from her mouth, which had drooped on one side in a **grotesque**[13] **palsy**[14], then set like melted wax. Drane visibly stiffened. It was Mrs Evans who spoke first.

---

1   **dispose of** *(v)* get rid of, do away with. *(s)* banish, discard, throw away, ditch. *(ant)* retain.

2   **robust** *(adj)* healthy and strong. *(s)* vigorous, tough, hardy, stout, sturdy, powerful. *(ant)* weak, feeble.

3   **deplete** *(v)* use up. *(s)* exhaust, consume, decrease, expend, drain, lessen, diminish, sap. *(ant)* replenish.

4   **complacently** *(adv)* in a complacent (smug, self-satisfied) manner. *(s)* arrogantly, contentedly. *(ant)* humbly.

5   **lament** *(v)* feel or express disappointment or regret. *(s)* deplore, rue, denounce, bemoan. *(ant)* celebrate.

6   **pulse** *(n)* a rhythmic throbbing of pumping blood. *(s)* beat, heartbeat, pounding, thump, pulsation.

7   **adrenaline** *(n)* a hormone (naturally produced chemical) that reduces reaction times in the body.

8   **dilate** *(v)* become or make larger, wider or more open. *(s)* expand, enlarge, increase, stretch. *(ant)* contract.

9   **rhetorical** *(adj)* asked for effect or to make a statement rather than get an answer.

10   **indistinct** *(adj)* not clear, sharply defined or distinguished. *(s)* nebulous, vague, undistinguishable. *(ant)* clear.

11   **ashen** *(adj)* pale because of shock, fear or illness. *(s)* wan, pasty, pallid, sallow, ghostly, ashy, grey. *(ant)* rosy.

12   **pallor** *(n)* a pale and unhealthy appearance. *(s)* whiteness, paleness, sallowness, pastiness. *(ant)* rosiness.

13   **grotesque** *(adj)* ugly and distorted (out of shape). *(s)* malformed, deformed, misshapen. *(ant)* attractive.

14   **palsy** *(n)* paralysis (inability to move), sometimes of one side of the face. *(ant)* mobility, sensation.

'Your sister will recover. Come inside and sit with her.' The woman spoke **demurely**[1], her manner unruffled and **placid**[2].

Claire approached Rebecca. 'Becca, what has he done to you?' she asked.

She glowered at Drane, who stood behind Rebecca. Looks of hatred streaked from her eyes as she perched on the arm of her sister's chair, stroking her hair. In a heartbeat, all the **bickering**[3], resentment and sibling **rivalry**[4] slid away, replaced by a **fierce**[5] emotional **bond**[6] only **kin**[7] evoked. She wanted her family with her right now, her mum, dad and Pete, but it was her and Becca, and she must be **resilient**[8] for them both. She had to do something special. She turned her gaze to Drane, holding it fast, unyielding, not flinching once until he lowered his eyes. Her back straightened, determined to guard Rebecca against further harm.

Drane backed a few steps away from Rebecca. His **beady**[9] eyes scanning the floor, avoiding Claire's glare. He looked uncomfortable, fiddling with his hands and shifting nearer to Mrs Evans. Claire **scrutinised**[10] him with **new-found**[11] **conviction**[12] as Rebecca drifted back into an uneasy **stupor**[13], **incomprehensible**[14] and **slumped**[15] on the tatty chair. Claire felt stronger, and she suspected Drane sensed it. He was **intimidated**[16]; she was sure of it. He'd stepped into the corner of the room nearer to Mrs Evans, who sat in absolute stillness. The

---

1   **demurely** *(adv)* in a demure (modest and reserved) manner. *(s)* shyly, meekly, mildly, quietly. *(ant)* boldly.

2   **placid** *(adj)* not excited, upset or bothered. *(s)* docile, tranquil, serene, composed, phlegmatic. *(ant)* agitated.

3   **bickering** *(n)* argument over trivial matters. *(s)* squabbling, quarrelling, disagreement. *(ant)* agreement.

4   **rivalry** *(n)* competition for the same thing. *(s)* jealousy, opposition, challenge, conflict. *(ant)* cooperation.

5   **fierce** *(adj)* powerful or heartfelt. *(s)* intense, keen, strong, extreme, profound, deep, ardent. *(ant)* mild, calm.

6   **bond** *(n)* a feeling that unites (joins) people in a shared emotion. *(s)* tie, link, relationship. *(ant)* separation.

7   **kin** *(n)* family and one's relations. *(s)* relatives, clansmen, kindred, lineage. *(ant)* non-relative.

8   **resilient** *(adj)* able to withstand difficulty. *(s)* hardy, tough, strong, robust, resistant. *(ant)* defeatist, weak.

9   **beady** *(adj)* (of the eyes) small, round and gleaming, keen and observant. *(s)* watchful, bright. *(ant)* dull.

10   **scrutinise** *(v)* look, inspect or examine closely and thoroughly. *(s)* study, search, survey, analyse. *(ant)* glance.

11   **new-found** *(adj)* recently found, discovered or established. *(s)* new, fresh, recent, novel. *(ant)* established, old.

12   **conviction** *(n)* a firmly held opinion or belief. *(s)* confidence, sureness, certainty. *(ant)* doubt.

13   **stupor** *(n)* a state of near unconsciousness or unawareness. *(s)* daze, torpor, blankness. *(ant)* consciousness.

14   **incomprehensible** *(adj)* not understandable. *(s)* incoherent, inarticulate, unintelligible. *(ant)* comprehensible.

15   **slump** *(v)* sit, lean or fall heavily and limply. *(s)* flop, sink, slouch, sag, droop, hunch. *(ant)* straighten, rise.

16   **intimidate** *(v)* force or frighten into submission. *(s)* threaten, bully, menace, overawe. *(ant)* assure.

woman had **adopted**[1] a resolute and **dignified**[2] silence, observing Drane through her thick glasses.

Then Drane barked an odd-sounding cough. Claire paused as he seemed to fight a slight choke. Dubious, she eyed him; his attitude had altered. She tried to read his mind like she thought she'd done before, but since entering the room, she couldn't hear any of their thoughts.

What's he doing? she thought as a horrid feeling of unease **resurfaced**[3]. He wasn't coughing at all; he appeared to be laughing. She sat upright, trying to hide her **disquiet**[4]. She sensed a worrying shift, a different air about him.

He stifled another cough, more a snigger, a **scoff**[5]. Claire's chest **contracted**[6], tightening horribly. He wasn't trying to conceal anything; he flaunted his **glee**[7] **flagrantly**[8]. He **chortled**[9], enjoying himself as Mrs Evans suddenly doubled over. The elderly Instinctive let out a horrifying groan, a howl so **despairing**[10], so ghastly, Claire leaped away from her sister.

'Mrs Evans! Mrs Evans?' she shouted. 'Drane, what have you done? What have you done to her?' she yelled as the **frail**[11]-looking lady writhed in agony. Claire dropped to her knees beside her, not sure what to do to help her. She looked at Drane, horrified.

In slow motion, he turned to Claire; a sick grin pulled at his mouth. Triumphantly, in a stark, chilling tone, he answered with a flippant shake of his head. 'Nothing, Claire, I've done nothing.'

Mrs Evans collapsed to her knees with such a crunch that Claire thought she must have broken something.

---

1   **adopt** *(v)* take on an attitude or position, behave in a certain way. *(s)* assume, acquire, embrace. *(ant)* reject.

2   **dignified** *(adj)* having a serious, respectful manner. *(s)* gracious, formal, noble, proper. *(ant)* undignified.

3   **resurface** *(v)* become evident again. *(s)* return, arise, reappear, recur, repeat, rematerialise. *(ant)* disappear.

4   **disquiet** *(n)* an anxious or worried feeling. *(s)* unease, concern, unrest, foreboding, anxiety. *(ant)* calmness.

5   **scoff** *(n)* an expression of mockery or derision. *(s)* sneer, ridicule, jeer, taunt, scorn. *(ant)* praise, respect.

6   **contract** *(v)* become tighter or shorter. *(s)* constrict, tense, shrink, diminish, wither. *(ant)* expand, grow.

7   **glee** *(n)* huge delight or gloating. *(s)* smugness, pleasure, elation, euphoria, hilarity, merriment. *(ant)* sadness.

8   **flagrantly** *(adv)* in a flagrant (obvious and offensive) manner. *(s)* deliberately, blatantly, overtly. *(ant)* covertly.

9   **chortle** *(v)* laugh in a loud, gleeful way. *(s)* snigger, titter, cackle, snort, guffaw. *(ant)* cry, lament.

10   **despairing** *(adj)* losing all hope. *(s)* desperate, anguished, desolate, pessimistic. *(ant)* hopeful, optimistic.

11   **frail** *(adj)* delicate and weak. *(s)* feeble, infirm, slight, unsound, puny, fragile. *(ant)* robust, sturdy, strong.

She wanted to punch away Drane's **self-righteous**[1] look, but her earlier confidence **evaporated**[2] at his superior, **victorious**[3] sneer. His eyes glittered as Mrs Evans shrivelled before him. Claire gasped as he took a threatening stride towards her. Gloating, in a low, smug hiss, he repeated, 'Why, Claire, I've done nothing, nothing at all.'

---

1   **self-righteous** *(adj)* convinced one is overly righteous. *(s)* smug, arrogant, haughty, supercilious. *(ant)* humble.

2   **evaporate** *(v)* cease to exist, melt away. *(s)* vanish, end, disappear, dissolve, vaporise. *(ant)* appear, solidify.

3   **victorious** *(adj)* having won a victory. *(s)* winning, vanquishing, triumphant, conquering. *(ant)* defeated.

10. The First Cut

The Master had studied Claire as she had grappled with her fear and had finally entered the museum's office, where her sister was held **captive**[1]. Instinctive or not, he had **concluded**[2] this plain young female posed no real threat.

He had surveyed the grand old hall, casting his **vulture's**[3] **leer**[4] into every **conceivable**[5] space. His highly trained boys **consistently**[6] performed with fail-safe precision; he accepted nothing less. Drane had chosen a suitable hostage, and the old knights Gwilym and Owain, albeit unwilling, had succumbed as planned.

Dewi, the Master, looked sharp. His **tailored**[7] suit and handmade leather shoes **complemented**[8] his lean frame and wide shoulders. Athletic, sculpted muscles rippled discreetly beneath his crisp, **starched**[9] shirt. A hint of **exclusive**[10] **cologne**[11] followed him. Thick hair, **styled**[12] in

---

1   **captive** *(adj)* held, caged or locked up. *(s)* imprisoned, incarcerated, detained, confined. *(ant)* free.

2   **conclude** *(v)* decide on or judge something by reasoning. *(s)* deduce, infer, determine, surmise. *(ant)* reject.

3   **vulture** *(n)* a horrid person who exploits (misuses) others, a large bird of prey. *(s)* predator. *(ant)* benefactor.

4   **leer** *(n)* an unpleasant look. *(s)* evil eye, grimace, sneer, smirk, stare, grin. *(ant)* smile.

5   **conceivable** *(adj)* capable of being understood or imagined. *(s)* imaginable, plausible. *(ant)* implausible.

6   **consistently** *(adv)* in a consistent (steady) manner. *(s)* reliably, dependably, constantly. *(ant)* inconsistently.

7   **tailored** *(adj)* made to fit exactly. *(s)* custom, smart, fitted, stylish, elegant, designed. *(ant)* misadjusted.

8   **complement** *(v)* enhance. *(s)* suit, set off, go with, add to, supplement, augment. *(ant)* contrast, diminish.

9   **starched** *(adj)* stiffened with starch (substance to stiffen fabric). *(s)* firm, rigid, inflexible. *(ant)* soft, pliant.

10   **exclusive** *(adj)* available to only a few. *(s)* high-class, restricted, limited, elite, select, special. *(ant)* inclusive.

11   **cologne** *(n)* scent or perfume. *(s)* aftershave, eau de toilette, fragrance, essence, toilet water.

12   **style** *(v)* make or design in a specific way. *(s)* cut, shape, form, adapt, fashion, tailor.

cutting-edge[1] London salons[2], striking eyes and snow-white teeth beguiled[3] everyone he met. His suave[4] disguise was most persuasive[5]. When he smiled, everyone yearned to know him, but right now, he didn't aim to fool anyone. The true Dewi emerged.

The Gwalch Gem bracelet was within his grasp. His covetous[6] glare finally locked on to it; his fingers itched to wield its power once again. The power he would use to manipulate time to influence[7] and exploit[8] the world for his gain.

Eerie and ghoulish[9], he appeared to almost skate across the deserted hall towards the bracelet. A conceited pout replaced the thin, fiendish[10] line of his lips. Tilting his head, he paused, savouring the moment as he reached into his pocket for the tiny metal box. His long, slender fingers opened the smooth lid and removed the Cutter. He twirled the tiny arrow in his manicured fingers. *How can something so flimsy[11] and dull deliver such a great prize? Yet it will,* he thought.

His greed and spirits soared as he leaned over the glass case, marvelling at the gem it contained, its deep green coupled with the Welsh gold Gwilym had mined. He salivated[12] as if embarking[13] on a gourmet[14] feast, his entire being devouring[15] the scene before him.

Holding the arrow, his right hand moved towards the glass as his left hand simultaneously[16] crawled along the case's edge. Methodically[17] he felt for the cutting point he must strike, the

---

1   **cutting-edge** *(adj)* the latest or most advanced. *(s)* leading, innovative, progressive. *(ant)* old-fashioned.

2   **salon** *(n)* a place where a hairdresser or beautician works. *(s)* barber shop, parlour.

3   **beguile** *(v)* enchant or charm (sometimes deceptively). *(s)* deceive, entrance, captivate, woo. *(ant)* repulse.

4   **suave** *(adj)* confident and elegant. *(s)* smooth, polished, refined, debonair, sophisticated. *(ant)* awkward.

5   **persuasive** *(adj)* able to persuade (convince) well. *(s)* compelling, believable, credible. *(ant)* unconvincing.

6   **covetous** *(adj)* desiring things belonging to others. *(s)* grasping, greedy, envious, avaricious. *(ant)* satisfied.

7   **influence** *(v)* persuade to change in some way. *(s)* affect, sway, manipulate, induce, impel. *(ant)* underwhelm.

8   **exploit** *(v)* benefit unfairly from. *(s)* abuse, use, ill-treat, misuse, manipulate, manoeuvre. *(ant)* respect.

9   **ghoulish** *(adj)* like a ghoul (phantom or evil spirit). *(s)* weird, deathly, fiendish, macabre. *(ant)* inoffensive.

10   **fiendish** *(adj)* cruel and wicked. *(s)* evil, villainous, malicious, malevolent, cunning, devilish. *(ant)* pleasant.

11   **flimsy** *(adj)* light and easily damaged. *(s)* insubstantial, fragile, delicate, slight. *(ant)* substantial, robust.

12   **salivate** *(v)* secrete (produce) saliva (spit). *(s)* slobber, dribble, drool, slaver, water, froth, ooze.

13   **embark** *(v)* board, begin or start. *(s)* commence, enter, launch, venture. *(ant)* disembark, cease, end, stop.

14   **gourmet** *(adj)* of high quality and prepared by an expert. *(s)* luxurious, opulent, decadent. *(ant)* poor.

15   **devour** *(v)* totally absorb or eat quickly. *(s)* consume, engulf, gobble, overwhelm. *(ant)* reject, abstain from.

16   **simultaneously** *(adv)* at the same time, all together. *(s)* concurrently, instantaneously. *(ant)* separately.

17   **methodically** *(adv)* in a methodical (systematic) way. *(s)* coherently, carefully, precisely. *(ant)* randomly.

imperfection[1] in the glass he knew existed. As he ran his nail across the glass, his snake's tongue flickered between his lips. The **defect**[2] existed – where should he aim the first blow with the Cutter? His fingertips **foraged**[3], feeling each minute **ridge**[4], sensing the slightest change in the glass case.

'Ahhh!' he sighed, **identifying**[5] the **chink**[6] in its armour. A weakness so minute, its **placement**[7] so **ingenious**[8], even its maker would struggle to find it again. But no ordinary seeker worked here. Here stood Dewi, the Master, the **estranged**[9] brother of the prince Llywelyn, poised to seize the prize that would be his again.

'Dewi,' said a soft voice from behind him.

The Master's touch **faltered**[10], but he stayed statue-still.

'Dewi,' the Welsh voice repeated, as **moderate**[11] and even as before.

Ignoring it, using the tiny Cutter, the Master's **immaculate**[12] hand delivered a precise blow to the glass case. The ageing case **quivered**[13] as swirling snakes of golden smoke escaped from the **impact**[14]. A faint, delicate smell, **reminiscent of**[15] flowers, dispersed into the air. Dewi gripped the Cutter, pushing harder into the glass until another translucent **helix**[16] curled upwards, shooting crackles of **fascinating**[17] sparks in its wake.

---

1   **imperfection** *(n)* an undesirable feature or fault. *(s)* flaw, deformity, defect, weakness, failing. *(ant)* perfection.

2   **defect** *(n)* a lack or imperfection. *(s)* shortcoming, flaw, deficiency, fault, weakness, failing. *(ant)* perfection.

3   **forage** *(v)* search widely for (often food). *(s)* look for, seek, hunt, rummage, scour, grub, root.

4   **ridge** *(n)* a narrow, raised band or bump on a surface. *(s)* crest, fold, crease. *(ant)* flat, furrow.

5   **identify** *(v)* recognise or distinguish. *(s)* spot, detect, discover, discern, pinpoint, locate. *(ant)* overlook, lose.

6   **chink** *(n)* a narrow opening or crack. *(s)* gap, breach, break, split.

7   **placement** *(n)* the act of placing, an arrangement or position. *(s)* location, situation.

8   **ingenious** *(adj)* clever, inventive and original. *(s)* innovative, smart, enterprising, creative. *(ant)* ignorant.

9   **estranged** *(adj)* no longer friendly or close to someone. *(s)* parted, alienated, distant, separated. *(ant)* united.

10   **falter** *(v)* lose momentum or strength. *(s)* hesitate, stall, delay, waver, pause, fade. *(ant)* rally, continue.

11   **moderate** *(adj)* medium or average, not intense. *(s)* controlled, measured, balanced, normal. *(ant)* extreme.

12   **immaculate** *(adj)* without flaw or mistake. *(s)* impeccable, faultless, pristine, perfect, spotless. *(ant)* defective.

13   **quiver** *(v)* tremble or shake. *(s)* shiver, quaver, shudder, vibrate, quake, tremor. *(ant)* steady, still.

14   **impact** *(n)* an instance of one object hitting another. *(s)* collision, crash, bang, blow, contact. *(ant)* avoidance.

15   **reminiscent of** *(adj)* reminding of or relating to, suggestive of. *(s)* similar to, redolent of, evocative of.

16   **helix** *(n)* a spiral or coiled form. *(s)* corkscrew, twirl, twist, whirl, whorl, loop.

17   **fascinating** *(adj)* extremely interesting. *(s)* engrossing, captivating, absorbing, riveting. *(ant)* boring.

'Dewi, stop!' Gwilym's voice roared so loud it **ricocheted**[1] around the hall, like a stray bullet. 'Stop now!' he repeated, even louder.

Dewi didn't move. Only his serpent's eyes swivelled towards the voice, and a mocking laugh hissed from his lips.

'You always were too **gallant**[2]', he spat, turning to face Gwilym. 'Asking me to stop! What do you intend to do, old friend?' he **jeered**[3] with **caustic**[4] derision. 'What, exactly, are you going to do to stop me?'

---

1   **ricochet** *(v)* rebound or echo off a surface, fly around. *(s)* reverberate, bounce, reflect.

2   **gallant** *(adj)* brave or noble. *(s)* honourable, principled, decent, polite, upright, chivalrous. *(ant)* unprincipled.

3   **jeer** *(v)* make mocking or rude remarks. *(s)* ridicule, taunt, scoff, deride, sneer, insult. *(ant)* compliment.

4   **caustic** *(adj)* bitter, scathing and sarcastic. *(s)* cutting, biting, scornful, sharp, harsh, unkind. *(ant)* mild, kind.

11. Teamwork

'Dewi, stop!' the Welsh voice boomed from outside the office.

That's Gwilym, thought Claire, panicking at his tone bellowing from the empty hall.

The pitch of Gwilym's voice terrified her. Unable to think, her brain seemed to **erase**[1] all **rational**[2] thoughts. Mrs Evans was still writhing on the office floor, and her sister was drooling, **incoherent**[3] in the chair. Josh Drane laughed. Gwilym **hollered**[4] again, even louder this time.

What should I do? she thought.

She felt as if time had stopped and the world was **unravelling**[5].

Slumping back against a protruding **lintel**[6], too dazed to feel the impact against her back, Claire started to cry. She wished she was anywhere but here. If only she could be at home. A **torrent**[7] of tears flowed in loud, **inconsolable**[8] sobs. No longer **coping**[9], she cried and cried.

What's that scratching noise? she thought, wiping her eyes. But she only looked up when a dull thump hit the office door.

Whack! It happened again, followed by an incessant scratching and persistent yapping.

'Jack?' she called. 'Jack!'

---

1   **erase** *(v)* remove or rub out. *(s)* expunge, obliterate, delete, eradicate, eliminate, destroy. *(ant)* preserve.

2   **rational** *(adj)* based on logic or reason. *(s)* sensible, wise, lucid, sane, reasonable, judicious. *(ant)* irrational.

3   **incoherent** *(adj)* unintelligible or delirious. *(s)* unclear, irrational, incomprehensible, inarticulate. *(ant)* coherent.

4   **holler** *(v)* shout or cry loudly. *(s)* bellow, bawl, roar, shriek, yell, howl, vociferate. *(ant)* whisper.

5   **unravel** *(v)* fall apart or unwind. *(s)* collapse, crumble, break down, fail. *(ant)* interlace, entwine.

6   **lintel** *(n)* a beam that supports a wall, door or window. *(s)* joist, girder, strut, rafter.

7   **torrent** *(n)* an overwhelming outburst (often of emotion). *(s)* flood, gush, rush, surge, deluge. *(ant)* trickle.

8   **inconsolable** *(adj)* unable to be comforted. *(s)* heartbroken, despairing, desolate. *(ant)* ecstatic.

9   **cope** *(v)* deal with something difficult. *(s)* contend, endure, handle, manage. *(ant)* fail, flounder, yield.

Ruff! Ruff! Jack barked louder.

Claire lunged at the door and yanked it open with such force that the handle hit the wall, making a **dent**[1].

A blur of legs and teeth snarled its way into the room. Jack went straight for Drane, obviously meaning business. He leaped, landing square in the boy's lap, and sank his sharp canines into the soft, fleshy part of his thigh. Drane howled. Jerking, he wheeled around from left to right, filling the cramped space, bouncing off the walls. His hands swooped and slapped in **involuntary**[2] **thrashes**[3], yet he didn't manage to hit Jack even once.

'Gerroff! Gerroff me!' he screamed.

His long legs **lashed**[4] up and down in ridiculous **spasmodic**[5] scissor kicks. Veering sideways, he spun in comical circles, trying to shake Jack off while a line of blood trickled down his torn trousers. Drane's arms flapped and **flailed**[6], **emulating**[7] a windmill, but Jack's jaw was locked to his leg like a **vice**[8].

Stumbling again, Drane snatched at a solid metal reading lamp perched on a desk in the corner. With a violent yank, the plug ripped out of the wall, whipping across the room towards Claire's face. Her head jerked backwards with a gross twist, **wrenching**[9] her neck. She managed to avoid the plug's metal **prongs**[10] as they careered **haphazardly**[11] towards her, **shaving**[12] her nose by a millimetre. Recovering her balance, she saw Drane lifting the heavy lamp, his arms extended high above his head. Letting out a vicious war cry, he hurled it down towards the terrier hanging from his thigh.

'Jack, off!' screamed Claire as she watched Josh Drane with horror.

---

1   **dent** *(n)* small hollow in a surface made by a blow or pressure. *(s)* dint, indentation, depression. *(ant)* lump.

2   **involuntary** *(adj)* done without will or conscious control. *(s)* automatic, reflex, spontaneous. *(ant)* voluntary.

3   **thrash** *(n)* flailing or jerking movement. *(s)* toss, flap, swing, wave, whip, lash, flay.

4   **lash** *(v)* move quickly and violently. *(s)* flail, jerk, swish, flick, whip, wag, swing, twitch.

5   **spasmodic** *(adj)* occurring in brief, irregular intervals. *(s)* erratic, fitful, intermittent, sporadic. *(ant)* continuous.

6   **flail** *(v)* swing or wave wildly. *(s)* thrash about, beat about, whirl, flap, flounder, lash.

7   **emulate** *(v)* copy. *(s)* imitate, reproduce, match, mimic, mirror, echo, rival. *(ant)* differ from.

8   **vice** *(n)* a metal tool with jaws for holding an object firmly in place. *(s)* clamp, brace, press, clasp.

9   **wrench** *(v)* twist or pull suddenly. *(s)* jerk, jolt, yank, sprain, injure, rick, turn, crick.

10   **prong** *(n)* a protruding metal part. *(s)* projection, point, tine.

11   **haphazardly** *(adv)* in a haphazard (random) way. *(s)* arbitrarily, chaotically, carelessly. *(ant)* systematically.

12   **shave** *(v)* pass closely, narrowly miss. *(ant)* hit, collide, connect, impact.

With obvious **barbaric**[1] intent, Drane roared and smashed the lamp down towards his thigh. He hadn't noticed an obedient Jack drop down and sit beside Claire's feet just before the makeshift **battering ram**[2] **bludgeoned**[3] into his flesh. When the almighty impact struck, his legs collapsed underneath him, and he lay utterly incapacitated on the floor alongside Mrs Evans, where he **bawled**[4], **squalling**[5] like a newborn baby.

---

1   **barbaric** *(adj)* cruel and savage. *(s)* barbarous, brutal, remorseless, fierce, ferocious, inhuman. *(ant)* gentle.

2   **battering ram** *(n)* a large object used for battering (hitting) something with. *(s)* club, bludgeon, cudgel, baton.

3   **bludgeon** *(v)* strike with a bludgeon (thick stick or club) or heavy object. *(s)* bash, batter, beat.

4   **bawl** *(v)* cry or shout noisily. *(s)* howl, wail, sob, weep, blubber, blub, roar, bellow. *(ant)* whisper.

5   **squall** *(v)* cry continuously and noisily. *(s)* yowl, wail, rage, bluster, howl, screech. *(ant)* laugh, smile.

12. Trust

As Drane lay nursing his battered leg on the office floor, on the other side of the door, in the exhibition hall, the Master continued to **goad**[1] and taunt his old **adversary**[2] Gwilym.

'What exactly are you going to do to stop me?' cackled Dewi, his eyes lit with raw threat; they exposed the **empathy**[3] of a shark. 'How are you going to save your precious gem?' he mocked, spitting his words at Gwilym.

Gwilym didn't blink; his gaze rested **defiantly**[4] on Dewi.

'The **devout**[5] and everlasting knight. The **perpetual**[6] hero. Underneath, you always were an **insipid**[7] fool,' Dewi **ridiculed**[8]. 'A slave to your people and **morality**[9], and where has it got you?' he hissed.

Not **retaliating**[10], Gwilym remained silent. His **stance**[11] exhibited neither threat nor **provocation**[12]. He simply stared at Dewi's dead expression.

---

1   **goad** *(v)* annoy or provoke into a reaction. *(s)* spur, hound, badger, incite, prod, push, stimulate. *(ant)* calm.

2   **adversary** *(n)* an opponent (rival). *(s)* enemy, foe, nemesis, challenger, opposition. *(ant)* supporter, ally.

3   **empathy** *(n)* the ability to understand the feelings of another. *(s)* compassion, sympathy. *(ant)* indifference.

4   **defiantly** *(adv)* in a defiant (disobedient) way. *(s)* boldly, rebelliously, cheekily, insolently. *(ant)* compliantly.

5   **devout** *(adj)* completely committed (dedicated) to a belief or cause. *(s)* devoted, staunch. *(ant)* uncommitted.

6   **perpetual** *(adj)* never changing or ending. *(s)* constant, eternal, permanent, undying. *(ant)* temporary.

7   **insipid** *(adj)* lacking the qualities that excite. *(s)* dull, vapid, boring, banal, bland, characterless. *(ant)* exciting.

8   **ridicule** *(v)* subject to unpleasant language or behaviour. *(s)* mock, humiliate, deride, tease, scorn. *(ant)* praise.

9   **morality** *(n)* principles discerning right and wrong. *(s)* ethics, decency, integrity, standards. *(ant)* immorality.

10   **retaliate** *(v)* react to or fight back. *(s)* respond, retort, reciprocate, counter. *(ant)* excuse, forgive.

11   **stance** *(n)* a person's outward attitude and behaviour. *(s)* bearing, pose, posture, position.

12   **provocation** *(n)* action or speech that stirs anger. *(s)* incitement, aggravation, vexation. *(ant)* pacification.

'What is it, old man? Are you too scared to take me on?' **rasped**[1] Dewi's **vengeful**[2] voice, his **repressed**[3] rage **erupting**[4] in response to Gwilym's grace and **composure**[5]. As he exploded, his fine features **contorted**[6] to bare his **immoral**[7] **soul**[8], that of a madman. 'You can't stop me, and you won't!' he screamed, aiming another stomach-**churning**[9] blow at the case with the Cutter.

It shuddered and groaned. Smoke poured out, but its previous soft gold colour had now turned an ominous black. **Fiery**[10] sparks flickered as the smoke **spewed**[11]. The sweet smell of flowers had vanished, replaced by an **acrid**[12], sickening burning. Dewi's victory was surely near; a third strike to the case might finish it. Snarling, with a **demented**[13] and **outlandish**[14] twist of his face, he stretched his arm upwards as if reaching for the ceiling; then, he crashed it down with such forcible might that a **hideous**[15], **unearthly**[16] vibration rang around the **capacious**[17] hall. Delicate cracks emerged, **rifts**[18] running in random branches throughout the glass, forming a complex **network**[19] of **venous**[20] tracks. Dewi snorted, licking his lips as he **hacked**[21] the case with the Cutter again.

'Gwilym, stop him! Stop him!' shouted Claire, running from the office. 'Don't just stand there!

---

1 **rasp** (*v*) say in a harsh, grating way. (*s*) croak, bark, snarl, growl. (*ant*) soothe.

2 **vengeful** (*adj*) seeking to gain revenge (payback). (*s*) unforgiving, resentful, ruthless, vindictive. (*ant*) forgiving.

3 **repressed** (*adj*) restrained or oppressed. (*s*) suppressed, controlled, curbed, inhibited, stifled. (*ant*) expressed.

4 **erupt** (*v*) explode physically or with emotion. (*s*) overflow, vent, burst forth, flare, rage. (*ant*) subside.

5 **composure** (*n*) the feeling of being calm and in control. (*s*) self-control, serenity, tranquillity, poise. (*ant*) agitation.

6 **contort** (*v*) bend or twist out of normal shape. (*s*) distort, deform, warp, misshape. (*ant*) align, straighten.

7 **immoral** (*adj*) not being moral (good). (*s*) wicked, depraved, dishonest, unscrupulous, corrupt. (*ant*) moral.

8 **soul** (*n*) a person's moral or emotional nature. (*s*) personality, spirit, persona, identity, inner self.

9 **churn** (*v*) turn and move (often in an anxious or excited way). (*s*) heave, mix, shake, roil, agitate. (*ant*) abate.

10 **fiery** (*adj*) burning, or having the colours of fire. (*s*) sizzling, hot, bright, brilliant, vivid, vibrant. (*ant*) icy, dull.

11 **spew** (*v*) expel or pour out rapidly. (*s*) eject, emit, spout, spurt, gush, flow, stream, spill. (*ant*) dribble, trickle.

12 **acrid** (*adj*) unpleasantly pungent or bitter. (*s*) choking, harsh, acidic, sharp. (*ant*) pleasant, sweet.

13 **demented** (*adj*) behaving irrationally (crazily). (*s*) deranged, unhinged, insane, lunatic, frenzied. (*ant*) rational.

14 **outlandish** (*adj*) unfamiliar and bizarre. (*s*) peculiar, eccentric, weird, queer, freakish, grotesque. (*ant*) usual.

15 **hideous** (*adj*) extremely unpleasant. (*s*) ugly, revolting, repugnant, appalling, monstrous. (*ant*) attractive.

16 **unearthly** (*adj*) mysterious or unnatural in a disturbing way. (*s*) weird, supernatural, eerie. (*ant*) normal.

17 **capacious** (*adj*) having lots of space inside. (*s*) spacious, vast, sizeable, extensive, huge, ample. (*ant*) cramped.

18 **rift** (*n*) a split or crack. (*s*) fissure, fracture, cleft, gap, hole, crevice, aperture, separation. (*ant*) closure.

19 **network** (*n*) a complex system of something. (*s*) maze, structure, web, arrangement.

20 **venous** (*adj*) relating to (like) veins. (*s*) veined, venose, veiny.

21 **hack** (*v*) cut with harsh, rough, heavy blows. (*s*) chop, slash, lacerate, hew, gash, slice.

You can't let him do that! You've got to stop him!' she shrieked.

Dewi **pivoted**[1] on his heel, shooting her a paralysing glare. He stilled, as if **hubristically**[2] assuming this present adversary posed minimal threat. Leering at her, he smirked an imperious, haughty sneer, then turned back to the case. Letting out a long, **vindictive**[3] laugh, he struck it again.

'Gwilym, what's wrong with you?' she shouted, her hands pushed together, beseeching him to act. 'He's gonna get the gem. Stop him! Do something! Stop him smashing the case!' Her screams were now **hysterical**[4]. Spluttering, she fanned away the caustic smoke and wiped her lips. 'Gwilym, please, he's going to get it,' she said, coughing. Her arms sagged to her sides in **resignation**[5]. 'Do something,' she begged, frowning at him, imploring him to answer.

'Claire, look behind you,' murmured Gwilym, his soft tone barely **perceptible**[6].

With the faintest tilt of his head, he gestured a subtle nod beyond her. She turned to see Drane dragging Rebecca from the office and into the hall. Rebecca could scarcely stand. At the same time, Jack sprinted across to Gwilym and sat by his feet. Claire was about to run over to Rebecca when a sound deafened her ears. The case finally **capitulated**[7], giving way beneath the might of the Cutter's **supernatural**[8] blows. The fragile cracks surged forth into myriad spreading **fissures**[9].

Claire looked from the case to Gwilym, baffled by his **apathy**[10]. A physical ache pulled at her chest as tears sprang again. Her hands, clenched tightly shut, were glued into fists of sweat.

'Trust, Claire' were Gwilym's only words as he turned and walked away, a **reliable**[11] Jack at his heel.

'What? Gwilym! Jack!' shouted Claire after them.

---

1   **pivot** *(v)* turn as if on a pivot (central point). *(s)* rotate, revolve, spin, swivel, whirl, pirouette.

2   **hubristically** *(adv)* in a hubristic (arrogant and presumptive) way. *(s)* conceitedly, haughtily. *(ant)* humbly.

3   **vindictive** *(adj)* seeking revenge (payback). *(s)* vengeful, revengeful, rancorous, malicious. *(ant)* benevolent.

4   **hysterical** *(adj)* expressing (showing) uncontrollable emotion. *(s)* frantic, frenzied, frenetic. *(ant)* composed.

5   **resignation** *(n)* acceptance of something undesirable yet inevitable. *(s)* tolerance, sufferance. *(ant)* defiance.

6   **perceptible** *(adj)* able to be noticed or seen. *(s)* audible, detectable, discernible. *(ant)* undetectable, inaudible.

7   **capitulate** *(v)* stop resisting an opponent or demand. *(s)* surrender, yield, submit, relent, cede. *(ant)* resist.

8   **supernatural** *(adj)* inexplicable in scientific terms. *(s)* paranormal, mystical, ghostly, uncanny. *(ant)* natural.

9   **fissure** *(n)* a narrow opening, split or crack. *(s)* crevice, chink, cleft, rift, slit, fracture, breach. *(ant)* closure.

10   **apathy** *(n)* lack of concern, interest or enthusiasm. *(s)* indifference, unconcern. *(ant)* curiosity, passion.

11   **reliable** *(adj)* trusted to perform without fail. *(s)* dependable, consistent, steadfast. *(ant)* unreliable, erratic.

They didn't look around. She knew they wouldn't. She knew they weren't coming back.

Torn, she looked away from the **maniac**[1] by the case and back towards the office. Mrs Evans lay on the floor, groaning – she would have to wait.

'Josh Drane!' she shouted, **outraged**[2]. 'Leave my sister alone!'

Drane didn't even look up; he yanked Rebecca, dragging her towards a fire exit.

'Drane,' she shrieked, 'put her down!' But her cries were futile.

'Claire? Claire?' Rebecca drawled.

'Shut up!' barked Drane into Rebecca's confused face. 'Shut up!' he hissed, shaking her with **ferocious**[3] jerks.

Lamentably[4], Rebecca looked sapped of any fight; she was **wilted**[5] and defenceless.

Livid[6] in a way like never before, Claire snapped. She charged at Drane shouting, 'YARRHHH!' circling her arms in opposing directions.

She'd seen Ben do something like this at his martial art competitions. Leaping as high as she could, she landed just over a metre from Drane. She **planted**[7] her feet firmly on the floor, bent her knees and crouched down low, ready to lunge, hands crossed before her chest.

Drane paused, a **bemused**[8] expression fleeting across his face; then he looked straight at her and burst out laughing. Throwing back his head, he howled, **inadvertently**[9] relaxing his grip on her sister. Claire seized the moment to karate chop hard at his arms, and Rebecca thumped to the floor.

Josh Drane's face portrayed a picture of shock and amazement. Stunned, he stared as Claire spun on one leg, built up momentum and speed, and in one **adept**[10] move, planted a perfect kick into the softest part of his stomach. As if feather-light, she landed back on her feet, ready and poised like a panther planning its next move.

---

1   **maniac** *(n)* a person behaving wildly, violently and dangerously. *(s)* lunatic, psychopath. *(ant)* sane person.

2   **outraged** *(adj)* very indignant, shocked or angered. *(s)* incensed, enraged, offended, affronted. *(ant)* placated.

3   **ferocious** *(adj)* great and extreme. *(s)* strong, vicious, aggressive, brutal, savage, barbarous. *(ant)* gentle, mild.

4   **lamentably** *(adv)* regrettably. *(s)* unfortunately, sadly, unluckily. *(ant)* fortunately.

5   **wilted** *(adj)* having lost energy or confidence. *(s)* languid, droopy, withered, faded, shrivelled. *(ant)* bolstered.

6   **livid** *(adj)* furiously angry. *(s)* seething, infuriated, incensed, enraged, outraged, fuming. *(ant)* pleased, calm.

7   **plant** *(v)* set or place in a specific position. *(s)* stand, deposit, lodge, put, stick, fix, set. *(ant)* move, uproot.

8   **bemused** *(adj)* confused or muddled. *(s)* bewildered, perplexed, flummoxed, stumped. *(ant)* understanding.

9   **inadvertently** *(adv)* in an inadvertent (unintended) manner. *(s)* accidentally, unwittingly. *(ant)* purposely.

10   **adept** *(adj)* highly skilled or proficient (good) at something. *(s)* competent, adroit, consummate. *(ant)* inept.

'Not laughing now, are you, Rat-Boy?' she taunted as her right foot left the ground, and her left flashed upwards after it, connecting cleanly under his chin.

She had **spectated**[1] at Ben's competitions most weekends, watching him make these moves, and this **skilful**[2] whipped strike landed right on target, flattening him with one sweet blow.

With Drane **dispatched**[3], Claire turned her focus onto her sister. 'Becca, wake up,' she said, gently shaking her. 'Becs, please wake up.'

Now out cold, Rebecca unmistakably needed to sleep off whatever Drane had given her. Claire removed her coat, as she was sweating, anyway, **fashioned**[4] it into a pillow, and laid it under her sister's head.

'Dewi.' Claire crouched frozen. Concerned for Rebecca, she'd forgotten he was there.

Swivelling around, she saw nothing but exhibits – Dewi had gone. An eerie silence filled the hall. **Incredulous**[5], she checked again; he'd seemingly **vaporised**[6]. She ran to the **smouldering**[7] case, a mass of cracks. Her heart tumbled. She'd saved Rebecca, yet Dewi must have got the gem and escaped. Gwilym was nowhere to be seen.

They had not foiled his attack. The Knights Hawk had failed. Dewi had been too **dominant**[8], and Gwilym too weak. Her sweet victory over Drane evaporated. The case's glass was so **fractured**[9] and **crazed**[10] she could barely see inside. As the remaining smoke thinned, she bent closer. *That's weird*, she thought, flaring her nostrils as a sweetness drifted upwards. *What's that smell?* she asked herself.

Sniffing the air, she ran her finger along the glass casing. **Razor**[11]-sharp **slivers**[12] lay in

---

1   **spectate** *(v)* watch rather than take part in. *(s)* view, observe, look, witness. *(ant)* participate.

2   **skilful** *(adj)* showing or having skill. *(s)* expert, accomplished, proficient, adept, competent. *(ant)* incompetent.

3   **dispatch** *(v)* deal with quickly. *(s)* finish, discharge, conclude, settle, destroy, kill. *(ant)* restore.

4   **fashion** *(v)* make into a specific form. *(s)* shape, mould, contrive, create, construct, fabricate. *(ant)* destroy.

5   **incredulous** *(adj)* not able to believe, unbelieving. *(s)* sceptical, doubtful, unconvinced. *(ant)* believing.

6   **vaporise** *(v)* vanish or disappear without trace. *(s)* evaporate. *(ant)* appear, emerge.

7   **smouldering** *(adj)* burning gently without flames but often emitting (producing) smoke. *(s)* glowing, smoking.

8   **dominant** *(adj)* influential and powerful over others. *(s)* strong, superior, forceful. *(ant)* submissive.

9   **fractured** *(adj)* broken, cracked or snapped. *(s)* shattered, splintered, split, ruptured. *(ant)* fixed, repaired.

10   **crazed** *(adj)* having lots of fine cracks. *(s)* flawed, damaged, shattered, splintered, split. *(ant)* unblemished.

11   **razor** *(n)* an incredibly sharp cutting or shaving instrument. *(s)* blade, knife, shaver, cutter.

12   **sliver** *(n)* a small, thin, narrow piece. *(s)* splinter, slice, shaving, fragment, shard, flake. *(ant)* whole.

wait, **snagging**[1] at her skin.

'Ouch!' She sucked at a tiny cut as she surveyed the damaged glass. *It's cracked but not broken*, she thought, examining it carefully.

Realising the significance of her words, and squinting through the cracks, she tried to work out what lay inside, but the criss-cross of **crevices**[2] made it impossible. She banged on it with her fist, but that just hurt. She pushed and **jostled**[3] it; still it would not budge. The **opaque**[4] glass blocked her view, and the abnormal sweet smell grew stronger. 'Lilies,' she **remarked**[5], realising what the smell was. 'I can smell lilies.' The **mysterious**[6] perfume wafted up from the case.

She followed the **origin**[7] of the smoke to find a wider **cleft**[8] she'd not seen a moment ago. Screwing one eye shut, she squinted through the tiny split with the other. Inside the case, nestling unperturbed on a red velvet cushion, sat the prettiest thing she'd ever seen. A **startling**[9] emerald hawk twinkled up at her. Magnificent, it sat **entwined**[10] within an intricate band of finely woven gold chain mail. Claire had seen gold before, yet none as **alluring**[11] as this. This gold shimmered and shone with life.

The Gwalch Gem bracelet **mesmerised**[12] her. Open-mouthed and held by its spell, she admired its beauty and **simplicity**[13]. Its colour gleamed an indescribable green, so lush, fresh and **joyful**[14]. The **extraordinary**[15] cut and sharp angles sparkled with a **lustre**[16] that **defined**[17] the

---

1   **snag** (*v*) catch or tear on something sharp. (*s*) rip, gash, cut, jag, hook, lacerate.

2   **crevice** (*n*) a narrow opening or crack (especially in rock). (*s*) gap, fissure, cleft, fracture, cranny. (*ant*) ridge.

3   **jostle** (*v*) push, bump or elbow something. (*s*) collide with, knock, shove, manhandle, shoulder.

4   **opaque** (*adj*) not able to be seen through. (*s*) cloudy, hazy, filmy. (*ant*) transparent.

5   **remark** (*v*) notice, say, or regard (look at) with attention. (*s*) comment, observe, state, utter.

6   **mysterious** (*adj*) difficult to identify, explain or understand. (*s*) bizarre, queer, inexplicable. (*ant*) explicable.

7   **origin** (*n*) where something begins or comes from. (*s*) source, derivation, start, origination. (*ant*) conclusion.

8   **cleft** (*n*) a split or fissure. (*s*) crevice, opening, breach, chasm, crack, rift, chink. (*ant*) closure, ridge.

9   **startling** (*adj*) alarming or shocking. (*s*) surprising, astounding, astonishing, staggering. (*ant*) placating.

10   **entwine** (*v*) twist, wind or weave together. (*s*) intertwine, interlace, interweave, interlink. (*ant*) unravel.

11   **alluring** (*adj*) powerfully attractive or fascinating. (*s*) appealing, charming, enticing, beguiling. (*ant*) repellent.

12   **mesmerise** (*v*) hold the complete attention of. (*s*) hypnotise, captivate, enthral, spellbind. (*ant*) bore.

13   **simplicity** (*n*) the quality of being simple. (*s*) purity, plainness, austerity. (*ant*) complexity, intricacy.

14   **joyful** (*adj*) causing huge pleasure and happiness. (*s*) bright, enjoyable, pleasing. (*ant*) joyless, glum.

15   **extraordinary** (*adj*) remarkable or extremely unusual. (*s*) exceptional, phenomenal, particular. (*ant*) normal.

16   **lustre** (*n*) sheen or glow. (*s*) brilliance, brightness, splendour, gloss, shine, radiance, gleam. (*ant*) dimness.

17   **define** (*v*) show or make clear the outline of. (*s*) determine, establish, specify, distinguish, clarify. (*ant*) distort.

hawk's shape. Luring her, it drew her closer.

The scent of lilies **intensified**[1], and even though she was looking through a narrow crack, an **unambiguous**[2] scene played out before her. She had little doubt as to the **participants'**[3] identities: a nobly **countenanced**[4] young man, **daubed**[5] with blood, sobbing and cradling a baby; the massive head of a shaggy grey dog resting beside him, a final stillness about it.

'Llywelyn? Llywelyn? Is that you?' she asked out loud.

But the scene suddenly changed, and so did the characters. A woman with a **shock**[6] of wavy blonde hair fanned into the picture. Claire saw the back of her head; the woman was looking towards a young man who seemed familiar. Claire couldn't see the woman's face, but she held something in her hands, lifting it up high before the man; it was unmistakably the sparkling Gwalch Gem bracelet.

Blowing into the crack to clear the **residual**[7] smoke, Claire pushed her eye nearer to the gap. The woman held the bracelet in her hands until she suddenly plucked the Gwalch Gem from the Welsh gold. Curling her fingers into a tight fist around the gem, the woman moved her arm towards the man, who looked on with what Claire thought was a terrible sadness. His eyes glazed, and his skin turned an ashen grey, as if the life within him had been **extinguished**[8].

Then, to Claire's horror, minuscule lines began to appear all over the man in random zigzags, like the case before her; his body cracked and crazed, but somehow he remained standing. Slowly, as if being injected with a vivid ink, the man's grey body started to change colour, gradually turning a stunning bright emerald green, just like the gem. The woman leaned forward and blew a sharp, hard breath towards him. The man's eyes took on a look that Claire could only describe as heartbroken. Then, shockingly, his body exploded, shattering into thousands of tiny, glistening shards, shooting outwards into an explosion of glittering green before disintegrating into specks of emerald dust. Had its meaning not been so distressing,

---

1   **intensify** *(v)* make or become more intense (strong). *(s)* strengthen, increase, escalate, sharpen. *(ant)* weaken.

2   **unambiguous** *(adj)* not open to misinterpretation. *(s)* unmistakable, clear-cut, explicit, definite. *(ant)* vague.

3   **participant** *(n)* something or someone who takes part in something. *(s)* contributor, member. *(ant)* observer.

4   **countenanced** *(adj)* having a look or expression. *(s)* faced, featured, expressed.

5   **daub** *(v)* smear, coat or paint in a clumsy way. *(s)* smudge, plaster, stain, cover, slop, splatter. *(ant)* clean.

6   **shock** *(n)* a thick mass of hair. *(s)* mane, head, crop, cascade.

7   **residual** *(adj)* remaining or left over. *(s)* lasting, surplus, remnant, enduring, outstanding. *(ant)* departed.

8   **extinguish** *(v)* put an end to or destroy. *(s)* terminate, annihilate, eradicate, snuff out, eliminate. *(ant)* create.

Claire could almost have described it as beautiful.

Claire shot upright, horrified at what she'd just seen. She was now fairly sure the man **depicted**[1] Gwilym.

She placed her eye back against the gap, squinting harder, but the grainy portrayal had gone. She had seen the Gwalch Gem wrenched out of the bracelet, and Gwilym had turned into emerald and shattered into thousands of pieces. What did this all mean? She wasn't sure, but she didn't like it. Bending down again, she screwed up her eye next to the glass, but she couldn't even find the opening this time. It seemed to have vanished. She couldn't smell lilies any more either.

What had she just seen, and what did it mean? She knew one thing for sure, the Gwalch Gem bracelet was untouched. **Miraculously**[2] the case had **withheld**[3] Dewi's **onslaught**[4] with the Cutter, and the bracelet had survived unharmed, lying before her in the case. But this joy was **quashed**[5] by the vision she had just seen. Had it been an **omen**[6], or even worse, a **premonition**[7]? If the Gwalch Gem was parted from the Welsh gold, would Gwilym die? Could all the Knights Hawk possibly die? She felt sick with worry.

'Ow! Urrrgghhh!' A loud groaning noise came from across the hall. Drane was rolling around the floor, whining and rubbing at his chin.

Ignoring him, Claire darted across the exhibition hall to the cinema and tore open the doors.

'Help!' she shouted as loud as she could. 'Help! My sister, Rebecca, needs help!' she yelled over the loud film.

Mr Hollie shot up from his seat, looking confounded. 'What? Who on earth are you?' he **stammered**[8]. 'Please refrain from behaving like a **feral**[9] animal. Speak **concisely**[10], girl,' he

---

1   **depict** *(v)* represent in some form. *(s)* portray, show, describe, paint, picture, illustrate. *(ant)* misrepresent.

2   **miraculously** *(adj)* in a remarkable and welcome way. *(s)* astoundingly, unbelievably. *(ant)* unremarkably.

3   **withhold** *(v)* suppress (put an end to) or hold back. *(s)* stop, refuse, deny, resist. *(ant)* permit, yield to.

4   **onslaught** *(n)* a vicious or destructive attack. *(s)* aggression, assault, offence, ambush, raid. *(ant)* defence.

5   **quash** *(v)* put an end to. *(s)* suppress, quell, repress, crush, curb, overwhelm, defeat, conquer. *(ant)* allow.

6   **omen** *(n)* a sign of something to come. *(s)* signal, portent, premonition, prophecy.

7   **premonition** *(n)* a feeling that something is about to happen. *(s)* forewarning, intuition, hunch.

8   **stammer** *(v)* speak with difficulty. *(s)* stutter, hesitate, falter, stumble, splutter, mumble. *(ant)* pronounce.

9   **feral** *(adj)* (especially of an animal) wild and untamed. *(s)* undomesticated, uncontrollable. *(ant)* tame, trained.

10   **concisely** *(adv)* in a concise (short but comprehensive) way. *(s)* succinctly, pithily. *(ant)* long-windedly.

said, **condescendingly**[1] looking down his nose at her.

'You have to come and help my sister. She's ill, and *you* left her with that horrible boy Drane, and Mrs Evans is ill too. Come now!' she demanded, ignoring his **rank**[2] of teacher.

'Yes, yes, of course,' he stuttered, tripping over his own feet. 'Miss Malik, wait with the class,' he instructed his assistant. 'Where is that curator **fellow**[3] Evans?' he **rambled**[4] on, following Claire back into the exhibition hall.

'What the blighter's happened here?' shouted the astonished teacher. 'Where the hell is Drane?' he asked with a **mystified**[5] look.

At that moment, the two security guards walked back into the hall, holding a boy by the **scruff**[6] of his neck. It was another of Hollie's pupils, the decoy boy who had been rocking the case to distract the guards earlier.

'Sir, will you stop **faffing**[7] about and help my sister now?' Claire shouted at Mr Hollie – she didn't know his name. 'Rebecca, help her now!' she ordered, pointing.

'Oh my word,' bleated Mr Hollie as he followed the direction of Claire's finger to see another of his **mislaid**[8] pupils.

Rebecca sprawled fast asleep on the floor. Drane, nearby, was nursing his bruised chin. His white school shirt hung out of his trousers, revealing a patch of blood across the bottom.

'What in the world have you done, boy?' Mr Hollie barked.

'Nothing, sir,' replied Drane. 'I didn't do anything.' He tried to tuck his bloody shirt into his trousers.

Noisy, **exuberant**[9] teenagers now poured out of the cinema, obviously desperate to join in the

---

1   **condescendingly** *(adv)* in a condescending (superior) manner. *(s)* imperiously, pompously. *(ant)* modestly.

2   **rank** *(n)* a position in an organisation. *(s)* standing, grade, level, status, title, place, category.

3   **fellow** *(n)* a man or boy. *(s)* person, individual, fella, character, chap, lad, bloke. *(ant)* woman.

4   **ramble** *(v)* talk in a confused or unimportant way. *(s)* prattle, blather, twitter, blether, digress.

5   **mystified** *(adj)* completely perplexed or bewildered. *(s)* nonplussed, bamboozled, stumped. *(ant)* enlightened.

6   **scruff** *(n)* (of an animal or person) the back of the neck. *(s)* scrag, nape, nucha.

7   **faff** *(v)* do something ineffectually (not having desired effect or outcome). *(s)* fuss, fluster, flap. *(ant)* achieve.

8   **mislaid** *(adj)* temporarily unable to be found. *(s)* misplaced, lost, forgotten, dropped. *(ant)* found.

9   **exuberant** *(adj)* full of cheer, energy or excitement. *(s)* boisterous, buoyant, spirited, vivacious. *(ant)* lethargic.

furore[1]. The young teaching assistant tried to **herd**[2] them back, but they ignored her. The two security guards tried to assist, joining the **fiasco**[3], but the kids disobeyed them all, running riot, clearly enjoying the tumult and **uproar**[4].

'Miss Malik,' Mr Hollie yelled, flapping about uselessly and **exacerbating**[5] the situation.

Claire looked on, despairing at the **bumbling**[6], incompetent adults. Exhausted, she knelt to Rebecca, who was still oblivious. Looking over at Drane, she shivered at an unexpected rush of excitement and pride. She'd floored him, and with style. Behind her the main doors to the museum flew open. Two **enormous**[7] policemen marched in, silencing everyone. They headed straight for Mr Hollie.

'Oh my,' he squeaked, looking faint.

'We received a report of an **attempted**[8] robbery,' the tallest boomed to the group in a **gravelly**[9] voice. 'Who's in charge here?' he demanded.

'That'll be me,' the fattest security guard announced, waddling across like an overfed duck. His **substantial**[10] **girth**[11] swayed as he moved.

He waded through the **throng**[12] of kids, who craned their necks to see everything.

'I'm in charge.' He glowed as he spoke. 'Dave Wise, head of security,' he added, holding in his belly and rocking onto tiptoe. He had spiky hair and sagging jowls, oddly resembling a pufferfish.

'Thank you, Mr Wise. What has happened here?' asked the tallest policeman as the other went over to inspect the damaged case.

---

1   **furore** *(n)* a disturbance caused by excitement or anger. *(s)* commotion, rumpus, hubbub. *(ant)* tranquillity.

2   **herd** *(v)* gather together or move in a group. *(s)* shepherd, assemble, steer, usher, drove. *(ant)* disperse.

3   **fiasco** *(n)* a complete failure, especially a ridiculous one. *(s)* debacle, shambles, farce, mess. *(ant)* success.

4   **uproar** *(n)* a loud noise or disturbance. *(s)* pandemonium, turmoil, hullabaloo, tumult, clamour. *(ant)* silence.

5   **exacerbate** *(v)* make worse. *(s)* aggravate, worsen, inflame, impair, intensify. *(ant)* alleviate.

6   **bumbling** *(n)* a confused or useless action. *(s)* blunder, bungle, ineptness, incompetence. *(ant)* efficiency.

7   **enormous** *(adj)* large in size or quantity. *(s)* giant, massive, colossal, vast, huge, immense. *(ant)* tiny, minute.

8   **attempted** *(adj)* failed despite effort to succeed. *(s)* unsuccessful, futile, ineffective. *(ant)* successful.

9   **gravelly** *(adj)* deep and rough in sound. *(s)* husky, gruff, raspy, hoarse, harsh. *(ant)* soft, velvety.

10   **substantial** *(adj)* of largish size, importance or worth. *(s)* considerable, sizeable, ample. *(ant)* small, minor.

11   **girth** *(n)* someone or something's middle (waist) measurement. *(s)* width, stomach, midriff.

12   **throng** *(n)* a dense, tightly packed crowd. *(s)* multitude, mob, mass, horde, gang, swarm. *(ant)* smattering.

'Some kid rocked one of the cases, setting the alarm off. But we **scuppered**[1] his **prank**[2] and removed him from the hall,' replied Dave, rubbing his double chin with a look of misplaced pride. 'We've got him though; no need to worry,' finished the guard.

'Well, **manifestly**[3], that *prank* may have been a **ruse**[4] for something more serious,' replied the police officer, gesturing towards Rebecca and then the case. 'Seems that one of your cases has been **irreparably**[5] damaged. We will need to tape it off for fingerprints and will require access to your CCTV footage. We will continue from here,' he stressed. 'I'll call an ambulance for these two. And keep this lot quiet.' He nodded at the **impudent**[6] pupils, throwing a pointed look at the two teachers.

Claire knelt by her sister as the 'police officers' worked the scene. Gwilym and Owain acted like they'd never clapped eyes on her before; *they* were dressed as two policemen!

She watched as they checked Rebecca's pulse and laid her in the recovery position, placing a **foil**[7] blanket over her. They attended Mrs Evans in the office, making her comfortable with a glass of water. Claire even allowed herself a smug smile as they searched Drane and found a small bag of white powder in his pocket. He'd also hidden a knife, which had **apparently**[8] **skewered**[9] his thigh, drawing blood.

'Who's in charge of these kids?' asked Gwilym.

'I am,' replied Mr Hollie, **scampering**[10] over, **simpering**[11] and panting like an adoring puppy. He extended his **clammy**[12] hand. 'Walter Hollie, head of history. Most people call me Wally,' he finished in all seriousness.

Gwilym ignored his hand and looked him straight in the eye.

---

1   **scupper** *(v)* prevent from working or succeeding. *(s)* ruin, wreck, foil, spoil, stymie. *(ant)* help, facilitate.

2   **prank** *(n)* a mischievous act or practical joke. *(s)* trick, stunt, caper, jape, lark, hoax, antic.

3   **manifestly** *(adv)* in a clear, evident or obvious way. *(s)* noticeably, clearly, undoubtedly. *(ant)* doubtfully.

4   **ruse** *(n)* an action intended to deceive (trick) someone. *(s)* con, subterfuge, stunt, smokescreen. *(ant)* truth.

5   **irreparably** *(adv)* in a way that is impossible to correct or repair. *(s)* permanently, irreversibly. *(ant)* reversibly.

6   **impudent** *(adj)* not showing respect for another. *(s)* cheeky, insolent, impertinent, brazen. *(ant)* respectful.

7   **foil** *(n)* thin, pliable (bendy) sheet or layer of metal. *(s)* aluminium foil.

8   **apparently** *(adv)* as far as one knows or can see. *(s)* supposedly, seemingly, evidently. *(ant)* implausibly.

9   **skewer** *(v)* pierce with something extremely thin and sharp. *(s)* stab, impale, spear, bayonet.

10   **scamper** *(v)* run with light, quick steps. *(s)* scurry, scuttle, scoot, hurry, romp, trot, hasten. *(ant)* dawdle, stroll.

11   **simper** *(v)* smile in an ingratiating (slimy, creepy, coy) manner. *(s)* grin, beam, smirk, pout. *(ant)* frown, scowl.

12   **clammy** *(adj)* unpleasantly damp and sticky. *(s)* sweaty, slimy, moist, wet. *(ant)* dry, warm, parched.

'**Evidently**[1], this lad deals in drugs and tried them on his girlfriend. She's had too much. We'll **analyse**[2] the **substance**[3]. His wounds are superficial, nothing serious. Take your class back to school, Mr Hollie, and we'll be in touch.'

'Yes, of course, sir,' exhaled the teacher, breathing again.

Relieved, he bowed his curly head in **deference**[4] towards the policeman. Then, resembling an **overenthusiastic**[5], **inept**[6] morris dancer, he swooshed off with a **giddy**[7] prance to round up the rest of his class.

With a disbelieving shake of his head, Gwilym frowned as the **hapless**[8] teacher tried to gather his pupils.

'The boy who set off the alarm, shall I get him?' asked Dave, the pufferfish security guard, practically saluting.

'Yes. We'll speak to him now,' replied Owain, stepping forward. 'Where is he?'

'This way,' replied the guard, leading Owain from the hall.

'And who are you, young lady?' Gwilym asked Claire, his tone so **matter-of-fact**[9] she answered in the same voice.

'I'm Claire Cadwallader … er … sir,' she replied. 'This is my sister, Rebecca; she's … er … here with her school.'

'Yes, Claire. We spoke with your teacher when you didn't arrive at school this morning. Did you follow your sister here because you wanted to come on the school trip too?' Gwilym frowned at her, but a **mirthful**[10] glint flickered in his eye. 'Your teacher remarked upon your love of history and said it would make sense if you were here. She also said something about you hating

---

1   **evidently** *(adv)* it would seem that. *(s)* apparently, seemingly. *(ant)* implausibly.

2   **analyse** *(v)* examine in detail. *(s)* inspect, study, investigate, evaluate, explore. *(ant)* overlook.

3   **substance** *(n)* a specific kind of thing. *(s)* matter, material, stuff, ingredient, constituent, element.

4   **deference** *(n)* polite respect and submission. *(s)* regard, esteem, reverence, admiration, awe. *(ant)* disrespect.

5   **overenthusiastic** *(adj)* having too much enthusiasm. *(s)* overzealous, ardent, fervent. *(ant)* unenthusiastic.

6   **inept** *(adj)* showing or having no skill. *(s)* amateurish, maladroit, bungling, incompetent. *(ant)* competent.

7   **giddy** *(adj)* frivolous and excitable. *(s)* silly, skittish, scatter brained, foolish. *(ant)* serious, solemn.

8   **hapless** *(adj)* unfortunate. *(s)* unlucky, luckless, woeful, ill-fated, doomed, pitiful. *(ant)* fortunate, fortuitous.

9   **matter-of-fact** *(adj)* unemotional. *(s)* impassive, deadpan, sober, aloof, cool. *(ant)* irrational, agitated.

10   **mirthful** *(adj)* full of mirth (amusement). *(s)* amusing, merry, light-hearted, joyful, jolly, jovial. *(ant)* mirthless.

cross-country.' He nodded. 'Playing **truant**[1] from school is a serious matter, and you won't do it again, will you, miss?' he added with a **grave**[2] tone.

She hung her head, feigning shame, hiding a smile as he **devised**[3] her cover story – her **alibi**[4]. Where had she been if people asked? Now she had her **corresponding**[5] story, everything would **corroborate**[6], thanks to Gwilym.

A man and a woman in **fluorescent**[7] green jackets bustled into the museum, **laden**[8] with boxes and bags.

'They're over here.' Gwilym gestured towards Rebecca and Drane on the floor.

The two **paramedics**[9] tended to Rebecca first, checking her pulse and placing various **instruments**[10] onto her fingers, and then an oxygen mask over her mouth.

'She's not going to die, is she?' Claire asked, suddenly scared.

'No,' replied the woman, smiling at her. 'She'll be fine; all her **vital signs**[11] are good. She'll be home before you know it,' she finished, winking at Claire.

Winking at traumatised relatives was most **unorthodox**[12], but this paramedic was no ordinary one; it was Felicity, last seen as the police officer they'd left guarding the entrance to the underground tunnel at the police station.

'Stand up,' Gwilym barked at Drane.

The **belligerent**[13] boy scowled an ugly look as Gwilym **cuffed**[14] his wrists.

Gwilym looked him straight in the eye and said, 'You're a foolish boy, carrying knives and

---

1   **truant** *(n)* a pupil missing school without permission. *(s)* absentee, non-attender, skiver. *(ant)* attendee.

2   **grave** *(adj)* serious or solemn. *(s)* sombre, sober, thoughtful, unsmiling, stony, gloomy. *(ant)* cheerful, upbeat.

3   **devise** *(v)* plan or invent. *(s)* conceive, formulate, concoct, contrive, create, develop. *(ant)* copy, replicate.

4   **alibi** *(n)* a claim that one was elsewhere whilst a wrong was done. *(s)* excuse, defence, proof.

5   **corresponding** *(adj)* similar or agreeing. *(s)* equating, suitable, parallel, relating, concurrent. *(ant)* differing.

6   **corroborate** *(v)* give support or confirm something. *(s)* agree, verify, endorse, validate, justify. *(ant)* disprove.

7   **fluorescent** *(adj)* vividly bright in colour. *(s)* luminous, shining, glowing, vibrant. *(ant)* dark.

8   **laden** *(adj)* heavily loaded or weighed down. *(s)* full, burdened, encumbered, overloaded. *(ant)* unburdened.

9   **paramedic** *(n)* a person skilled in emergency medical care. *(s)* ambulance attendant, medical technician.

10   **instrument** *(n)* a tool or implement. *(s)* device, gadget, apparatus, contraption, mechanism.

11   **vital signs** *(n)* measurements that indicate the function of a person's body (pulse, blood pressure, etc.).

12   **unorthodox** *(adj)* contrary (opposite) to what is usual. *(s)* unconventional, unusual. *(ant)* orthodox.

13   **belligerent** *(adj)* aggressive and hostile. *(s)* threatening, confrontational, bellicose. *(ant)* peaceful, friendly.

14   **cuff** *(v)* put on handcuffs. *(s)* handcuff, secure, shackle, restrain, fetter. *(ant)* uncuff, release.

dealing drugs. You're in trouble, deep trouble,' he warned.

Claire, by now, realised Gwilym's plan. He'd **concocted**[1] a cover story for the relevant people, an alibi concealing the gem's truth and the real attempted theft. Due to the knife Drane was carrying, no one would ever know a dog had bitten him. She had so many burning questions to ask Gwilym, but she knew they'd have to wait for now.

'Claire, love! Rebecca?' An anguished voice rose **amid**[2] the fall of running footsteps.

'Dad? What are you doing here?' Claire squealed, throwing herself at Vince. 'How did you know where we were?' she asked.

'We came over a day early to do some shopping,' he replied, smothered by Claire. 'On the way, your mum phoned me. Her car's in the garage, so we came straight here as fast as we could.'

Claire's dad glanced behind him towards the entrance. A vision of loveliness with legs like a **gazelle's**[3] entered the hall.

'Jayne!' shouted Claire.

She wanted to run up and throw her arms around her, but Jayne looked too perfect to spoil. Her thick blonde hair tumbled down, resting on her shoulders in soft, natural curves. An **understated**[4] cream trouser suit **flattered**[5] her legs as she seemed to glide into the building. Complementing **beige**[6] heels took her to a slender six feet tall.

As easy as a model on a catwalk, Jayne **sashayed**[7] in long, **masterful**[8] strides across the museum, a gorgeous waft of perfume in her wake. Her feline eyes twinkled, smiling at Claire. The schoolchildren who were leaving with Mr Hollie fell quiet as she crossed the hall, and the teacher's jaw gaped open. One of the teenagers let out a low whistle.

Mr Hollie tutted and muttered, '**Insufferable**[9] kids.' Then he gushed a **profuse**[10] apology to

---

1   **concoct** *(v)* devise or create a story or plan. *(s)* dream up, fabricate, invent, contrive, conceive. *(ant)* copy.

2   **amid** *(prep)* surrounded by, in the middle of. *(s)* among, within, amidst, between, during. *(ant)* outside.

3   **gazelle** *(n)* a small, slender antelope with long, slim legs.

4   **understated** *(adj)* not excessively showy. *(s)* modest, simple, tasteful, sensible. *(ant)* flamboyant, ostentatious.

5   **flatter** *(v)* show off to the best advantage. *(s)* enhance, complement, suit, improve. *(ant)* mar, spoil.

6   **beige** *(adj)* a pale fawn colour (like sand). *(s)* buff, taupe, oatmeal, biscuit, stone.

7   **sashay** *(v)* walk in an exaggerated yet casual manner. *(s)* swagger, prance, strut. *(ant)* slouch, shuffle.

8   **masterful** *(adj)* powerful and able to control others. *(s)* imposing, commanding, dominant. *(ant)* feeble.

9   **insufferable** *(adj)* too extreme to deal with. *(s)* intolerable, unbearable, obnoxious, impossible. *(ant)* bearable.

10   **profuse** *(adj)* abundant. *(s)* plentiful, copious, generous, gushing, effusive. *(ant)* scant.

Jayne, almost bowing in **servitude**[1] as he spoke. **Swooning**[2], he straightened his tie and turned **crimson**[3].

Jayne had this effect on people. Busy rooms fell quiet, and crowds would part to let her pass, people **gawking**[4] in admiration. She **emitted**[5] a **magnetic**[6] **aura**[7]. Claire sometimes wondered why Jayne liked her dad. They were totally different characters, but she was glad Jayne did.

'Claire, darling,' Jayne said, clearly upset. 'Are you OK? What on earth has happened here?' she asked, hugging her.

Claire inhaled, **eager**[8] to pour out her heart, but then Gwilym stepped forward.

'Claire, tell your story later,' he said in a quiet yet insistent voice. 'When you are home. It's time to go now.'

'Oh, OK,' she responded, **abashed**[9]. 'OK.'

In a slow, **deliberate**[10] manner, Jayne pivoted to face the policeman.

'Thank you for helping the girls today,' she acknowledged in a cool, **eloquent**[11] voice. 'Their father and I very much appreciate your assistance,' she continued. **Polite**[12] and professional, she smiled broadly, exposing her **faultless**[13] white teeth. Her gaze bored into Gwilym.

Even Gwilym looks dazzled, thought Claire, smiling in his direction.

'Our pleasure; we are here to help,' he replied as professionally as Jayne had.

Claire watched them as they spoke.

Gwilym looks funny, she thought, grinning. *All men act funny near Jayne.* She giggled to herself.

---

1   **servitude** *(n)* the state of being subject to someone more powerful. *(s)* subjugation, subjection. *(ant)* freedom.

2   **swoon** *(v)* be overcome with admiration or other strong emotion. *(s)* weaken, be overwhelmed. *(ant)* fortify.

3   **crimson** *(adj)* deep, rich purplish-red colour. *(s)* ruby, scarlet, rouge, carmine, cherry, cerise.

4   **gawk** *(v)* stare stupidly. *(s)* gape, gaze, gawp, rubberneck, ogle, goggle, watch. *(ant)* glance, ignore.

5   **emit** *(v)* produce and discharge (give off). *(s)* release, effuse, issue, vent, secrete, radiate. *(ant)* absorb.

6   **magnetic** *(adj)* attractive and alluring. *(s)* charming, irresistible, compelling, captivating. *(ant)* repellent.

7   **aura** *(n)* a subtle (fine) impression or quality exuded (given off). *(s)* air, quality, characteristic, feeling.

8   **eager** *(adj)* wanting to do or have something keenly. *(s)* impatient, enthusiastic, ready. *(ant)* unenthusiastic.

9   **abashed** *(adj)* embarrassed, ashamed or disconcerted. *(s)* humiliated, deflated, mortified. *(ant)* undaunted.

10   **deliberate** *(adj)* careful and unhurried. *(s)* measured, steady, cautious. *(ant)* hasty, careless.

11   **eloquent** *(adj)* indicating or expressing something clearly. *(s)* articulate, expressive, fluent. *(ant)* inarticulate.

12   **polite** *(adj)* showing respectful and considerate behaviour. *(s)* civil, courteous, deferential. *(ant)* rude, aloof.

13   **faultless** *(adj)* free from error or defect. *(s)* perfect, flawless, spotless, immaculate. *(ant)* imperfect, blemished.

'We will contact the parents if we have any more information.'

'I'm sure you will,' Jayne replied **cordially**[1], smiling wider. Gracefully she tossed her hair over her shoulder and twirled around on her high heels. 'Come on, Claire, darling, let's get you home.'

Jayne wrapped a loving arm around Claire's shoulder and ushered her towards the exit, where Vince was accompanying Rebecca into the ambulance.

As they left, Claire glanced back from Jayne's protective **embrace**[2], looking for Gwilym. He stood alone, watching her leave. Searching for answers, her **keen**[3] eyes queried his **cryptic**[4] yet impassive face. He caught her eye and gave her the slightest nod of his head. Her eyes lingered on his, moistening and crinkling into a smile as they did. Swallowing hard, she battled to banish the hideous vision of him shattering into thousands of pieces, then turned and headed out of the museum with Jayne.

---

1   **cordially** *(adv)* in a cordial (warm and friendly) manner. *(s)* pleasantly, genially, convivially. *(ant)* unpleasantly.

2   **embrace** *(n)* the act of holding in one's arms. *(s)* hug, cuddle, clasp, grasp, squeeze, clinch. *(ant)* exclusion.

3   **keen** *(adj)* sharp and intense. *(s)* astute, perceptive, deep, bright, responsive. *(ant)* insensitive, indifferent.

4   **cryptic** *(adj)* having a mysterious or obscure (unclear) meaning. *(s)* enigmatic, puzzling. *(ant)* straightforward.

13. Exhibition Case 111

Gwilym watched as Claire left the museum's chaotic exhibition hall, the beautiful woman's arm wrapped in a protective shield around Claire's shoulder. He could not help but be beguiled by the unique **fragrance**[1] she left behind her. It left an **indelible**[2] stamp on his senses; he would recognise it anywhere and at any time.

He headed towards the cracked exhibition case and, like any good policeman would, began to investigate the attempted theft. His partner, Owain, had recovered the two young Mal-Instinctive accomplices from the basement, where he had left them earlier, and was striding over to their teacher, a boy grasped in each hand.

'Are these two with you?' Owain **addressed**[3] Hollie, who was still flapping and **flouncing**[4] about with **incompetence**[5], **ineffectually**[6] trying to round up his **rebellious**[7] class, who were **having a ball**[8] now.

Mr Hollie **blanched**[9]. **Flabbergasted**[10], he stared aghast at the two **bedraggled**[11] boys. The

---

1   **fragrance** *(n)* a pleasant smell. *(s)* scent, perfume, bouquet, aroma, cologne, eau de toilette. *(ant)* stench.

2   **indelible** *(adj)* unable to be forgotten. *(s)* lasting, permanent, enduring, ineradicable. *(ant)* fleeting.

3   **address** *(v)* speak to. *(s)* lecture, talk to, discuss with, make a speech to.

4   **flounce** *(v)* move in an exaggerated manner. *(s)* sweep, prance, sashay, mince, stomp, strut. *(ant)* shuffle.

5   **incompetence** *(n)* inability to do something successfully. *(s)* ineptitude, stupidity, ineffectiveness. *(ant)* ability.

6   **ineffectually** *(adv)* in an ineffectual (unsuccessful) manner. *(s)* incompetently, fruitlessly. *(ant)* effectively.

7   **rebellious** *(adj)* tending to rebel (fight) authority or control. *(s)* defiant, disobedient, unruly. *(ant)* obedient.

8   **have a ball** *(v)* have a great deal of fun. *(s)* enjoy oneself, party, celebrate, make merry.

9   **blanch** *(v)* become white or pale. *(s)* whiten, lighten, grey, blench, bleach, drain, fade. *(ant)* blush, colour.

10   **flabbergasted** *(adj)* greatly surprised. *(s)* stunned, astonished, staggered, flummoxed, stupefied. *(ant)* sedate.

11   **bedraggled** *(adj)* dirty and dishevelled. *(s)* disarranged, messy, unkempt, rumpled. *(ant)* neat, clean.

teacher's mouth opened and closed. His long, **spindly**[1] legs **buckled**[2] like two pieces of spaghetti.

'How did I ever manage to lose these boys as well?' he muttered, trying to **compose himself**[3] and deal with the **renegade**[4] youths. 'Er … yes, they are,' he stuttered, fluttering his hands, trying to get his assistant's attention.

Ever an **extrovert**[5], Miss Malik smiled at him and waved enthusiastically back.

Attempting to cover his **ineptitude**[6], but failing **spectacularly**[7], Hollie twirled in nervous one-footed circles, busying himself by calling out to his students. He stumbled to a clumsy halt at Owain's feet, and Owain looked down at him, straight-faced.

'And you are?' Owain asked the teacher, an **official**[8] edge to his voice.

'Walter Hollie, Chorlton High,' panted the teacher, standing up and sticking out a **feminine**[9] hand.

Owain ignored it and spoke to Hollie. 'These two were **larking**[10] around in the basement. Up to you what you do with them. I wouldn't be too **lenient**[11] though,' he warned.

'No! Er … no, of course not,' Mr Hollie replied, wondering if he'd be **sacked**[12], certain he'd be **demoted**[13], his **reputation**[14] now **tarnished**[15].

Owain thrust the two young attackers towards their teacher. The bruising grip, together with the marks it would leave, conveyed an **unequivocal**[16] threat. As he stepped back from the

---

1   **spindly** *(adj)* tall or long and thin. *(s)* skinny, lanky, gangling, gangly, twiggy, spindling. *(ant)* sturdy, stout.

2   **buckle** *(v)* bend and give way under strain or pressure. *(s)* crumple, collapse, fold, warp. *(ant)* straighten.

3   **compose oneself** *(v)* calm oneself. *(s)* pull oneself together, recover one's composure. *(ant)* fluster, panic.

4   **renegade** *(adj)* rejecting authority and control. *(s)* rebellious, mutinous, traitorous. *(ant)* loyal, obedient.

5   **extrovert** *(adj)* friendly, confident and outgoing. *(s)* sociable, gregarious, uninhibited. *(ant)* introvert.

6   **ineptitude** *(n)* lack of know-how, skill and ability. *(s)* incompetence, incapacity. *(ant)* competence.

7   **spectacularly** *(adv)* in a spectacular (dramatic) way. *(s)* enormously, magnificently. *(ant)* unspectacularly, dully.

8   **official** *(adj)* relating to a position of authority or power. *(s)* authorised, formal, lawful. *(ant)* informal, casual.

9   **feminine** *(adj)* having qualities associated with a woman. *(s)* womanly, womanlike, ladylike. *(ant)* masculine.

10   **lark** *(v)* have fun and mess around. *(s)* joke, prank, cavort, caper, romp, frolic.

11   **lenient** *(adj)* easy-going, not harsh or strict. *(s)* tolerant, gentle, forgiving, moderate, merciful. *(ant)* severe.

12   **sack** *(v)* dismiss from employment (one's job). *(s)* get rid of, kick out, fire, can, discharge. *(ant)* employ, hire.

13   **demote** *(v)* move to a lower rank or position. *(s)* downgrade, relegate, reduce, lower, devalue. *(ant)* promote.

14   **reputation** *(n)* a general opinion of someone. *(s)* character, name, stature, renown, repute, status.

15   **tarnished** *(adj)* less respected or valued. *(s)* sullied, blemished, blotted, soiled, harmed. *(ant)* enhanced.

16   **unequivocal** *(adj)* with or leaving no doubt. *(s)* plain, clear, unmistakable, unambiguous, sure. *(ant)* equivocal.

disgraced[1] boys, a lingering glare reiterated the stark warning he'd given to them both.

Mr Hollie half bowed before the policeman. 'Thank you, thank you, sir. I cannot apologise enough for the behaviour of my pupils,' he stuttered.

He'd noticed nothing of Owain's physical **veiled**[2] threats to the Mal-Instinctive boys, too distracted by **inwardly**[3] **rehearsing**[4] the speech he would be giving to the headmistress in about an hour. She was one tough lady; he'd have to **grovel**[5]. Sweating now and swallowing **copiously**[6], he led the two Mal-Instinctives away, none the wiser as to who, or what, they really were.

From the sidelines, Dave the security guard **lumbered**[7] up to Owain and handed over the decoy boy he'd been holding secure for him.

'Here's the other lad for you,' he informed Owain in an **officious**[8] voice. 'Thank you, Mr Wise,' said Owain. 'Mr Hollie,' beckoned Owain, **detaining**[9] the third Mal-Instinctive by the scruff of his collar.

Mr Hollie swooned.

Without speaking, Owain thrust the boy towards him.

The teacher **promptly**[10] gripped his third **delinquent**[11] pupil by the arm and whisked him away.

Meanwhile, over by the broken glass case, Felicity approached Gwilym.

'Sir, Drane is in the ambulance with the girl and her father. We are about to leave. May I **clarify**[12] which hospital is prepared? The usual?' she asked in discreet tones.

---

1   **disgraced** *(adj)* fallen from favour. *(s)* dishonoured, discredited, tarnished. *(ant)* dignified, honoured.

2   **veiled** *(adj)* partially hidden, disguised or obscured. *(s)* covered, shrouded, masked, cloaked. *(ant)* revealed.

3   **inwardly** *(adv)* in an inward manner. *(s)* internally, secretly, privately, silently. *(ant)* outwardly, openly.

4   **rehearse** *(v)* practise or prepare (sometimes mentally). *(s)* recite, list, review, repeat, iterate. *(ant)* improvise.

5   **grovel** *(v)* act obsequiously (humbly and creepily). *(s)* crawl, beg, plead, cringe, fawn, kowtow. *(ant)* dominate.

6   **copiously** *(adv)* in copious (large) quantities. *(s)* profusely, abundantly, extravagantly. *(ant)* barely.

7   **lumber** *(v)* move in an awkward, heavy and slow way. *(s)* shamble, waddle, trudge, plod, galumph. *(ant)* glide.

8   **officious** *(adj)* overenthusiastic and overly helpful. *(s)* meddlesome, interfering, self-important. *(ant)* subdued.

9   **detain** *(v)* stop from proceeding by holding back. *(s)* hold, delay, restrain, hinder, obstruct. *(ant)* release, free.

10   **promptly** *(adv)* in a prompt (immediate) manner. *(s)* swiftly, rapidly, straight away, hastily. *(ant)* slowly.

11   **delinquent** *(adj)* tending to commit minor (small) crimes. *(s)* lawless, errant, troublesome. *(ant)* dutiful.

12   **clarify** *(v)* make clearer and less confusing. *(s)* simplify, confirm, elucidate, explain, explicate. *(ant)* confuse.

Even in **shapeless**[1] fluorescent work **garments**[2], Felicity's prettiness shone. 'Yes. We'll meet you there, Flic,' replied Gwilym, using her **abbreviated**[3] name.

*

The vast exhibition hall had finally been **evacuated**[4] and the alarms switched off. **Dopey**[5] Dave and blundering Bert had slouched off upstairs and were back to normal, stuffing down popcorn and **guffawing**[6] at a movie. After all, the police were in charge now.

Owain approached a solitary Gwilym, who now stood by the cracked case. 'Sir, I sense your unease and **preoccupation**[7] towards the **fledgling**[8] Instinctive.'

'I hope she is **resourceful**[9].' Gwilym frowned as he spoke to Owain. 'She is faced with such **onerous**[10] **adversity**[11] so soon.'

'She has already begun to prove herself,' replied Owain, touching Gwilym's shoulder. 'You are **weary**[12], my friend.'

'Yes, perhaps I am a little tired,' replied Gwilym as they walked across the hall, approaching Mrs Evans still sitting in the office chair.

'Marjorie, how are you now?'

'I am fine now, sir,' she replied. 'Do we have any word from Robert? Do we know if the Cutter is safe?' As she spoke, her **taut**[13] skin pulled over her **skeletal**[14] cheekbones and ashen face. Her **hollow**[15] voice faltered to a mere croak, barely audible even in the small office.

---

1   **shapeless** *(adj)* having no specific shape. *(s)* formless, unattractive, baggy, loose-fitting. *(ant)* defined, fitting.

2   **garment** *(n)* an item of clothing. *(s)* clothes, outfit, garb, attire, dress, vestment, costume, apparel, raiment.

3   **abbreviated** *(adj)* (of words) shortened. *(s)* reduced, cut, contracted, condensed, truncated. *(ant)* lengthened.

4   **evacuate** *(v)* leave or remove. *(s)* vacate, clear, empty, abandon, void, desert. *(ant)* fill, occupy, enter.

5   **dopey** *(adj)* foolish and idiotic. *(s)* daft, dim-witted, slow, stupid, simple. *(ant)* intelligent, bright, smart.

6   **guffaw** *(v)* laugh heartily and loudly. *(s)* roar, howl, chortle, hoot, cackle. *(ant)* sob, moan, whine.

7   **preoccupation** *(n)* extreme concern. *(s)* engrossment, anxiety, absorption. *(ant)* nonchalance.

8   **fledgling** *(adj)* inexperienced or underdeveloped (still learning). *(s)* emergent, budding, novice. *(ant)* expert.

9   **resourceful** *(adj)* able to overcome difficulties. *(s)* capable, ingenious, quick-witted. *(ant)* unimaginative.

10   **onerous** *(adj)* involving effort or difficulty. *(s)* burdensome, troublesome, arduous, excessive. *(ant)* easy, facile.

11   **adversity** *(n)* an unpleasant or difficult situation. *(s)* hardship, distress, danger, misfortune. *(ant)* advantage.

12   **weary** *(adj)* extremely tired. *(s)* exhausted, fatigued, drained, whacked, shattered. *(ant)* fresh, refreshed.

13   **taut** *(adj)* tense, not relaxed. *(s)* stretched, strained, tight, stressed, worried. *(ant)* slack, relaxed, loose.

14   **skeletal** *(adj)* relating to the skeleton, extremely thin. *(s)* emaciated, gaunt, skinny, wasted. *(ant)* obese.

15   **hollow** *(adj)* empty and expressionless. *(s)* flat, dull, void, muffled, muted, dead, heavy. *(ant)* expressive.

Gwilym watched her; she appeared changed, **sunken**[1] with **fretfulness**[2] and **fatigue**[3].

'Not yet, though no doubt we will soon,' he responded. 'You must rest, Marjorie. Close the museum for a while and wait for him. If he contacts us first, we will let you know,' said Gwilym, encouraging her as he spoke.

'Yes, sir. Of course, you are right,' she **concurred**[4].

Concerned, Gwilym watched her get up and **hobble**[5] away, her gait stiff and laborious, but they must leave her.

'Come, Owain,' beckoned Gwilym. 'We still have work to do.'

As the two knights left the museum, a faint crinkle of an echo followed them, its cheerful, **melodic**[6] notes drifting in waves across the empty hall, akin to wind chimes tinkling in **unison**[7] as if pushed by a **languid**[8] summer breeze. A smell of fresh lilies swirled upwards, once again filling the air with sweet perfume. Then slowly, one by one, every crack, every split, every fissure in the glass case **retraced**[9] its original tracks with **pinpoint**[10] mathematical precision, until there were none.

Case 111 looked exactly as it had that morning.

---

1   **sunken** *(adj)* weakened or diminished. *(s)* haggard, drawn, drooping, sagging. *(ant)* healthy, boosted.

2   **fretfulness** *(n)* the feeling of distress. *(s)* worry, unease, anxiety, apprehension. *(ant)* confidence, unconcern.

3   **fatigue** *(n)* extreme tiredness. *(s)* exhaustion, weariness, lethargy, lassitude, weakness. *(ant)* refreshment.

4   **concur** *(v)* agree with. *(s)* accord, acquiesce, correspond, coincide, accede, consent, assent. *(ant)* disagree.

5   **hobble** *(v)* walk in an awkward way. *(s)* limp, shuffle, falter, shamble, totter, stumble. *(ant)* stride, glide.

6   **melodic** *(adj)* tuneful and pleasant. *(s)* musical, harmonious, agreeable, sweet, dulcet. *(ant)* discordant.

7   **unison** *(n)* harmonious and simultaneous performance. *(s)* chorus, harmony, unity, union. *(ant)* discord.

8   **languid** *(adj)* peaceful and relaxed. *(s)* leisurely, unenergetic, unhurried, lethargic, indolent. *(ant)* vigorous.

9   **retrace** *(v)* go back over, trace back. *(s)* review, redo, repeat, reconstruct, return.

10   **pinpoint** *(adj)* precise and to the best degree. *(s)* exact, accurate, clear-cut, correct, meticulous. *(ant)* vague.

14. Luxury in Defeat

Outside the museum, Claire didn't see the **chauffeur**[1]-driven black Bentley glide past them; she was too busy strapping herself into the front of Jayne's smart four-wheel drive. As her seat belt connected and she glanced outside, she narrowly missed the handsome, stylishly attired man in the back, who scrutinised her through the tinted window. He had **misjudged**[2] her; he wouldn't make that mistake twice.

He rolled a matchstick-sized object in one hand and held an **oblong**[3] metal box in the other. Fascinated, he studied the Cutter between his fingers. Why had it failed him? Why had the glass not succumbed to its targeted blows? What had that **shrewd**[4], **sly**[5] little knight Evans done to it?

Curious, he checked it from all angles, observing its plain yet **bewitching**[6] form. His eyes flashed but his face matched that of stone. Only the rhythmic tapping of his foot, like the swish of a cat's **vexed**[7] tail, hinted at his seething irritation. The Knights Hawk had won this round. A seasoned businessman, he'd lost deals before but always found other ways to win. **Resilience**[8] and, of course, **ruthlessness**[9] were the key to success. He had plenty of both.

Holding the unique object with care, he laid it back in the purpose-built box. He paused,

---

1   **chauffeur** *(n)* a person employed to drive a car. *(s)* driver, operator, cab driver. *(ant)* passenger.

2   **misjudge** *(v)* form a wrong opinion of. *(s)* miscalculate, underestimate, misinterpret. *(ant)* understand.

3   **oblong** *(adj)* rectangular in shape. *(s)* quadrilateral, four-sided.

4   **shrewd** *(adj)* having sharp judgement. *(s)* astute, clever, cunning, crafty, sharp-witted. *(ant)* naive, slow.

5   **sly** *(adj)* deceitful (dishonest) and cunning in nature. *(s)* crafty, wily, devious, evasive, sneaky. *(ant)* honest.

6   **bewitching** *(adj)* enchanting and delighting. *(s)* charming, beguiling, captivating, fascinating. *(ant)* repulsive.

7   **vexed** *(adj)* annoyed. *(s)* displeased, irked, riled, irritated, aggravated, exasperated. *(ant)* pacified, calm.

8   **resilience** *(n)* the ability to recover swiftly from difficulty. *(s)* toughness, hardiness, durability. *(ant)* fragility.

9   **ruthlessness** *(n)* a lack of pity for others. *(s)* callousness, heartlessness, mercilessness. *(ant)* mercy.

before closing the lid and tucking it into the breast pocket of his Savile Row suit.

His long, manicured nail tapped on the opaque glass that separated him from the front. His tap turned the screen **transparent**[1], revealing his female driver. Catching her eye in the rear-view mirror, he nodded once, then tapped the screen again, returning it to **privacy**[2] mode, then **reclined**[3] into the **decadent**[4] **opulence**[5] of **plush**[6] cream leather. He directed his eyes up towards the **extravagant**[7] vehicle's leather-trimmed roof and **gesticulated**[8] his hand in a dismissive wave. A screen made from ultra-thin graphene glided down, halting at eye level. **Columns**[9] of rapid figures flickered, shifting from red to green then back to red again. His intelligent eyes scanned the ever-changing columns of numbers. He absorbed the fast-changing digits, computing each meaningful and **consequential**[10] detail with ease. He swiped at the air with his finger, flipping the view. More rows flickered in different **time zones**[11]; his gaze followed the **erratic**[12] changes of this morning's **financial**[13] markets. Satisfied, he gestured again, and the graphene screen retracted.

It would be a long journey, time to **ponder**[14] his next move. He signalled into the air again. The **rapturous**[15] piano notes of Rachmaninoff's Concerto Number Two in C **Minor**[16] **filtered**[17]

---

1   **transparent** *(adj)* can be seen through. *(s)* see-through, clear, translucent. *(ant)* opaque, blocked, cloudy, dark.

2   **privacy** *(n)* a state where one is private (unseen or alone). *(s)* seclusion, isolation, solitude. *(ant)* public.

3   **recline** *(v)* lean or lie back with one's back supported. *(s)* relax, repose, lounge, loll, rest, sprawl. *(ant)* stand.

4   **decadent** *(adj)* luxurious and self-indulgent (spoiling oneself). *(s)* hedonistic, deluxe. *(ant)* restrained.

5   **opulence** *(n)* great wealth or luxury. *(s)* lavishness, affluence, prosperity. *(ant)* poverty, simplicity.

6   **plush** *(adj)* expensive and luxurious. *(s)* deluxe, lavish, posh, swanky, swish, lush. *(ant)* spartan, cheap.

7   **extravagant** *(adj)* highly or overly priced. *(s)* profligate, excessive, exorbitant, big-budget, costly. *(ant)* cheap.

8   **gesticulate** *(v)* use gestures (movements) to communicate. *(s)* wave, signal, motion, indicate.

9   **column** *(n)* vertical arrangement. *(s)* list, line, string, procession, file. *(ant)* row.

10   **consequential** *(adj)* having a consequence (importance or relevance). *(s)* significant. *(ant)* inconsequential.

11   **time zone** *(n)* a geographical area where a common standard time is used.

12   **erratic** *(adj)* not regular or even. *(s)* abnormal, irregular, bizarre, unpredictable, inconsistent. *(ant)* consistent.

13   **financial** *(adj)* relating to finance (money management). *(s)* commercial, fiscal, economic.

14   **ponder** *(v)* think carefully about. *(s)* consider, contemplate, deliberate, muse, cogitate, reflect. *(ant)* disregard.

15   **rapturous** *(adj)* causing rapture (intense pleasure). *(s)* ecstatic, joyful, blissful, divine. *(ant)* depressing.

16   **minor** *(adj)* a musical term indicating a key or mode based on a minor scale. *(ant)* major.

17   **filter** *(v)* slowly enter. *(s)* trickle, flow, seep, permeate, ooze. *(ant)* flood, pour.

with **unobtrusive**[1] clarity into the Bentley's **ostentatious**[2] back seat. The sound quality **sublime**[3] and **orchestral**[4].

Goosebumps prickled his arms. Rarely affected by emotions, he was moved by this music. He **unwound**[5], resting his head back and inhaling the fine-smelling leather of his **exorbitant**[6] yet tasteful **customised**[7] car. *I must allow more **leisure**[8] time,* he **reprimanded**[9] himself. *Perhaps a **yacht**[10],* he thought.

He lifted a heavy glass up towards the light, inspecting the rising **amber**[11] bubbles. He popped his minute **thermometer**[12] into the top of his champagne **flute**[13]. The digital reader displayed the **extortionate**[14] **beverage's**[15] exact temperature.

Obsessive[16] attention to detail was one of his key **attributes**[17]; he prided himself on precision and accuracy – some may have even called him **eccentric**[18]. Smiling, he loosened his tie and savoured a **liberal**[19] sip of perfectly chilled **vintage**[20] champagne. Uninterrupted and absorbing the divine music, he quashed his anger, closed his eyes and enjoyed the luxurious ride home.

---

1   **unobtrusive** *(adj)* not intruding or attracting attention. *(s)* inconspicuous, tasteful, discreet. *(ant)* obtrusive.

2   **ostentatious** *(adj)* designed to impress. *(s)* showy, flashy, flamboyant, grandiose, extravagant. *(ant)* modest.

3   **sublime** *(adj)* of great beauty or excellence. *(s)* moving, uplifting, superb, heavenly. *(ant)* inferior, poor.

4   **orchestral** *(adj)* relating to (like) an orchestra. *(s)* symphonic, instrumental, classical, musical.

5   **unwind** *(v)* relax and de-stress. *(s)* rest, repose, quieten, recline, wind down, chill out, laze. *(ant)* tense, stress.

6   **exorbitant** *(adj)* unreasonably or very highly priced. *(s)* extortionate, excessive. *(ant)* cheap, reasonable.

7   **customise** *(v)* modify (change) to suit specific tastes or needs. *(s)* personalise, tailor. *(ant)* generalise.

8   **leisure** *(n)* free time for enjoyment. *(s)* freedom, holiday, rest, ease, relaxation. *(ant)* work, labour.

9   **reprimand** *(v)* address disapproval to (tell off). *(s)* rebuke, chastise, scold, reproach, chide. *(ant)* praise.

10   **yacht** *(n)* a medium to large boat. *(s)* pleasure boat, cruiser, sailing boat.

11   **amber** *(adj)* a honey-yellow colour (like amber resin). *(s)* golden, ochre, tawny.

12   **thermometer** *(n)* an instrument for measuring and indicating temperature. *(s)* temperature gauge.

13   **flute** *(n)* a narrow and tall wine glass.

14   **extortionate** *(adj)* very or too high in price. *(s)* exorbitant, inflated, outrageous, extravagant. *(ant)* reasonable.

15   **beverage** *(n)* any drink, but not usually water unless it is bottled. *(s)* libation, potable, potation.

16   **obsessive** *(adj)* tending to obsess (think, talk or do continually). *(s)* fanatical, compulsive. *(ant)* moderate.

17   **attribute** *(n)* a feature or quality seen as a characteristic. *(s)* trait, element, aspect, part, quirk, feature, mark.

18   **eccentric** *(adj)* unconventional (unusual) and slightly odd. *(s)* peculiar, abnormal, bizarre. *(ant)* conventional.

19   **liberal** *(adj)* generous. *(s)* ample, considerable, substantial, large, abundant, copious. *(ant)* measly.

20   **vintage** *(adj)* from the past and high quality. *(s)* prime, select, first-rate, first class. *(ant)* inferior.

15. Sticking to the Story

Unaware the Master's Bentley had just glided past her window, Claire, sighing with exhaustion and relief, melted into the **sumptuous**[1] front passenger seat of Jayne's car.

The spacious **interior**[2] smelled of leather and Jayne's **arresting**[3] yet irresistible perfume. **Gadgets**[4] to do this, switches to do that. Heated seats and a talking computer that phoned people if you asked it to. Claire was used to squashing into her mum's battered old **banger**[5] – and that was when it started.

What's my mum going to say about school? she thought as reality shattered her reverie.

Her mum drove her mad sometimes, yet Claire realised how tough juggling three kids and a full-time job must be as a single parent. Despite how different her mum was from Jayne, she appreciated how she kept things **afloat**[6], and she knew for sure her mum would never leave them. Dee's own childhood had been **dire**[7], and she had always **vowed**[8] not to repeat the same mistakes, no matter how dreadful things got for her.

'How are you feeling, darling?' asked Jayne, keeping her eyes on the road.

'Worried about Mum – she's gonna flip. I know she can be a bit of an **airhead**[9], but she's so

---

1   **sumptuous** *(adj)* splendid and expensive-looking. *(s)* luxurious, lavish, plush, extravagant, grand. *(ant)* meagre.

2   **interior** *(n)* the inner part of something. *(s)* inside. *(ant)* exterior, outside.

3   **arresting** *(adj)* attracting attention. *(s)* attractive, fascinating, bewitching, engaging. *(ant)* repellent.

4   **gadget** *(n)* a small and clever mechanical or electronic device or tool. *(s)* implement, thingamajig, widget.

5   **banger** *(n)* an old car or vehicle in poor condition. *(s)* heap, jalopy, wreck, rattletrap, beater. *(ant)* new car.

6   **afloat** *(adj)* out of difficulty or debt (owing money). *(s)* above water, stable, solvent, steady. *(ant)* insolvent.

7   **dire** *(adj)* of an extremely bad quality. *(s)* terrible, dreadful, calamitous, disastrous, appalling. *(ant)* wonderful.

8   **vow** *(v)* make a solemn (serious) promise. *(s)* swear, affirm, assure, guarantee, assert, pledge.

9   **airhead** *(n)* a silly or dreamy person. *(s)* dreamer, idealist, birdbrain, ninny, space cadet. *(ant)* realist.

against us missing school she'll freak,' answered Claire.

'I'm sure she won't,' replied Jayne. 'Not when she realises why you did it, and not when she hears what you *actually* did. You're a **bona fide**[1] heroine, my darling.' Jayne glanced over, smiling.

Claire blushed, brushing off the **compliment**[2], although she had no idea what *bona fide* meant. Her confidence from earlier had all but seeped away – it all felt such a **fantasy**[3]. She knew it was a complete **cliché**[4], yet it did feel like a dream. But it *had* happened; she had even made some of it happen. Miles away, she caught Jayne examining her.

'What happened to you and Rebecca today?' asked Jayne, turning her head back to the road. 'You gave your dad such a shock.'

'I know,' replied Claire. 'I'm scared of what he's gonna say too,' she added. 'Will you have a word with him for me, please?' she begged, blinking at Jayne with puppy-dog eyes.

'Of course,' replied Jayne, flicking on the **indicator**[5]. 'I'm sure he'll show you **mercy**[6],' she laughed. 'You can tell me what happened today. I won't be **judgemental**[7].'

Claire longed to tell Jayne everything; she trusted her, but she also remembered Gwilym's face when he'd stopped her from telling Jayne at the museum. His attitude had struck her as odd, one she'd struggled to read. She'd decided there and then to discuss today only with members of the Knights Hawk, but she wondered if she'd ever see Gwilym and Owain again or whether Gladys was back at home with Jack and Thomas. But how could she keep this from Ben? It would be so difficult – yet she'd have to.

'So, what happened?' asked Jayne again, encouraging Claire to talk, but then the phone rang. Her dad's number flashed up on the screen.

'It's Dad!' squealed Claire. 'Can I talk to him on your hands-free?' she asked.

'Of course,' answered Jayne.

'Claire, it's Dad here. Are you OK, love?' he asked, sounding strained.

---

1   **bona fide** *(adj)* real and genuine. *(s)* true, actual, authentic, legitimate, valid, official. *(ant)* bogus, artificial.

2   **compliment** *(n)* an expression of praise or admiration. *(s)* tribute, accolade, approval, kudos. *(ant)* criticism.

3   **fantasy** *(n)* an idea or thing not based on reality. *(s)* dream, illusion, imagination, fiction. *(ant)* reality.

4   **cliché** *(n)* an expression used by many people. *(s)* banality, saying, stereotype. *(ant)* originality, novelty.

5   **indicator** *(n)* a flashing vehicle light that indicates (shows) manoeuvres (movements). *(s)* blinker, signal.

6   **mercy** *(n)* forgiveness and compassion. *(s)* clemency, leniency, pity, sympathy, tolerance. *(ant)* cruelty.

7   **judgemental** *(adj)* overly critical (disapproving). *(s)* fault-finding, negative. *(ant)* uncritical.

'Yeah, I'm fine, Dad. I'm really, really sorry for not going to school. You're not too mad, are you?' she blurted.

'Mad? No! I'm just glad you're both OK,' he replied. 'And anyway, you missed school to go to a history museum, Claire,' he laughed. 'Don't EVER do it again though,' he added.

'Phew! Sorry, Dad. Honestly, I am,' she said **sincerely**[1].

Vince's voice lifted. 'Jayne?'

'Yes, darling?'

'Dee's at home, **distraught**[2]. Could you drop Claire there, please? Rebecca's going to be fine; she'll need lots of fluid and rest. There is some **justice**[3] though – the police have arrested that **revolting**[4] boy Drane.'

'Yes, of course, no problem,' replied Jayne. 'I'll drop her off; then I'll message you.'

'Great. See you in a bit, then.'

'Bye, Dad,' Claire shouted.

*

They were almost home; Chorlton wasn't far from town, though the rush hour commuters **congested**[5] the roads into an irritating **gridlock**[6]. Claire peered through the window, finding some **solace**[7] in Drane's arrest, and trying to make sense of the day. Too tired and hungry to think **coherently**[8], she tipped her head back against the headrest and closed her eyes.

'Penny for those thoughts?' Jayne asked, nudging Claire's arm as they sat in traffic.

'I'm thinking of school on Monday,' she answered. 'I hope they don't **expel**[9] me.' Horrified at the thought, she turned an anguished face towards Jayne.

---

1   **sincerely** *(adv)* in a sincere (true and heartfelt) or genuine way. *(s)* honestly, earnestly. *(ant)* insincerely.

2   **distraught** *(adj)* extremely worried and upset. *(s)* distressed, hysterical, fraught, desperate. *(ant)* calm, serene.

3   **justice** *(n)* fair treatment or behaviour. *(s)* integrity, impartiality, rightness, justness. *(ant)* injustice, unfairness.

4   **revolting** *(adj)* causing disgust. *(s)* sickening, repellent, repulsive, nauseating. *(ant)* delightful, enchanting.

5   **congest** *(v)* obstruct or block. *(s)* jam, clog, halt, choke, overcrowd, overfill. *(ant)* free, clear, unblock.

6   **gridlock** *(n)* severe (bad) traffic congestion. *(s)* stoppage, deadlock, bottleneck, snarl, tailback.

7   **solace** *(n)* comfort in a bad situation. *(s)* condolence, consolation, support, relief, help. *(ant)* aggravation.

8   **coherently** *(adv)* in a coherent (logical) manner. *(s)* rationally, reasonably, lucidly, clearly. *(ant)* incoherently.

9   **expel** *(v)* officially ask to leave school permanently. *(s)* exclude, remove, eject, oust, banish. *(ant)* include.

'Of course they won't. You're hardly a **serial**[1] **offender**[2], and it's a history museum, not a nightclub. Still, I guess you're **liable**[3] to be in some trouble,' she added, throwing Claire a **rueful**[4] glance.

In truth, Claire wasn't concerned about school; it **paled**[5] into insignificance right now. That image of Gwilym turning emerald and shattering as that woman plucked the gem from the gold dominated her thoughts.

I must see Gladys, she thought. *My mum's bound to ground me tonight, but I hope she lets me out this weekend*, she worried, not convinced she would.

'Pretty much home now,' said Jayne as they turned onto Barlow Moor Road. 'Not going to spill the beans about today, then?' she asked Claire with a grin.

'It's nothing really. That rat-boy Josh Drane wouldn't let go of Becca, so I **clouted**[6] him,' Claire replied, being **economical**[7] with the truth.

'Wow, Claire, that was brave, but a bit risky. What if he'd hurt you? You won't do that again, will you?' she said with a serious shake of her head.

'No,' replied Claire. 'I acted without thinking.' *It's a half-truth*, she thought guiltily, grimacing at the queues of traffic gassing the air.

She thought of how she'd escaped the boy in the woods and kicked Drane so accurately. She'd not heard anyone else's thoughts since being outside the office, and now she wasn't sure she ever had. But what if these were her talents that Gwilym had **alluded**[8] to? What if she could actually do those things again? Even though everything had dimmed into a hazy blur, she held on to that thought as hard as she could. Besides, even if she could tell Jayne the real story, Jayne would think she was bonkers.

'Course I won't do it again,' Claire reiterated, her eyes angled downwards, looking at her twiddling fingers, which she had crossed as she spoke. She'd never been the best liar.

---

1   **serial** *(adj)* repeatedly following the same behaviour. *(s)* repeat, persistent, regular, ongoing. *(ant)* one-time.

2   **offender** *(n)* a person or thing that does something wrong. *(s)* culprit, delinquent, wrongdoer. *(ant)* hero.

3   **liable** *(adj)* likely to be or do something. *(s)* bound, predisposed, prone, inclined, susceptible. *(ant)* unlikely.

4   **rueful** *(adj)* showing regret or sorrow, especially in an ironic or humorous way. *(ant)* unrepentant.

5   **pale** *(v)* seem or become less important. *(s)* diminish, fade, lessen, reduce. *(ant)* intensify, worsen, deepen.

6   **clout** *(v)* hit hard with the hand or an object. *(s)* smack, thump, slap, cuff, wallop, beat, whack.

7   **economical** *(adj)* using or giving no more than is necessary. *(s)* sparing, careful, frugal. *(ant)* lavish, careless.

8   **allude** *(v)* call attention to indirectly, suggest. *(s)* hint at, imply, indicate, insinuate. *(ant)* announce, elucidate.

They drove into Beech Road, and Claire felt sick in anticipation. Her mum would flip! Rain began to pelt down onto the roof as they indicated to pull in and stopped outside Claire's house, Jayne's **automatic**[1] **ignition**[2] switching off.

'Maybe tell me all about it on Sunday after the theatre. If you feel up to it.'

'That's if my mum still lets me go,' Claire said, flat and **despondent**[3].

'Of course she will; I'll tell your dad what to say to her, and hopefully, there'll be no **veto**[4],' said Jayne, leaning over and patting Claire's arm.

Reassured, Claire went to leave the car. 'Noooo! I left my school bag at the museum. I'm gonna be in even more trouble now.' She plonked her head into her hands, feeling **wretched**[5]. 'I'm such an idiot!'

'Go on, Claire, your mum's at the door. We'll sort your bag; don't fret. Go on.' And with a gentle tap of her arm, she nudged Claire to leave the car.

Claire didn't dare hug Jayne goodbye in case Dee saw from the doorway.

'Go!' Jayne mouthed, grinning as her car sprang back into life.

Dreading the inevitable, Claire pushed open the heavy door. As she jumped down into a puddle, she **baulked**[6] at the sight of a white-faced Dee. She braced herself.

'I'm sorry, Mum. Honestly, I am. I won't do it again, I promise, not ever.'

Dee yanked Claire towards her and gave her such a crushing hug the air squeezed out of her lungs with a grunt. Dee didn't let go. **Taken aback**[7] as Dee squished harder, Claire winced, waiting for the **tirade**[8] to hit – only it didn't. Astounded at Dee's reaction, she squeezed her mum back.

'Has Princess Jayne and her pricey perfume driven off yet? I can smell it,' Dee whispered into the back of Claire's neck.

'Yes, Mum,' replied Claire, looking over her mum's wet shoulder, 'she's gone.'

---

1   **automatic** *(adj)* working by itself. *(s)* self-regulating, self-executing, computerised, programmed. *(ant)* manual.

2   **ignition** *(n)* a mechanism or electronics that activate a car engine. *(s)* starter.

3   **despondent** *(adj)* feeling low from loss of hope. *(s)* downcast, crestfallen, discouraged. *(ant)* hopeful.

4   **veto** *(n)* a ban. *(s)* rejection, embargo, refusal, sanction, quashing, prevention. *(ant)* approval, permission.

5   **wretched** *(adj)* extremely unhappy or unfortunate. *(s)* miserable, desolate, dejected, abject. *(ant)* happy.

6   **baulk** *(v)* hesitate or be unwilling. *(s)* recoil, resist, refuse, cringe, flinch. *(ant)* proceed, accept, advance.

7   **take aback** *(v)* surprise or shock. *(s)* confuse, startle, astonish, throw off. *(ant)* reassure.

8   **tirade** *(n)* a lengthy, angry speech, criticism or accusation. *(s)* outburst, rant, diatribe, harangue. *(ant)* praise.

'What the heck were you thinking?' her mum asked in her irritated but not-quite-angry voice. 'I've been worried sick all day,' said Dee before Claire could speak. 'School phoned and said you hadn't come in; you didn't call for Ben; no one could find you. I thought something terrible had happened to you!' she said, beginning to shout now and squeezing Claire even harder. 'And this business with Becca. What's that all about?' Dee hadn't stopped to take a breath yet.

'I'm not sure, Mum,' fibbed Claire. 'Dad will have to fill you in. He's with Becs now, and the police, I think.'

Drenched[1], she followed her mum into the house, which looked untidy, as usual. Pete perched on the edge of the couch, headphones hiding his ears. His body swayed, flinching at the **sporadic**[2] **blood-curdling**[3] screams coming from the TV. He was busy on his Xbox, dodging and vaporising the aliens invading the giant screen.

'Turn that rubbish off!' ordered Dee, yanking his headphones off. 'Come and see your sister; she's home!' she shouted at Pete.

'No need to shout, Mum,' he replied, pointing at his ears. 'My headphones are in your hand,' he added with an **insolent**[4] sarcasm.

Dee whacked him playfully with them.

'Hiya, Pete.' Claire **sidled**[5] into the lounge, a **sheepish**[6] look on her face.

'Well, get you, Eclair-Girl. **Kudos**[7]. Who's the big hero, then?' he teased.

'Don't call her Eclair,' shouted Dee. 'Leave her be; she's not a bloomin' cake.'

Claire raised an eyebrow at her mum sticking up for her.

'Some security bloke posted a clip of someone **decking**[8] a lad who looks just like Josh Drane, and I reckon that someone is you, sis.' Pete wagged a finger in Claire's face, but his eyebrows were raised in admiration.

---

1   **drench** *(v)* wet thoroughly. *(s)* soak, saturate, drown, douse, flood, deluge. *(ant)* dry, parch.

2   **sporadic** *(adj)* occurring irregularly. *(s)* occasional, periodic, intermittent, erratic, random. *(ant)* regular, even.

3   **blood-curdling** *(adj)* expressing or causing terror. *(s)* frightening, chilling, fearsome. *(ant)* comforting.

4   **insolent** *(adj)* rude and lacking respect. *(s)* cheeky, brazen, disrespectful, impudent. *(ant)* respectful.

5   **sidle** *(v)* walk in a furtive (secretive) or timid (shy) manner. *(s)* sneak, creep, slink, slip, edge. *(ant)* stride.

6   **sheepish** *(adj)* embarrassed from shame. *(s)* uncomfortable, hangdog, awkward, guilty. *(ant)* unashamed.

7   **kudos** *(n)* compliments or congratulations. *(s)* respect, praise, credit, prestige, cachet. *(ant)* infamy.

8   **deck** *(v)* knock to the ground with a strike. *(s)* floor, punch, thump, hit.

'What?' Panic choked her. 'Let me see it!' she shouted, grabbing at the phone he **brandished**[1] before her.

'Hang on, speedy.' He held his phone above his head and pushed her away.

'Is it you?' Dee's **quizzical**[2] eyes narrowed at Claire, a hint of pride sneaking across her face.

'Give it here! Let me see it!' shouted Claire, managing to snatch the phone.

Her heart hammered as she pressed play. Thankfully, no sound accompanied the clip. A vague shot of a chunky girl running towards an **adolescent**[3] boy played out; then the screen blanked out before coming back to life to show the boy lying flat on the floor.

'It's you, isn't it?' Pete's eyes were **alight**[4] with astonishment and admiration. 'It is you!' he said again. 'She'd deny it otherwise, Mum. Our Claire's too honest – it's defo her.'

Claire wasn't listening; she'd crashed down onto the couch in a state of utter relief. The clip had **broadcast**[5] nothing significant.

'Is it you, love?' Dee asked, sitting down beside her. 'Did you do that to that boy?'

Claire didn't answer. She stared stubbornly up at the ceiling, **contemplating**[6] the entire crazy day.

'Claire?' Dee nudged her. 'Is it you in the clip?'

'Might be,' she answered defensively, her eyes now aimed at her feet.

'See, I told you it's her. I told you.' Pete jumped around the lounge, shouting and pointing at Claire.

'Jeez, Claire, you'll be the talk of Chorlton,' he joked.

'What happened, love?' asked Dee, moving closer. 'What did he do to you?'

Here goes, Claire thought, squirming inside.

'I don't know exactly, Mum. I was looking at the exhibits in the main hall, and I saw him. He had hold of Becca, dragging her. She looked terrible, Mum; something was so wrong. He wouldn't leave her.' Claire stalled, not wanting to upset her mum any more than she needed to.

---

1   **brandish** *(v)* wave as a threat or in excitement. *(s)* flourish, shake, wield, flash, display, flaunt. *(ant)* conceal.

2   **quizzical** *(adj)* puzzled or amused. *(s)* questioning, curious, enquiring, sceptical. *(ant)* certain, uninterested.

3   **adolescent** *(adj)* developing from a child into an adult. *(s)* teenage, pubescent, juvenile. *(ant)* baby, adult.

4   **alight** *(adj)* shining brightly. *(s)* lit, sparkling, aglow, burning, blazing, ablaze, flaming. *(ant)* dark, dull, dim.

5   **broadcast** *(v)* transmit content. *(s)* circulate, publish, air, show, screen, spread, announce. *(ant)* suppress.

6   **contemplate** *(v)* think about. *(s)* ponder, consider, deliberate, reflect on, ruminate on. *(ant)* disregard.

'Go on, love,' said Dee. 'It's OK.'

'I asked him a few times to leave her alone, nicely at first,' she fibbed, 'but he laughed at me, so I whacked him. I must have caught him exactly right,' she added as an **afterthought**[1].

Dee and Pete gawped at her, open-mouthed. Nobody uttered a word.

If only you knew what really happened, thought Claire.

'What!' Pete shrieked, breaking the silence. 'My kid sister sorting out Josh Drane! You are gonna be, like, soooo famous around here,' he boasted, proud of her. 'Respect,' he added, flicking his fingers.

'OK, enough now!' said Dee to Pete. 'Claire, I'm so proud of you sticking up for Becca like that, I really am, BUT … you can't just go around hitting people, and what's worse is he could have killed you. I can't **abide**[2] that boy, and I've told Becs hundreds of times to keep away from him,' she said **vociferously**[3]. 'Maybe she'll learn her lesson now.'

'Yeah, Mum, I know.' Claire looked at the floor again. 'I don't know what came over me, really. He was hurting her; he shook her so hard I saw red. I flipped.'

'Come here, you daft thing.' Dee held her daughter close just as the doorbell rang.

'That'll be your dad.' Suddenly **jittery**[4], Dee rearranged her damp hair in the mirror, **dabbing**[5] at her cheeks. With a strained smile on her face, she went over and opened the door.

'Rebecca!' she cried, ignoring Claire's dad, who was **virtually**[6] propping up their daughter. 'What in God's name happened to you?' She grabbed Rebecca's arm to help Vince bring her in. Rebecca wavered, her walk unsteady and weak. Between them they laid her down on the couch.

'Mum,' Rebecca said, bursting into tears.

Claire felt so sorry for her. Rebecca looked **crestfallen**[7] and vulnerable. The spider-

---

1   **afterthought** *(n)* something that is thought of or added later. *(s)* addition, second thought. *(ant)* forethought.

2   **abide** *(v)* tolerate or endure (deal or put up with). *(s)* bear, stand, take, stomach, accept. *(ant)* ban, reject.

3   **vociferously** *(adv)* in a vociferous (loud and forceful) manner. *(s)* vocally, noisily, stridently. *(ant)* quietly.

4   **jittery** *(adj)* nervous and unable to relax. *(s)* edgy, anxious, jumpy, frazzled, skittish, fidgety. *(ant)* calm, still.

5   **dab** *(v)* repeatedly press lightly against something. *(s)* touch, pat, daub, blot, stroke.

6   **virtually** *(adv)* almost. *(s)* nearly, effectively, practically, essentially, fundamentally. *(ant)* entirely, actually.

7   **crestfallen** *(adj)* sad, disappointed, low in confidence. *(s)* downcast, despondent, disconsolate. *(ant)* upbeat.

lashes were **smeared**[1] into black **tendrils**[2] of **mascara**[3]; her hair was **matted**[4], her clothes **dishevelled**[5]; and her discarded, **scuffed**[6] heels dangled from Vince's hand.

'What on earth happened to you?' said Dee.

'I can't remember, Mum,' said Rebecca in a small voice. 'One minute I'm in the cinema at the museum; the next thing I remember is seeing Claire and then waking up in hospital with Dad. That's all I can remember,' she blubbed.

'The police reckon Drane drugged her,' said Vince angrily. '**Allegedly**[7], he's been selling the stuff at school, so they've arrested him. The head had better kick him out now,' he added.

'I'm sorry, Mum … and Dad,' Rebecca said between sobs. 'I swear I didn't take any drugs. I had no idea; I wouldn't ever do that.'

'I know, love,' Dee sighed. 'You're daft, but not that flippin' daft.' She had always drummed into her kids that drugs were not worth the risk, not ever.

'Mum, can I have a drink, please?' asked a **subdued**[8] Rebecca.

'Get her a drink, Vince,' Dee snapped.

'OK! Course,' Vince replied, jumping to it. 'Anyone else?'

'Yes, please, Dad,' said Claire. 'Water for me, thanks.'

Rebecca tried to sit up, but still too **woozy**[9], she **withered**[10] back down on the couch.

'Claire,' Rebecca managed to mutter, 'what did you do to Josh? What was he doing? Why did he give me that stuff?' she asked, **perplexed**[11].

Unable to offer any **plausible**[12] answer, too unsure of what to say, Claire shrugged.

Dee stroked Rebecca's hair. 'Our Claire flattened that bully,' said Dee, answering for her. 'And

---

1   **smeared** *(adj)* spread or coated over something. *(s)* wiped, rubbed, streaked, smudged.

2   **tendril** *(n)* something resembling (like) a tendril (slim, curly branch of a plant). *(s)* strand, finger, thread.

3   **mascara** *(n)* a cosmetic for darkening or thickening eyelashes.

4   **matted** *(adj)* tangled into a thick mess. *(s)* knotted, entangled, intertwined, snarled. *(ant)* disentangled.

5   **dishevelled** *(adj)* (hair or clothes) made untidy. *(s)* mussed, tousled, ruffled, unsettled. *(ant)* tidy, groomed.

6   **scuffed** *(adj)* marked by scraping against something. *(s)* shabby, scratched, damaged, abraded. *(ant)* polished.

7   **allegedly** *(adv)* according to claims without proof. *(s)* supposedly, purportedly. *(ant)* evidently.

8   **subdued** *(adj)* quietened, overcome or controlled. *(s)* subjugated, suppressed, humbled. *(ant)* encouraged.

9   **woozy** *(adj)* unsteady, dazed or dizzy. *(s)* light-headed, faint, groggy, nauseous. *(ant)* clear-headed, lucid.

10   **wither** *(v)* decline or weaken. *(s)* deflate, wilt, shrink, droop, fade, shrivel. *(ant)* rise, bloom, thrive.

11   **perplexed** *(adj)* completely confused. *(s)* baffled, confounded, foxed, flummoxed, bemused. *(ant)* enlightened.

12   **plausible** *(adj)* seeming probable (likely) or reasonable (sensible). *(s)* believable, feasible. *(ant)* implausible.

I've told her off for it too,' she added, realising she was **condoning**[1] violence.

'Thanks, Dad.' Claire smiled up at her father and took her drink.

Rebecca sipped hers, then handed it back to Vince.

'Thanks, Claire,' said Rebecca earnestly. 'I mean it. Thanks.'

She tried to smile, but her head **lolled**[2] to one side, and in what seemed like one second, she fell asleep.

Vince's phone chimed. Fidgeting and looking uncomfortable, he glanced at the message. 'I'd best be off now. Are we still OK to have Claire on Sunday as arranged?' he asked his estranged wife.

'I suppose so,' Dee said grudgingly, yet she sounded grateful to have Claire home.

'Does that mean I can still go with Ben to his contest tomorrow?'

'Don't push it, young lady,' her mum warned.

But Claire could tell by Dee's face she'd be able to go.

'Thanks, Mum,' she squealed, planting a kiss on her cheek.

'Right, then.' Vince cleared his throat, stood up and brushed his palms down his thighs in a final, awkward gesture.

Her mum didn't move; uncomfortable seconds lingered, the same way they always did when her dad was saying goodbye.

Poor Mum, thought Claire. Her dad was going back to Jayne, and her mum would be here, lonely. Her dad's **career**[3] had prospered since meeting Jayne, and he looked more handsome, well dressed and confident these days.

'See you on Sunday, Claire. Let me know how Becs gets on, would you, please, Dee?' Vince walked towards the door.

'Yes,' said Dee. 'Claire will be all ready and waiting in her Sunday best for you,' she added with a biting, **sardonic**[4] ring to her voice. She yanked the door open as he said, 'Bye,' then slammed it

---

1   **condone** (*v*) accept behaviour that is considered wrong. (*s*) allow, disregard, overlook, excuse. (*ant*) punish.

2   **loll** (*v*) hang loosely or droop. (*s*) dangle, flop, sag, dip, drop, slump. (*ant*) lift, rise.

3   **career** (*n*) a long-term occupation (job). (*s*) profession, vocation, employment. (*ant*) unemployment.

4   **sardonic** (*adj*) cynical (bitter) or mocking. (*s*) scornful, ironic, sarcastic, derisive, scathing. (*ant*) sincere, kind.

closed behind him. **Diplomacy**[1] had never been her **strong suit**[2].

Claire watched as her **dejected**[3] mum walked back into the lounge. Dee wore little make-up, and her damp blonde hair fell onto her shoulders. Her casual jeans and T-shirt flattered her boyish shape. Claire adored this look, young and natural; her mum didn't need all the **garish**[4] make-up she'd taken to wearing since her dad had left. Her mum was **inherently**[5] pretty, but Claire could see the lines creasing her eyes and the telltale dark shadows underneath. They **confessed**[6] a different truth, one of fragility and sorrow.

'Mum, I'm so sorry if I worried you.'

'Don't be daft,' replied Dee with a brave smile. 'I'm so happy you're here now. What do you want for your tea?' she asked, heading towards the kitchen.

⋆

Nothing changes overnight, thought Claire half an hour later, chewing on an overcooked, almost-**inedible**[7] piece of chicken. Still, she was grateful to be home. Rebecca was still fast asleep on the couch, snoring, and no doubt Pete had gone out to tell all his mates of his sister's triumph – he wouldn't be able to keep his mouth shut.

'Muuuuum?' Claire asked.

'What?' replied Dee, suspicious of Claire's tone.

'Can I go out to Ben's for a bit? It is Friday night,' she asked as casually as she could, pushing her luck to the limit now.

Dee didn't answer; she drummed her fingers on the table.

'Mmmm …' Dee teased, **prolonging**[8] Claire's agony. 'You can,' she answered, 'BUT … take Becca's phone with you and be back in an hour, no more. Do you hear me, young lady? One hour, then you're back.'

'Thanks, Mum,' squealed Claire, springing up and flinging her arms around Dee's neck.

---

1 **diplomacy** *(n)* the ability to deal with people in a polite way. *(s)* tact, sensitivity, discretion. *(ant)* tactlessness.

2 **strong suit** *(n)* a person's strong point. *(s)* forte, metier, strength, speciality, asset. *(ant)* weakness, flaw.

3 **dejected** *(adj)* made sad. *(s)* dispirited, disheartened, discouraged, demoralised, depressed, saddened. *(ant)* elated.

4 **garish** *(adj)* showy and bright. *(s)* brash, loud, brassy, gaudy, overbright, lurid, tasteless. *(ant)* tasteful, stylish.

5 **inherently** *(adv)* in an inherent (born with) way. *(s)* naturally, genetically, innately. *(ant)* superficially.

6 **confess** *(v)* admit or make known. *(s)* tell, reveal, divulge, disclose, assert, affirm. *(ant)* deny, hide, conceal.

7 **inedible** *(adj)* not suitable or fit for eating. *(s)* unpalatable, tasteless, unappetising, disgusting. *(ant)* edible.

8 **prolong** *(v)* cause to continue or last longer. *(s)* extend, lengthen, protract, elongate, persist. *(ant)* curtail.

'Help me clear up first though,' Dee **bargained**[1].

'Of course I will,' Claire chirped, scooping up the dirty plates and putting them into the sink. She grabbed the packet of bread from the table and opened the bread bin. The lonely fossil of a doughnut was still there, now showing early signs of a blue mould.

She laughed to herself as she hooked the doughnut out of the bread bin and threw it into the bin. She grabbed her coat and Rebecca's phone, and shouted, 'Bye, Mum. See you in a bit.' Slamming the door shut behind her, she sprinted straight to Gladys's house.

---

1   **bargain** *(v)* negotiate (discuss) to get what one wants. *(s)* haggle, barter, trade, broker, compromise.

16. Finding Gladys

Red-faced and sweating, Claire contemplated Gladys's closed curtains. Doubled over, nursing a painful **stitch**[1], she was panting hard, resting her hands on her burning thighs for support. She'd sprinted past Ben's, hoping she wouldn't be spotted.

Gladys's house looked exactly as Claire had left it that morning. Knocking on the front door, she thought it was unlikely Gladys would be home if she'd been in Anglesey only a few hours earlier. She crossed her fingers, chewed her lip and waited in hope for Jack's usual greeting. None came. **Deflated**[2], she knocked again.

Maybe they're in the backyard, she thought.

Pressing her nose to the window, she peeked through a gap in the curtains, but there was no sign of life. She concluded Gladys really wasn't at home.

Desperate to speak to someone, she toyed with going to Ben's, then decided against it. What could she tell him? She didn't want to lie to him either. She'd sleep on it and meet him in the morning, as they'd arranged yesterday.

Despondently she walked back towards the shops and decided to have a **snoop**[3] of Rebecca's phone. **Anecdotes**[4] about Becca and Drane were already circulating on **social media**[5]; none of it was the truth, all of it **overblown**[6], exaggerated **hearsay**[7]. She tutted and switched the phone off,

---

1   **stitch** *(n)* a sharp pain in a person's side when exercising. *(s)* twinge, pang, spasm.

2   **deflate** *(v)* suddenly lose confidence. *(s)* dispirit, subdue, dismay, disappoint. *(ant)* boost.

3   **snoop** *(n)* a secret investigation. *(s)* nose, poke, ferret, intrusion, search.

4   **anecdote** *(n)* a short amusing or interesting story. *(s)* tale, narrative, sketch, yarn, hearsay.

5   **social media** *(n)* websites and applications for people to share content and engage in social networking.

6   **overblown** *(adj)* made to seem more important or impressive. *(s)* exaggerated, overstated. *(ant)* understated.

7   **hearsay** *(n)* information received that cannot be verified (proved). *(s)* rumour, gossip, tittle-tattle. *(ant)* fact.

carrying on past the **trendy**[1] cafes and bars, up past the newsagent's and then the chippy.

It was early Friday evening now, and already busy. Outside the pub, workmen held **frothy**[2] pints, debating football. Further along, friends chatted **gregariously**[3] at tables, laughing as they sipped wine and ate **tapas**[4].

Crossing the road, she passed the **bustling**[5] playground. Dogs yapped outside the railings, and carefree children kicked their legs high on the swings, their **joyous**[6] chuckles accentuating her sudden feeling of loneliness. Seeing the dogs made her pine for Jack's **wiry**[7] white face and his soft black-and-tan ears. One of the dogs was barking so loudly Claire stopped and investigated the playground; everything seemed fine, just a kid digging in the sand. As the dog's barking increased, she checked the playground again but realised the sound was coming from behind her. Turning around, she walked back a few metres towards the road and the newsagent's. There, further down the street, tugging on his lead, pulled a determined Jack. He was barking incessantly, yapping and yanking poor Gladys towards the park – he'd seen Claire.

'Gladys! Gladys!' she shouted, **bombing**[8] across the side street, narrowly missing a passing car. 'Gladys, wait!'

Claire ran towards Gladys, flinging herself at her and Jack in turn. 'Why's Jack on the lead?' panted Claire. 'You never use a lead.'

'Slow down, Claire – you nearly got yourself run over,' Gladys said, ticking her off. 'He's found a liking for his lead after you took him out on it. Forever bringing it to me in his teeth. He's a cheeky lad; drops it at my feet every five minutes. That's why we're here, on an **errand**[9] to buy my **lottery**[10] ticket,' she laughed, looking down at Jack.

'Oh, Gladys, I'm so glad to see you. I've got to be home soon. Can I come around to yours for

---

1   **trendy** *(adj)* up to date or fashionable. *(s)* modish, popular, contemporary, hip, cool, chic. *(ant)* unfashionable.

2   **frothy** *(adj)* covered with a mass of bubbles. *(s)* bubbly, foamy, effervescent, gassy, fizzy. *(ant)* still, flat.

3   **gregariously** *(adv)* in a gregarious (sociable, friendly) manner. *(s)* convivially, openly, extrovertly. *(ant)* shyly.

4   **tapas** *(n)* small Spanish savoury dishes or snacks.

5   **bustling** *(adj)* (of a place) full of people and activity. *(s)* busy, vibrant, hectic, lively. *(ant)* deserted, empty.

6   **joyous** *(adj)* full of joy and happiness. *(s)* jolly, exuberant, merry, delighted, elated, cheery, blissful. *(ant)* sad.

7   **wiry** *(adj)* resembling wire in texture or form. *(s)* coarse, rough, bristly, scratchy. *(ant)* soft, sleek, smooth.

8   **bomb** *(v)* run extremely quickly. *(s)* leg it, sprint, bolt, hotfoot, tear, shoot. *(ant)* dawdle, saunter, amble.

9   **errand** *(n)* a short journey undertaken to do a job. *(s)* chore, task, mission, favour, assignment.

10   **lottery** *(n)* a competition to raise money by selling tickets and then drawing one at random for a prize. *(s)* raffle.

a bit to talk, please?' Claire asked, dancing about on the spot, anxious for her to agree.

'Of course. Come on, I'll put the kettle on.' And at that, the three of them trotted off.

Five minutes later they were in Gladys's **hospitable**[1] kitchen. Wherever Gladys was, there was sure to be tea.

Claire stroked Jack's velvety ear between her fingers. The soft **texture**[2] was such a contrast to the rest of his bristly coat. She thought of Lady, the pony; she was convinced she could still smell the faint horsey scent lingering on her hands. The memories seemed from long ago, not earlier on that day. It all sounded so **ludicrous**[3], so unreal, that she felt awkward **broaching**[4] the subject with Gladys. She fiddled with her finger, poking it through a hole in the tablecloth.

'Gladys, can I ask you a bit of a funny question?'

'Of course, Claire. What is it?'

'Why would a Knight Hawk buy a lottery ticket?' she asked in all seriousness.

Chuckling, Gladys put down the teapot and rubbed her hands on her apron. 'You are funny,' she answered, sitting down. 'The lottery money helps **fund**[5] the museum where you've spent most of today,' she laughed. 'We knights must pay our way.'

'Ahhh, I get it,' Claire nodded as Gladys **pottered**[6] about.

Gladys put two mugs on the table and sat back down.

'Where's Thomas?' asked Claire, looking around.

'We're not sure at the moment,' Gladys replied.

'What do you mean, not sure?' Claire frowned.

Gladys, Jack and Thomas were inseparable. Why didn't she know where Thomas was, and why wasn't she worried about him?

Gladys poured the steaming tea into the mugs and added milk from a blue-and-white jug, its pattern identical to the **crockery**[7] she'd seen on the dresser in Wales.

---

1   **hospitable** *(adj)* welcoming and friendly. *(s)* congenial, sociable, cordial, warm, open, kind. *(ant)* inhospitable.

2   **texture** *(n)* the way something feels or looks. *(s)* touch, structure, consistency, appearance, character.

3   **ludicrous** *(adj)* so foolish, stupid or unreasonable as to be amusing. *(s)* absurd, farcical, comical. *(ant)* sensible.

4   **broach** *(v)* raise a difficult subject for discussion. *(s)* propose, approach, introduce, mention, open. *(ant)* close.

5   **fund** *(v)* provide with money. *(s)* pay for, subsidise, sponsor, finance, support, maintain. *(ant)* withdraw.

6   **potter** *(v)* move around in an unhurried way. *(s)* tinker, fiddle, amble, saunter, shuffle. *(ant)* hurry.

7   **crockery** *(n)* earthenware utensils (articles) for eating, drinking and serving from. *(s)* tableware.

'When I got home, he had gone,' she said.

'But is he OK?' asked Claire, splashing her tea onto the table.

'Yes, we're sure he's fine, cariad. He is **self-sufficient**[1] and will be gathering valuable information for us. Cats are excellent at **surveillance**[2].'

'Surveillance?' asked Claire quizzically.

'Yes. Cats make **superb**[3] spies,' said Gladys, calmly stirring her tea.

'Spies, wow,' laughed Claire. 'Old Thomas is a spy? Amazing!' she said, thrilled. 'Thomas Bond!' she giggled.

'Yes, he is – a spy, that is,' said Gladys. 'When he has relevant information for the Knights Hawk, he will return.'

Gladys curled her **papery**[4] hands around her mug and blew a gentle **ripple**[5] across the tea's surface.

'Do you have any idea who he's spying on?' asked Claire.

Gladys paused. 'He's **tracking**[6] the Cutter,' she eventually answered. 'Wherever the Cutter is, Thomas will be also.'

'So he's at the museum, then?' asked Claire.

'No, Claire, Thomas won't be at the museum; the Cutter is no longer there.'

'Really?' Claire sat up, shocked. 'The bracelet *is* safe, isn't it?' She fidgeted in her seat, fear rising at the thought of the scene she'd witnessed in the gem.

'The bracelet is safe; however, half of the Cutter is gone.'

'What do you mean, half? Where's it gone?' asked Claire.

'The Master only **obtained**[7] half of the Cutter, the other half is safe with us, in Robert Evans's keeping.'

'You mean the creepy curator guy from the museum who was on the train today?' Claire flinched, regretting what she said the moment the words left her mouth.

---

1   **self-sufficient** *(adj)* needing no help. *(s)* independent, self-reliant, autonomous. *(ant)* dependent, needy.

2   **surveillance** *(n)* close observation (watching). *(s)* investigation, scrutiny, reconnaissance. *(ant)* inobservance.

3   **superb** *(adj)* excellent. *(s)* supreme, outstanding, superlative, magnificent, first-rate. *(ant)* abysmal.

4   **papery** *(adj)* dry and thin. *(s)* delicate, wrinkled, fragile, frail, paperlike. *(ant)* tough, sturdy, robust.

5   **ripple** *(n)* a small wave or series of waves on a surface. *(s)* wavelet, undulation, wrinkle.

6   **track** *(v)* follow the movements or trail of. *(s)* pursue, shadow, stalk, trace, trail, locate. *(ant)* lead, guide.

7   **obtain** *(v)* acquire, get or secure something. *(s)* find, attain, achieve, take, procure, gain, capture. *(ant)* lose.

Gladys fell silent, a **pensive**[1] look on her face.

Claire cringed again, mortified at her **rude**[2] comment. She mentally **scolded**[3] herself; Evans was a Knight Hawk, after all. However, if she was being honest, she didn't like the way he made her feel. The ensuing painful silence from Gladys proved ample punishment for her lack of tact.

'Did you say Robert Evans was on the train with you earlier?' Gladys eventually asked in a quiet voice.

'Yes, he was. After seeing him today when we arrived through that awful tunnel, I assumed you or Gwilym had sent him,' answered Claire, relieved that Gladys hadn't told her off for her comment, or, being **diplomatic**[4], had seemingly **sidestepped**[5] it.

'So there are two bits to the Cutter, then?' continued Claire, trying to fill the awkward silence.

'Yes. The Knights Hawk sealed the Gwalch Gem bracelet in the case. The glass is impenetrable unless both parts of the Cutter are used to open it. Two tiny, identical arrows. Alone they are useless; together they are all-powerful. Today Dewi discovered more to the gem's security than he realised.'

Claire massaged Jack's ear again. 'So if Dewi has half of the Cutter, Mr Evans has the other?' asked Claire.

'Yes, Robert Evans has it. Today at the museum, Evans recognised Drane's **accomplished**[6] Mal-Instinctive power and knew the Master was close. Evans acted without hesitation to save the Gwalch Gem bracelet.'

'Accomplished? Rat-Boy Drane? He can't be that great if I managed to beat him.'

'Maybe it says more about you than you realise,' Gladys replied.

Claire felt a huge rush of pride and couldn't disguise her grin at the thought of what she'd done. 'Where's Mr Evans now, then?'

Gladys hesitated. 'We're not **entirely**[7] certain.'

---

1   **pensive** *(adj)* thoughtful. *(s)* reflective, contemplative, preoccupied, meditative. *(ant)* thoughtless.

2   **rude** *(adj)* bad-mannered or impolite. *(s)* cheeky, insolent, audacious, offensive, discourteous. *(ant)* polite.

3   **scold** *(v)* tell someone off angrily. *(s)* reprimand, berate, rebuke, admonish, chastise. *(ant)* praise, commend.

4   **diplomatic** *(adj)* showing tact (diplomacy) and sensitivity (feeling). *(s)* tactful, politic, discreet. *(ant)* tactless.

5   **sidestep** *(v)* avoid discussing or dealing with. *(s)* dodge, evade, circumvent, elude, skirt, bypass. *(ant)* confront.

6   **accomplished** *(adj)* highly trained or skilled. *(s)* expert, proficient, consummate, adept. *(ant)* incompetent.

7   **entirely** *(adv)* to a full extent or degree. *(s)* utterly, completely, absolutely, totally, wholly. *(ant)* partially.

'What do you mean, you're not certain? You're *never* not certain about anything, Gladys!'

Gladys got up and took a cloth from the sink and mopped the tea splashes from the worn **vinyl**[1] tablecloth.

'There are far-reaching tunnels that run from the edges of the museum's basement and beyond. They are most complicated, intertwining and **unforgiving**[2]. No Mal-Instinctive knows them as well as they would like. They are **primarily**[3] Evans's work, and he **traverses**[4] them better than any other knight.'

'Gosh,' said Claire. Maybe she *had* underestimated Evans.

'Evans escaped with one arrow before Dewi reached him. He left the other for Dewi to find, to throw him off the trail. Dewi thought he had the whole Cutter until it failed to break through the glass, but we are still waiting to hear from Evans,' she finished.

'Is that unusual?' asked Claire. 'Should you have heard from him by now?'

'Possibly, although not necessarily.'

'Why *was* he on the train with me this morning?' Claire asked, but Gladys didn't answer.

'I suspect you are wondering what happens now, cariad.'

'Yes,' Claire blurted. 'Yes, I am.'

Gladys smiled a weary smile and said, 'You have no **obligation**[5] to us; everything you pursue is your choice, and always has been.'

'Yes,' Claire mouthed in a half whisper. 'Yes, I suppose it is,' she finished, expecting her future would prove more complicated than she'd anticipated.

'It's getting late. You mustn't put your mum through any more **heartache**[6]; she has suffered enough for one day.'

'Gosh, yes. Is that the time?' She plopped Jack down from her lap and kissed his head. 'See you Monday, **buddy**[7].'

---

1   **vinyl** *(n)* a man-made substance often used for covering materials and turntable records. *(s)* plastic.

2   **unforgiving** *(adj)* (of a place) difficult, harsh or hostile. *(s)* hard, demanding, taxing, challenging. *(ant)* easy.

3   **primarily** *(adv)* for the most part. *(s)* mainly, mostly, essentially, principally, predominantly. *(ant)* barely.

4   **traverse** *(v)* move through or across. *(s)* negotiate, navigate, criss-cross, cross, cover.

5   **obligation** *(n)* the act of being bound (forced) into a promise. *(s)* commitment, requirement, duty. *(ant)* option.

6   **heartache** *(n)* emotional pain. *(s)* agony, anguish, grief, distress, despair, despondency, affliction. *(ant)* joy.

7   **buddy** *(n)* a good friend. *(s)* chum, pal, mate, companion, partner, sidekick, comrade, confidant. *(ant)* enemy.

Standing to leave, she fastened her coat and stuck her hands into her pockets, swaying from foot to foot.

'Gladys?'

'Yes, cariad? What is it?'

'Today's been so crazy for me, unreal, but something else has felt wrong.'

'What has felt wrong, Claire?'

'Well, the day seems longer somehow. In a way, it feels like it's taken forever.'

Gladys smiled, **mulling**[1] over what Claire had said.

'Yes, I suppose it has felt strange to you. You're not used to it, as we are.'

'Not used to what?' Claire's round face crinkled.

Gladys smiled. 'We tangled time for you,' declared Gladys.

'You did *what*?' Claire asked, stunned.

'We tangled time for you,' Gladys said, allowing her words to sink in.

'What do you mean, tangled time? I thought the Gwalch Gem bracelet was the only thing that could change time,' asked Claire.

'We have other means. Although time-tangling does come at a cost, today it was necessary. We could not have achieved all we did without it.'

Claire **recalled**[2] the day: the journeys, how long they had taken, the lack of people along the way.

'So that's why no one was around when I woke up, why Ben had gone and there was no traffic. Is that why my clock didn't work?' She didn't wait to let Gladys answer.

'Yes, Claire, that's more or less right. We had to confuse the Mal-Instinctives and needed more time than we had, so we tangled time to change that.'

'Wow! Tangled time.' Claire blew out a long, low whistle – impressed. 'You knights can change time without the bracelet.'

Gladys nodded.

'How do you do that?' asked Claire.

But Gladys just smiled and tapped Claire's shoulder.

---

1 **mull** (*v*) think about. (*s*) ponder, consider, contemplate, deliberate, muse, reflect, ruminate. (*ant*) disregard.

2 **recall** (*v*) bring something back into one's mind. (*s*) remember, recollect, reminisce. (*ant*) repress, forget.

'Come on now, your mum will be worried. Although you don't always see it, she tries her utmost for you children, and you should head home to her now. Jack and I will still be here on Monday.'

'And Thomas?' added Claire.

'Yes, and perhaps Thomas too,' Gladys answered, dropping her gaze.

'Will I ever see Gwilym again? And Owain and Anwen?' said Claire, tears filling her eyes.

'I'm sure you will, Claire. This is the beginning of your Instinct journey.'

Gladys curled a soothing arm around Claire's shoulder and steered her towards the door.

Claire swooped Jack up one more time and kissed his nose; he licked hers in return. 'Yuck! Doggy breath,' she joked, plonking him down.

She hugged Gladys on the doorstep, and tears didn't fail her. 'I've done this a lot today,' she sniffled, wiping them away on her **mucky**[1] sleeve. 'Are you OK, Gladys? You look worried about something,' Claire asked.

'I'm fine; it's been a long, long day, as you now know,' said Gladys, winking at Claire.

'See you on Monday with Ben, I suppose, then.' Claire sniffed, not entirely convinced she believed Gladys, who she now knew could keep things from her.

'Yes, cariad, see you on Monday.' Gladys waved as Claire walked down the short path.

Claire glanced back, waved, then left, closing the creaky metal gate to head home.

'Claire! Claire!'

Claire spun around, worried by Gladys's tone. Gladys stood at her front door, pointing upwards.

'What is it?' asked Claire, striding back to her.

But Gladys didn't answer; she just stared **skywards**[2].

Claire turned towards what looked like a speck hanging high up in the sky. Screwing up her eyes, she strained to see what it was, but couldn't make it out. Gladys persisted, pointing to the dot growing in the sky. Blinking, Claire realised that in the distance, but rapidly nearing them, was a helicopter. It flew towards them until it was almost above them; then it lowered

---

1 **mucky** *(adj)* covered with muck (dirt or filth). *(s)* grubby, grimy, messy, soiled, unclean, grotty. *(ant)* clean.

2 **skywards** *(adv)* in the direction of the sky. *(s)* upwards, heavenwards, aloft, overhead. *(ant)* downwards.

altitude[1] to a steady hover, **suspended**[2] above the green.

A moment later a strong surge turned the **responsive**[3] blades faster, and the aircraft did a full three-hundred-and-sixty-degree pirouette, dropped its nose and bowed before them. Then, in a graceful **manoeuvre**[4], the yellow helicopter **banked**[5] and flew away, Gwilym at the controls.

Claire, who had been waving madly, smiled as it disappeared into the distance.

'How do you knights have access to RAF helicopters and jets?' asked Claire.

Gladys smiled. 'The Sea King and Hawk T1 are **decommissioned**[6] aircraft. The RAF doesn't use them any more, so we do. We have resourceful friends. Now, Claire, *go home* and get some well-earned rest.'

'But, Gladys, there's something else I meant to ask you, something I saw, something about the gem,' said Claire anxiously.

'No more questions now, Claire,' replied Gladys. 'Your mum will be waiting.'

'But, Gladys,' persisted Claire.

'Your mum, cariad; it's late.'

Claire knew she'd pushed her mum far enough for one day, and if she **overstepped the mark**[6] now, she'd never let her go to Ben's competition in the morning.

'You're right, Gladys. I'll see you on Monday.'

And with that, she headed home.

---

1   **altitude** *(n)* the height of something relating to sea or ground level. *(s)* elevation, highness.

2   **suspend** *(v)* hang from or over something. *(s)* swing, dangle.

3   **responsive** *(adj)* reacting speedily. *(s)* active, reactive, receptive. *(ant)* sluggish, unresponsive.

4   **manoeuvre** *(n)* one or several movements requiring care and skill. *(s)* action, procedure, exercise.

5   **bank** *(v)* tilt to make a turn. *(s)* lean, slant, incline, cant, pitch, veer, slope. *(ant)* right, level out.

6   **decommission** *(v)* withdraw (remove) from service. *(s)* mothball, retire, discharge. *(ant)* introduce, activate.

6   **overstep the mark** *(v)* go beyond what is allowed. *(s)* transgress, exceed, violate.

17. How Evans Tangled Time Alone

Whilst Claire slept at home, more truth to the story unfolded deep in the underground tunnels.

Busy foraging for food in the damp black recess, beetles, bugs and insects scurried about their daily **duties**[1]. A **swollen**[2] cocoa-brown **cockroach**[3] **deposited**[4] her precious eggs in the peaceful, moist crevice she had **fortuitously**[5] discovered in the nook behind the man's knees. This unusual **incubator**[6] had lain still long enough to present her with the ideal **hatching**[7] place for her egg case, although she didn't realise her eggs would never quite reach the forty-something days required for **maturation**[8].

Like a full-term **babe**[9] **cocooned**[10] in its mother's **womb**[11], Robert Evans lay still, curled up in the soggy soil, bent knees pulled up close, locked to his chest, small, **petulant**[12] fists tucked away in angry balls above them. His bony, bare feet protruded from shredded trousers, and a scant,

---

1 **duty** *(n)* an action required as part of one's job. *(s)* task, chore, assignment, function, obligation, responsibility.

2 **swollen** *(adj)* enlarged. *(s)* bloated, expanded, increased. *(ant)* contracted, compressed.

3 **cockroach** *(n)* a beetle-like insect with long antennae and legs. *(s)* roach, bug, creepy-crawly.

4 **deposit** *(v)* lay or put down. *(s)* deliver, set, leave, place, consign, store, stow, drop. *(ant)* withdraw, remove.

5 **fortuitously** *(adv)* in a fortuitous (by chance) way. *(s)* luckily, serendipitously, accidentally. *(ant)* intentionally.

6 **incubator** *(n)* a warm space for hatching eggs or keeping small babies warm. *(s)* hatchery, brooder, nursery.

7 **hatching** *(n)* (of an egg) the act of opening to produce a young animal. *(s)* emergence, incubation, brooding.

8 **maturation** *(n)* the process of maturing (growing). *(s)* development, evolution, growth. *(ant)* retrogression.

9 **babe** *(n)* a baby. *(s)* newborn, infant, tot, child. *(ant)* elder, adult.

10 **cocoon** *(v)* envelop (wrap in) in a protective or comforting way. *(s)* surround, swathe, cosset. *(ant)* expose.

11 **womb** *(n)* the organ where a baby develops. *(s)* uterus, belly.

12 **petulant** *(adj)* sulky and ill-tempered. *(s)* crabby, fractious, irritable, peevish, cantankerous. *(ant)* affable, nice.

ragged[1] shirt partially exposed the **sullied**[2] dirty-white skin on his arms. A neat black beaver-cloth **waistcoat**[3], **intact**[4] and still buttoned, had endured the ordeal. **Prim**[5] and **incongruous**,[6] it **swaddled**[7] his upper **torso**[8] as if he were **aptly**[9] dressed for a morning at church.

Silent and still, he appeared at peace. Sleeping, perhaps. However, this **refuge**[10] offered little **nurturing**[11]. No such loving, **matriarchal**[12] comfort blanket existed here.

How long he had **languished**[13] there, dormant, was difficult to **gauge**[14]. How **injurious**[15] his unpreventable sacrifice would be was not yet apparent, because earlier today this **diminutive**[16] man had surpassed all other Knights Hawk; he had tangled time alone. **Eclipsing**[17] all others, he had reached the **pinnacle**[18] of his **existence**[19] and changed the landscape permanently. Robert Evans hoped his heroic deed would go down in history for **millennia**[20] to come, for in his fist, he still clutched the tiny arrow. One half of the precious Cutter, which he had snatched from the fairy figurine whilst attempting his one desperate hope of escaping his sinister **pursuer**[21] – Dewi, the Master.

---

1   **ragged** *(adj)* unkempt, torn or old. *(s)* tattered, ripped, frayed, shabby, raggedy, tatty, untidy, dirty. *(ant)* neat.

2   **sullied** *(adj)* dirty or polluted. *(s)* soiled, stained, contaminated, foul, discoloured. *(ant)* clean, washed.

3   **waistcoat** *(n)* a sleeveless garment typically worn under a suit. *(s)* gilet, vest.

4   **intact** *(adj)* not impaired or damaged. *(s)* complete, whole, unbroken, unharmed. *(ant)* broken.

5   **prim** *(adj)* disapproval of anything improper. *(s)* formal, tidy, stuffy, prissy, fussy, moralistic. *(ant)* informal.

6   **incongruous** *(adj)* unusual or out of keeping in some way. *(s)* odd, inappropriate. *(ant)* appropriate.

7   **swaddle** *(v)* wrap in something. *(s)* bundle, envelop, enfold, bandage, sheathe, shroud, cloak. *(ant)* unwrap.

8   **torso** *(n)* the trunk (body without head or limbs) of a human. *(s)* upper body.

9   **aptly** *(adv)* in an apt (suitable) manner. *(s)* appropriately, fittingly, pertinently. *(ant)* inappropriately.

10   **refuge** *(n)* a safe place. *(s)* shelter, sanctuary, security, protection, asylum, harbour, retreat, haven. *(ant)* hazard.

11   **nurturing** *(n)* protection and care whilst growing. *(s)* rearing, support, encouragement, raising. *(ant)* neglect.

12   **matriarchal** *(adj)* relating to powerful female roles. *(s)* motherly, maternal, maternalistic. *(ant)* patriarchal.

13   **languish** *(v)* be forced to remain in a poor situation. *(s)* suffer, rot, decay, moulder, decline. *(ant)* thrive.

14   **gauge** *(v)* measure or estimate the amount of. *(s)* judge, assess, evaluate, determine, calculate.

15   **injurious** *(adj)* causing damage. *(s)* harmful, hurtful, detrimental, distressing, adverse. *(ant)* beneficial.

16   **diminutive** *(adj)* small or unusually small. *(s)* little, tiny, petite, undersized, wee. *(ant)* immense, gargantuan.

17   **eclipse** *(v)* surpass or deprive of power or importance. *(s)* outshine, overshadow, outdo, exceed. *(ant)* lose to.

18   **pinnacle** *(n)* the highest or most successful point. *(s)* highpoint, peak, acme, zenith. *(ant)* bottom, nadir.

19   **existence** *(n)* time alive. *(s)* life, being, presence, survival, actuality. *(ant)* non-existence.

20   **millennium** *(n)* a period of one thousand years (plural: *millennia*).

21   **pursuer** *(n)* something or someone that pursues (chases) another. *(s)* follower, stalker, hunter. *(ant)* prey.

After many hours of **fleeing**[1] through his web of underground tunnels, the **sheer**[2] effort of it all had taken its **toll**[3]. Evans now lay confused and exhausted in a **queer**[4] state of live **rigor mortis**[5]. His rigid fingers would require **severing**[6] to release their contents. Even in this hushed **fetal**[7] form, he would rather die than **relinquish**[8] what would deliver greatness to him once again.

Now, in the depths of the **dingy**[9] tunnels, **ailing**[10] and **paralysed**[11] with cold, his chaotic mind flooded with the **harrowing**[12] images of what had happened to him just hours before. Shivering **feverishly**[13], remembering the intense terror of escaping the Master, **degraded**[14] to the **status**[15] of a hunted animal, he now relived every step of his escape in minute detail.

*

He tried his utmost to outrun Dewi in the basement, but the Master's athleticism easily surpassed that of Evans. Even though Evans took the most direct route to the Cutter, the Master came **gravely**[16] *close.*

Never had Evans been required to run through the basement passages, but today he moved as fast as his short, unfit legs could carry him. Petrified, he realised Dewi's strength had grown throughout the years, and somehow Dewi had become aware of the basement's layout. Evans had disastrously **underrated**[17] *his pursuer.*

---

1 **flee** *(v)* run away. *(s)* depart, escape, vanish, abscond, bolt, fly, leave. *(ant)* linger, remain.

2 **sheer** *(adj)* unrestricted. *(s)* pure, utter, absolute, total, downright, outright, unmitigated. *(ant)* restricted.

3 **toll** *(n)* the adverse (unfavourable) effect of something. *(s)* harm, damage, detriment, injury. *(ant)* benefit.

4 **queer** *(adj)* strange or odd. *(s)* funny, weird, curious, peculiar, bizarre, outlandish. *(ant)* normal.

5 **rigor mortis** *(n)* the temporary stiffening of the body after death.

6 **sever** *(v)* cut off. *(s)* remove, amputate, separate, detach, chop off, cleave. *(ant)* unite, attach, combine, join.

7 **fetal** *(adj)* denoting posture typical of a fetus (developing offspring, baby). *(s)* curled. *(ant)* straight.

8 **relinquish** *(v)* give up. *(s)* abandon, hand over, cede, surrender, quit, yield. *(ant)* keep, retain, hold, acquire.

9 **dingy** *(adj)* drab and gloomy. *(s)* dismal, sombre, dark, grim, dirty, murky, soiled, cheerless. *(ant)* bright, clean.

10 **ailing** *(adj)* in poor health. *(s)* sickly, poorly, weak, infirm, indisposed, feeble, frail. *(ant)* well, healthy, fit.

11 **paralysed** *(adj)* partly or wholly incapable (unable) of movement. *(s)* disabled, incapacitated. *(ant)* mobilised.

12 **harrowing** *(adj)* distressing. *(s)* disturbing, shocking, troubling, traumatic, devastating. *(ant)* comforting.

13 **feverishly** *(adv)* in a feverish (hot or nervous) manner. *(s)* agitatedly, anxiously, nervously. *(ant)* calmly.

14 **degrade** *(v)* reduce to a lower rank. *(s)* relegate, devalue, demote, downgrade. *(ant)* elevate, promote.

15 **status** *(n)* social or professional standing. *(s)* situation, condition, position, class, grade, level.

16 **gravely** *(adv)* in a grave (serious) way. *(s)* dangerously, critically, profoundly, fatefully, acutely. *(ant)* trivially.

17 **underrate** *(v)* underestimate (misjudge) something. *(s)* undervalue, miscalculate, devalue. *(ant)* overrate.

The basement was dimly lit, but Evans didn't need light; he could navigate it **blindfolded**[1]. *With sweat soaking his coarse* **woollen**[2] *suit, and the temperature soaring as the Master's dark energy neared, he stooped to where the walls met the dusty floor, fishing around until he found what he needed. He curled his hand around a chunky* **cable**[3], *and with one quick, hard pull, he plunged his surroundings into* **medieval**[4] *darkness. Stumbling back up and breaking into his fastest run, he hoped the darkness would buy him the precious seconds required to succeed.*

Scuttling towards the side room that held both halves of the Cutter, his feet skidded through the basement passages. He realised he would not outrun the Master and stopped. Aware the Knights Hawk had tangled time once today to help the girl, he knew risking it a second time would, in itself, be **perilous**[5], *but attempting this feat alone could kill him. Until today, tangling time* **unaided**[6] *remained* **unattempted**[7], *and therefore* **untested**[8].

Hyperventilating[9], *he* **delved**[10] *into the* **sodden**[11] *left pocket of his waistcoat. At the end of a fine chain, his fingers found the item they* **sought**[12]. *Attached to a length of* **interwoven**[13] *links lay a* **circular**[14] *object. Although less than five centimetres in diameter and one centimetre thick, the weight of it hinted at its worth, its expert* **casting**[15] *in solid Welsh gold. In the middle, surrounded by intricate* **engravings**[16], *sat a dull round stone.*

Not all knights carried this exotic piece, this **faceless**[17] *pocket watch that did not tell the time, but*

---

1 **blindfolded** *(adj)* deprived of (denied) sight by tying a blindfold around the head. *(s)* masked. *(ant)* unmasked.

2 **woollen** *(adj)* made of or containing wool. *(s)* woolly, woven, warm.

3 **cable** *(n)* insulated (covered) wire that transmits electricity. *(s)* lead, cord, flex.

4 **medieval** *(adj)* of or relating to the Middle Ages. *(s)* old, early, feudal, Gothic, primitive. *(ant)* current, modern.

5 **perilous** *(adj)* full of extreme risk or danger. *(s)* unsafe, hazardous, treacherous, precarious, chancy. *(ant)* safe.

6 **unaided** *(adj)* without help. *(s)* alone, solo, single-handed, unaccompanied, unassisted. *(ant)* assisted, aided.

7 **unattempted** *(adj)* not tried or tested. *(s)* untested, untried. *(ant)* attempted, established, done.

8 **untested** *(adj)* not subjected to examination or trial. *(s)* experimental, untried, unproven, new. *(ant)* tested.

9 **hyperventilate** *(v)* breathe rapidly in an anxious or excited way. *(s)* overbreathe, pant, gasp. *(ant)* suffocate.

10 **delve** *(v)* reach inside something and search. *(s)* rummage, dig, root, rootle, scrabble, fish. *(ant)* withdraw.

11 **sodden** *(adj)* soaked through with liquid. *(s)* saturated, soaking, sopping, drenched, wringing. *(ant)* dry.

12 **seek** *(v)* try to find (past tense: *sought*). *(s)* look for, hunt for, search for, pursue. *(ant)* lose.

13 **interwoven** *(adj)* woven together. *(s)* intertwined, entwined, linked. *(ant)* unwoven, separate.

14 **circular** *(adj)* like a circle in shape. *(s)* round, rounded, disc-like, discoid.

15 **casting** *(n)* the act of shaping (typically metal) by pouring into a mould while molten (melted). *(s)* forming.

16 **engraving** *(n)* a design cut into a hard surface. *(s)* inscription, scoring, etching, scratch.

17 **faceless** *(adj)* having no face. *(s)* plain, featureless. *(ant)* faced.

altered it. Just as the Cutter was fashioned from a fragment of the Gwalch Gem, so had the Time-Tanglers been crafted.

Holding the piece, Evans feared his **impending**[1] *forfeit*[2], because when a knight tangled time, part of their hard-earned Instinct was lost forever. Changing time alone posed a terrifying unknown.

With all hope of **eluding**[3] the Master gone, Evans knew he must try, or face losing control of the Cutter, and with it his chance of achieving greatness once more.

Swaying, **awash**[4] with the waves of adrenaline surging to keep him upright, he struggled to hold the Time-Tangler steady in the flat of his left palm. Needing to **apply**[5] an exact touch, he placed his right thumb onto the matt stone. His digit rotated, moving in precise anticlockwise circles. With tentative touches, he gradually increased minuscule amounts of pressure and speed.

Buffing and polishing the rock, he worked swiftly until his skin burned. From where he stood, Evans could see the side room that contained the Cutter, but all would end here if he was unable to tangle time now. Dewi would inevitably discover both halves of the Cutter.

As his own **depreciating**[6] energy **leached**[7] from him into the **passive**[8] stone, his sacrifice had already begun, the **extent**[9] of which he would later discover.

Without warning, the stone within the Time-Tangler sprang to life. Random shards of spiny crystals shot in all directions, slicing his skin. Yet he was beyond sensation as the once-**innocuous**[10] **entity**[11] transformed into a gleaming, dangerous jewel. The **razored**[12] points and **flawless**[13], **reflective**[14] surfaces glinted from the centre of this magnificent artefact.

---

1   **impending** *(adj)* about to happen. *(s)* imminent, looming, approaching, threatening, brewing. *(ant)* receding.

2   **forfeit** *(n)* something lost or given up because of something else. *(s)* sacrifice, loss, penalty. *(ant)* award, gain.

3   **elude** *(v)* avoid or escape. *(s)* evade, dodge, flee, circumvent, foil, outrun, thwart. *(ant)* embrace, pursue.

4   **awash** *(adj)* flooded or covered with. *(s)* oversupplied, swamped, inundated, overflowing. *(ant)* dry, deficient.

5   **apply** *(v)* use or exert. *(s)* employ, administer, handle, execute, exercise, utilise, implement.

6   **depreciate** *(v)* decrease over time. *(s)* decline, diminish, dwindle, reduce. *(ant)* appreciate, increase.

7   **leach** *(v)* drain or pass through slowly. *(s)* empty, leak, trickle, seep, filter, discharge. *(ant)* pour, gush, fill.

8   **passive** *(adj)* not reacting to external force. *(s)* lifeless, inactive, unreceptive, idle, dormant. *(ant)* active.

9   **extent** *(n)* degree or amount. *(s)* scale, level, intensity, magnitude. *(ant)* limitation.

10   **innocuous** *(adj)* not offensive or harmful. *(s)* harmless, innocent, safe, weak, inoffensive. *(ant)* harmful.

11   **entity** *(n)* a thing that exists. *(s)* object, unit, item, article, individual, being, creature. *(ant)* nonentity.

12   **razored** *(adj)* sharp-edged and razor-like. *(s)* sharpened, bladed, honed. *(ant)* blunted, rounded.

13   **flawless** *(adj)* without defect (fault) or imperfection. *(s)* perfect, unblemished, faultless, pure. *(ant)* flawed.

14   **reflective** *(adj)* reflecting light. *(s)* shining, glistening, glinting. *(ant)* unreflective, dull.

His right thumb, his unique print, must stick fast to the **nucleus**[1] of the **pulsating**[2] stone, the **umbilical**[3] **parasite**[4] that had sparked into life, its selfish heart throbbing as it drained the life of its **host**[5].

As the Master drew **nigh**[6], sending the temperature in the passageway to scorching levels, Evans believed he was out of time. Turning his head away so as not to look his assailant in the eye, he pressed his thumb onto the Time-Tangler and waited for the Master's **forthcoming**[7] onslaught. **Resigned**[8] to this destiny, **devoid**[9] of energy, his knees buckled beneath him.

He fell with a deafening crack and was **propelled**[10] backwards at bullet-like speed, his back smacking into the wall. Dazed and in a **stupefied**[11] heap, a brilliant flash blinded him. Shooting out between his clenched fingers, strips of **incandescent**[12] light flooded the passage with flowing **rods**[13] of fluorescent green. A circle of emerald lasers burst from the jewel's centre, their **unerring**[14] **symmetrical**[15] rays **converging**[16] to a single point in the centre of the door ahead.

Fighting unconsciousness, Evans gripped the Time-Tangler in his palm. A mini **vortex**[17], no bigger than a swirl of water escaping a small **plughole**[18], appeared from the **core**[19] of the green dot

---

1   **nucleus** *(n)* the central and most important part. *(s)* centre, heart, core, nub, kernel. *(ant)* outside, edge.

2   **pulsate** *(v)* expand and contract regularly. *(s)* beat, throb, pulse, palpitate, pound.

3   **umbilical** *(adj)* connected to something for vital supplies. *(s)* linked, joined, bound, attached. *(ant)* separate.

4   **parasite** *(n)* something that exists by living with and taking from another. *(s)* dependant, taker. *(ant)* host.

5   **host** *(n)* something or someone on which a parasite (dependant) lives. *(s)* donor, contributor. *(ant)* parasite.

6   **nigh** *(adv)* near. *(s)* close, nearby. *(ant)* away, remote.

7   **forthcoming** *(adj)* about to appear or happen. *(s)* imminent, oncoming, approaching, impending. *(ant)* distant.

8   **resigned** *(adj)* accepting what cannot be avoided. *(s)* compliant, acquiescent, unresisting. *(ant)* resistant.

9   **devoid** *(adj)* completely lacking or free from. *(s)* empty, without, wanting, bereft, deficient. *(ant)* full, filled.

10   **propel** *(v)* drive or push into a specific direction. *(s)* move, boost, thrust, shoot, force, impel, launch. *(ant)* pull.

11   **stupefy** *(v)* shock and astonish. *(s)* astound, amaze, stagger, stun, daze, overwhelm, confuse. *(ant)* enlighten.

12   **incandescent** *(adj)* glowing brightly with heat. *(s)* aglow, radiant, luminescent, flaring, fluorescent. *(ant)* dark.

13   **rod** *(n)* a thin, straight bar or pole. *(s)* baton, cylinder, stick, shaft, strip.

14   **unerring** *(adj)* always accurate or right. *(s)* unfailing, perfect, correct, infallible, error-free. *(ant)* faulty, erring.

15   **symmetrical** *(adj)* looking or appearing to be the same. *(s)* regular, even, balanced, equal. *(ant)* asymmetrical.

16   **converge** *(v)* meet at the same point. *(s)* merge, join, touch, unite, congregate, intersect. *(ant)* diverge.

17   **vortex** *(n)* whirling air or liquid. *(s)* spiral, whirlpool, swirl, whirlwind, twister, maelstrom.

18   **plughole** *(n)* a hole where water drains but can be stopped by a plug. *(s)* outlet, drain.

19   **core** *(n)* the part that is central. *(s)* centre, nucleus, heart, hub, middle, interior, midpoint. *(ant)* edge, outside.

*projecting onto the door. Expanding outwards, its **velocity**[1] drew in dirt and dust **particles**[2], which whirled and twisted, obscuring the passageway as a **tornado**[3] of grit and grime lashed at his face, pelting him with a **hail**[4] of tiny stones.*

* **Summoning**[5] his last drop of physical and mental strength, Evans hurled himself head first at the **intersecting**[6] lasers. As his feet left the ground, he flew like a rag doll and was sucked into the vortex through the door.*

* Catapulted through time, then thrown into a disorientated heap onto a floor, Evans pushed the Time-Tangler back into his pocket and **groped**[7] in the dark for clues as to where he was. The dust and smell told him he was in one of the museum's familiar side rooms. Patting at the low, crowded shelves, he prayed he'd landed in the right one.*

* Pushing himself onto his knees, steadying his dizziness, he felt along the rows of shelving. He fingered archived items, reading their shapes from memory, and he recognised the collection. He was a **fastidious**[8] curator, and he soon realised this was the correct room.*

* After pulling himself precariously onto his feet, he reached for the delicate fairy and took one arrow from her quiver. Gripping it in his fist, he patted the wall with his other hand, feeling for the door. Then suddenly, with a resounding crash, it flew open, and a faint light flicked on.*

* Evans collapsed, his legs **liquefying**[9] with fear, because towering in the doorway before him was the Master. Now face to face with Dewi, he knew it was all over. **Cowering**[10] beneath his **captor**[11], Evans grasped the tiny arrow tighter in his fist. As Dewi took a **menacing**[12] stride closer to him, Evans watched helplessly as the Master's eyes swept the room. Then, as if to*

---

1   **velocity** *(n)* the speed of something in a given direction. *(s)* rate, rapidity, haste, quickness.

2   **particle** *(n)* a minute fragment or quantity of matter (substance). *(s)* bit, fleck, speck, grain, scrap. *(ant)* chunk.

3   **tornado** *(n)* a mobile vortex (swirl) of violent and destructive winds. *(s)* whirlwind, cyclone, tempest.

4   **hail** *(n)* a large number of things thrown violently through the air. *(s)* barrage, shower, deluge.

5   **summon** *(v)* try to produce from within oneself. *(s)* call, muster, rouse, find, mobilise, rally. *(ant)* suppress.

6   **intersect** *(v)* cross at a point. *(s)* interconnect, meet, overlap, criss-cross, converge. *(ant)* diverge, divide.

7   **grope** *(v)* feel or search about for blindly with the hands. *(s)* fumble, scrabble, finger, fish. *(ant)* withdraw.

8   **fastidious** *(adj)* fussy about accuracy and detail. *(s)* scrupulous, meticulous, exact. *(ant)* careless.

9   **liquefy** *(v)* make, turn or become liquid. *(s)* dissolve, soften, melt. *(ant)* solidify, harden, set.

10   **cower** *(v)* crouch or squat in fear. *(s)* shrink, recoil, grovel, flinch, quail, cringe, tremble. *(ant)* stand tall.

11   **captor** *(n)* one who takes a prisoner by force. *(s)* detainer, capturer, jailer, keeper. *(ant)* liberator.

12   **menacing** *(adj)* threatening or dangerous. *(s)* ominous, intimidating, sinister, fearsome. *(ant)* reassuring.

bait[1] *him, Dewi cackled, and made his move.*

Recoiling, Evans screamed, shielding his face with his hands, the arrow falling to the floor. But no strike fell. No blows rained down from above.

*Evans peeked **bewilderedly**[2] through his trembling fingers. Totally ignoring him, the Master turned to face the shelves, his hands hovering in peculiar floating motions above the objects.*

But why? *thought Evans.* Why has Dewi not attacked me and taken the Cutter?

*Drawn by the slight warmth emanating from his waistcoat pocket, Evans reached into it for the faceless watch. The stone, now smooth and no longer pulsating, glowed the faintest fading green. Suddenly, **injected**[3] with a rush of hope, Evans found his answer. The Master could not see him, as the Time-Tangler had brought them to the same place but in different times – time was still tangling them both.*

*Before the stone could stop glowing, before the jaws of time snapped back to the present, Evans stuffed the Time-Tangler back into his pocket and snatched the arrow from the floor. Crawling to the door, without looking back, he stood and fled the room, heading for the long, **bleak**[4] tunnels, taking one half of the Cutter with him.*

*

Now, hours later, as he lay frozen, his mind drifting from memories back into the present, relief **coursed**[5] through Robert Evans's veins as he felt the tiny arrow still gripped in his fist. Had he failed, Dewi would have detected both halves of the Cutter and succeeded in stealing the Gwalch Gem bracelet.

But what price had Evans paid for his **ambitions**[6] to deliver half of the Cutter to its rightful **recipient**[7]? The **imperative**[8] delivery that would **restore**[9] him to a great man. The

---

1   **bait** *(v)* deliberately taunt (provoke) or annoy. *(s)* tease, torment, goad, harass, irk, rag. *(ant)* delight, soothe.

2   **bewilderedly** *(adv)* in a bewildered (confused) way. *(s)* perplexedly, bemusedly. *(ant)* understandingly.

3   **inject** *(v)* introduce into something. *(s)* instil, infuse, imbue, impregnate. *(ant)* drain.

4   **bleak** *(adj)* dark, stark and not encouraging or favourable. *(s)* unwelcoming, austere, desolate. *(ant)* appealing.

5   **course** *(v)* move through without obstruction. *(s)* flow, pour, run, gush, race, surge, stream. *(ant)* trickle.

6   **ambition** *(n)* great desire to achieve or do something. *(s)* objective, aim, hope, aspiration, goal. *(ant)* apathy.

7   **recipient** *(n)* a person or thing that receives something. *(s)* receiver, beneficiary, awardee. *(ant)* giver, donor.

8   **imperative** *(adj)* of vital (key) importance. *(s)* crucial, essential, urgent, critical. *(ant)* unimportant.

9   **restore** *(v)* return to a former position or place. *(s)* reinstall, reinstate, re-establish. *(ant)* remove.

delivery that remained **unaccomplished**[1].

His future now see-sawing precariously in an **unpredictable**[2] balance, Evans lay immobile beneath the **gargantuan**[3] **foundations**[4] of the **headquarters**[5] of the world's most **progressive**[6] **tech**[7] company, Via-Corp. At the **forefront**[8] of **artificial intelligence**[9], its **enigmatic**[10] but **reclusive**[11] president, David Lewis, had **amassed**[12] a **fortune**[13] and was **heralded**[14] as one of the century's greatest **innovators**[15] and **philanthropists**[16]. Modest, seldom seen in public, he declined all **interviews**[17].

Via-Corp often stole news **headlines**[18] for its shunning of **convention**[19], **extolling**[20] its **unorthodox**[21] **enticement**[22] of youngsters still in school, emphasising they no longer needed **costly**[23] degrees to **flourish**[24]. **Disadvantaged**[25] but **gifted**[26] children whose parents could neither

---

1   **unaccomplished** *(adj)* not finished or carried out. *(s)* incomplete, unexecuted. *(ant)* accomplished.

2   **unpredictable** *(adj)* unable to be predicted (foreseen). *(s)* changeable, uncertain, capricious. *(ant)* predictable.

3   **gargantuan** *(adj)* huge. *(s)* large, enormous, massive, colossal, mammoth, vast, immense, gigantic. *(ant)* tiny.

4   **foundation** *(n)* an underground, weight-bearing part of a building. *(s)* base, footing, substructure.

5   **headquarters** *(n)* the command and control centre of an organisation. *(s)* head office, nerve centre. *(ant)* branch.

6   **progressive** *(adj)* favouring innovation (newness) and change. *(s)* modern, innovative. *(ant)* conservative.

7   **tech** *(n)* short for *technology*. *(s)* automation, computer, science, machinery.

8   **forefront** *(n)* the leading or most important position. *(s)* head, vanguard, spearhead, cutting-edge. *(ant)* back.

9   **artificial intelligence** *(n)* computer technology that simulates intelligent behaviour.

10   **enigmatic** *(adj)* mysterious and hard to make out. *(s)* unknowable, inscrutable, puzzling. *(ant)* straightforward.

11   **reclusive** *(adj)* avoiding the company of others. *(s)* solitary, isolated, withdrawn, asocial. *(ant)* sociable.

12   **amass** *(v)* gather together over time a large amount of. *(s)* accumulate, collect, stockpile. *(ant)* distribute.

13   **fortune** *(n)* a large amount of money or assets (things of value). *(s)* wealth, prosperity. *(ant)* poverty.

14   **herald** *(v)* praise publicly. *(s)* proclaim, tout, publicise, acclaim, applaud, commend. *(ant)* criticise.

15   **innovator** *(n)* someone who introduces new ideas or products. *(s)* leader, pioneer, trailblazer. *(ant)* imitator.

16   **philanthropist** *(n)* one who cares about others and often gives money. *(s)* humanitarian. *(ant)* misanthropist.

17   **interview** *(n)* a meeting or conversation, often for public use. *(s)* discussion, talk, audience.

18   **headline** *(n)* the most important item of news. *(s)* front page, title, caption, leader. *(ant)* back page, unimportant.

19   **convention** *(n)* the way that something is usually done. *(s)* rule, principle, standard, custom. *(ant)* innovation.

20   **extol** *(v)* praise highly. *(s)* acclaim, celebrate, commend, exalt, laud, worship. *(ant)* deprecate, criticise.

21   **unorthodox** *(adj)* contrary (opposite) to what is usual. *(s)* unconventional, nonconformist. *(ant)* orthodox.

22   **enticement** *(n)* something used to lure (attract). *(s)* temptation, incentive, invitation, bribery. *(ant)* deterrent.

23   **costly** *(adj)* costing a lot of money. *(s)* expensive, dear, pricey, overpriced, inflated. *(ant)* inexpensive, cheap.

24   **flourish** *(v)* grow or develop rapidly and successfully. *(s)* succeed, thrive, prosper, bloom. *(ant)* deteriorate.

25   **disadvantaged** *(adj)* in a poor position, especially socially and financially. *(s)* deprived. *(ant)* privileged.

26   **gifted** *(adj)* having excellent natural ability or talent. *(s)* accomplished, expert, adept, talented. *(ant)* inept.

dream of nor afford **elite**[1] universities were encouraged to train there, and Via-Corp also **sponsored**[2] **refugees**[3] escaping from **war-torn**[4] countries.

Flaunting[5] an audacious self-belief, Lewis had **brazenly**[6] **constructed**[7] **futuristic**[8] offices in **obscure**[9], **deprived**[10] areas, **bypassing**[11] the predictable, affluent towns and cities normally favoured by the giant **corporates**[12]. If a **candidate**[13] passed the Via-Corp intelligence tests, state-of-the-art on-site **accommodation**[14] came as part of a **seductive**[15] and **lucrative**[16] **salary**[17] package. All this ensured the future talent of his company, which was **radically**[18] **disrupting**[19] the **employment**[20] **practices**[21] of young people. No longer did students have to follow the well-trodden path to success; they could come and join the Via-Corp family. It all seemed perfect.

Oblivious to the time slipping dangerously by, Robert Evans eventually prised one sticky eyelid open, hoping his pupils would soon adjust to the dark. He waited. Would his **fate**[22] be

---

1   **elite** *(adj)* superior or influential because of ability or wealth. *(s)* best, exclusive, top-notch. *(ant)* worst.

2   **sponsor** *(v)* provide funds (money) for. *(s)* pay, finance, support, subsidise, bankroll, back, help. *(ant)* extort.

3   **refugee** *(n)* a person from another country seeking refuge from war or disaster. *(s)* escapee. *(ant)* citizen.

4   **war-torn** *(adj)* devasted (ruined) by war. *(s)* war-wearied, war-scarred, disrupted. *(ant)* peaceful.

5   **flaunt** *(v)* display ostentatiously (openly) to cause envy, admiration or defiance. *(s)* parade, exhibit. *(ant)* hide.

6   **brazenly** *(adv)* in a brazen (bold and shameless) way. *(s)* blatantly, plainly, audaciously. *(ant)* discreetly.

7   **construct** *(v)* make or build. *(s)* erect, establish, create, assemble, fabricate, raise. *(ant)* demolish, destroy.

8   **futuristic** *(adj)* involving or having modern technology or design. *(s)* innovative, revolutionary. *(ant)* outdated.

9   **obscure** *(adj)* not well known or important. *(s)* unknown, minor, humble, little-known. *(ant)* known, famous.

10   **deprived** *(adj)* suffering a lack of basic material and cultural needs. *(s)* disadvantaged. *(ant)* privileged.

11   **bypass** *(v)* avoid. *(s)* omit, shun, ignore, decline, neglect, sidestep, evade. *(ant)* include, embrace.

12   **corporate** *(n)* a business, company or group. *(s)* firm, corporation.

13   **candidate** *(n)* a person who applies for a job or position. *(s)* applicant, contender, hopeful. *(ant)* employer.

14   **accommodation** *(n)* a place where a person can live or lodge (stay). *(s)* dwelling, housing, living quarters, residence.

15   **seductive** *(adj)* attractive and tempting. *(s)* enticing, alluring, inviting, appealing. *(ant)* unappealing, repellent.

16   **lucrative** *(adj)* producing a good profit. *(s)* profitable, well paid, rewarding, worthwhile. *(ant)* unprofitable.

17   **salary** *(n)* a person's income (regular pay) from employment (work). *(s)* wages, earnings, remuneration.

18   **radically** *(adv)* in a radical (thorough) way. *(s)* totally, drastically, fundamentally. *(ant)* superficially.

19   **disrupt** *(v)* interrupt or change by causing a disturbance or problem. *(s)* upset, unsettle. *(ant)* maintain.

20   **employment** *(n)* the action of giving work to someone. *(s)* engagement, hiring. *(ant)* dismissal.

21   **practice** *(n)* the way that something is usually done. *(s)* process, system, method, habit, mode.

22   **fate** *(n)* a future outcome that is out of one's control. *(s)* destiny, upshot, fortune, luck, lot.

such a futile waste? Was his destiny to **perish**[1] alone, **unfound**[2] and forgotten, down here in the emptiness of the tunnels he had designed?

Unable to move, he winced as an **industrious**[3] army of ants marched **fervently**[4] across his cheeks. A **vehement**[5] **multitude**[6] of legs tickled and irritated intensely, but his arms were incapable of swiping them off. Blinking madly, he blew sharp **wafts**[7] of **rank**[8] air up through **brittle**[9], cracked lips, trying hopelessly to fan these persistent foot soldiers away.

Continuing to blow, he directed his rapid, stale breaths onto his **solidified**[10] hands. The faster he blew, the more his head whirled and his ears buzzed. A fuzzy black image seemed to dart by, startling him with flashes of colour. Almond-shaped **lanterns**[11] of yellow-green light briefly confused his eyes. Dizzying, he slowed his breaths; he could lose **consciousness**[12] and **hallucinate**[13] again if he exerted himself this **strenuously**[14] so soon. But he must **thaw**[15] his fingers. **Verging**[16] on **hypothermia**[17], he forced himself to inhale deeper, puffing the **tepid**[18] warmth onto his solid fists.

Suddenly he flinched, startled by **spherical**[19] drops of water dripping onto his taut face.

---

1   **perish** *(v)* die, especially suddenly. *(s)* expire, succumb, decease, depart, fade, pass away. *(ant)* live, survive.

2   **unfound** *(adj)* not found. *(s)* lost, undiscovered, undetected, unexposed. *(ant)* found, discovered, exposed.

3   **industrious** *(adj)* hard-working and diligent. *(s)* conscientious, untiring, busy, assiduous. *(ant)* lazy, indolent.

4   **fervently** *(adv)* in a fervent (enthusiastic) manner. *(s)* passionately, ardently, zealously. *(ant)* indifferently.

5   **vehement** *(adj)* showing strong feeling. *(s)* fervent, vigorous, forceful, ardent, emphatic. *(ant)* apathetic.

6   **multitude** *(n)* a large number. *(s)* gathering, host, swarm, legion, horde, mass, throng. *(ant)* handful, few.

7   **waft** *(n)* a gentle movement or current of air. *(s)* blow, wave, breath, puff, gust, draught.

8   **rank** *(adj)* having a foul smell. *(s)* sour, pungent, fetid, reeking, rancid, noxious, putrid. *(ant)* fresh, sweet.

9   **brittle** *(adj)* hard but easily cracked or broken. *(s)* stiff, inelastic, breakable, fragile, delicate, crisp. *(ant)* pliant.

10 **solidify** *(v)* make or become solid and unpliant. *(s)* harden, set, freeze, stiffen, firm, fix. *(ant)* soften, melt.

11 **lantern** *(n)* a portable (moveable) lamp with a handle. *(s)* light.

12 **consciousness** *(n)* the state of being conscious, aware and responsive. *(s)* awareness. *(ant)* unconsciousness.

13 **hallucinate** *(v)* see or experience something that isn't real. *(s)* imagine, fantasise, visualise.

14 **strenuously** *(adv)* in a strenuous (strong) manner. *(s)* energetically, vigorously. *(ant)* half-heartedly.

15 **thaw** *(v)* warm enough to soften or melt. *(s)* unfreeze, defrost, liquefy. *(ant)* freeze, harden, solidify.

16 **verge** *(v)* be close to or about to. *(s)* near, approach, edge, brink, border. *(ant)* retreat, leave.

17 **hypothermia** *(n)* dangerously low body temperature. *(s)* chill, cold, shivers, freezing. *(ant)* fever.

18 **tepid** *(adj)* slightly warm. *(s)* lukewarm, warmish, mild, temperate. *(ant)* cold, icy, boiling.

19 **spherical** *(adj)* like a sphere (round). *(s)* globular, rotund, circular, orbicular, bulbous. *(ant)* flat.

Desperate to **slake**[1] his thirst, he winced, twisting his stiff neck towards the falling drips, and opening his parched mouth, gratefully catching a few.

Eventually, Evans's body defrosted sufficiently, and he hauled himself up to a stoop. In these low tunnels, reaching his **destination**[2] would be an **arduous**[3] **undertaking**[4], yet he would not **squander**[5] this one chance by **deviating**[6] from his plan. He would heave himself there if it killed him.

Strangely, hunger didn't **hamper**[7] him, although an **intolerable**[8] thirst and **debilitating**[9] weakness **dramatically**[10] hindered his progress. Thankfully, his knowledge of his underground engineering had stayed with him. With one hand **buttressed**[11] firmly against the earthy tunnel, and the other grasping the Cutter, he limped along the dark tunnels, deeper into the vast foundations. Spitting **foul**[12]-tasting grime from his **dehydrated**[13] mouth, he wondered how long he had been down there. Oxygen deprivation clouded his senses and **judgement**[14]. He **craved**[15] the smell of the **invigorating**[16] Welsh mountain air. He yearned for the shine of simple sunlight to **nourish**[17] and **energise**[18] his **sallow**[19] skin. The **gratuitous**[20] luxuries **appreciable**[21]

1   **slake** *(v)* satisfy a thirst. *(s)* quench, allay, assuage, sate, satiate, mollify, relieve, extinguish. *(ant)* exacerbate.

2   **destination** *(n)* the place where someone or something is going to. *(s)* objective, target. *(ant)* starting point.

3   **arduous** *(adj)* difficult and tiring. *(s)* strenuous, onerous, taxing, laborious, gruelling, toilsome. *(ant)* easy.

4   **undertaking** *(n)* a task. *(s)* responsibility, mission, duty, venture, attempt, endeavour, pursuit.

5   **squander** *(v)* waste an opportunity or money. *(s)* blow, lose, misuse, misspend, frivol, trifle. *(ant)* save, hoard.

6   **deviate** *(v)* change or leave an established (planned) course. *(s)* diverge, digress, stray, differ. *(ant)* conform.

7   **hamper** *(v)* hinder (slow) or obstruct (block) movement or progress. *(s)* impede, restrain. *(ant)* assist.

8   **intolerable** *(adj)* not able to be endured. *(s)* unbearable, insufferable, impossible, excruciating. *(ant)* bearable.

9   **debilitating** *(adj)* tending to weaken or hinder. *(s)* incapacitating, draining, enervating. *(ant)* invigorating.

10   **dramatically** *(adv)* in a dramatic (powerful) way. *(s)* greatly, radically, noticeably, severely. *(ant)* modestly.

11   **buttressed** *(adj)* placed for support. *(s)* braced, bolstered, shored, propped.

12   **foul** *(adj)* offensive to the senses. *(s)* disgusting, revolting, polluted, rank, fetid. *(ant)* fresh, clean.

13   **dehydrated** *(adj)* having lost water. *(s)* dry, parched, drained, desiccated, shrivelled. *(ant)* hydrated, wet.

14   **judgement** *(n)* the ability to make decisions or come to conclusions. *(s)* sense, intelligence. *(ant)* stupidity.

15   **crave** *(v)* feel great desire for. *(s)* want, yearn for, require, hanker after, wish for, long for. *(ant)* dislike, spurn.

16   **invigorate** *(v)* give energy or strength to. *(s)* refresh, revitalise, rejuvenate, galvanise. *(ant)* exhaust.

17   **nourish** *(v)* provide life or health with necessary food or substances. *(s)* feed, sustain, nurture. *(ant)* deprive.

18   **energise** *(v)* give vitality (life). *(s)* boost, invigorate, strengthen, revitalise. *(ant)* drain, enervate.

19   **sallow** *(adj)* unhealthily pale or yellowish in colour. *(s)* wan, pasty, ashen, sickly, pallid, washed out. *(ant)* rosy.

20   **gratuitous** *(adj)* costing no money. *(s)* free, gratis, complimentary, costless. *(ant)* paid for, chargeable.

21   **appreciable** *(adj)* capable of being recognised, seen and appreciated. *(s)* perceptible. *(ant)* unnoticeable.

only when withheld, he wanted those back.

Above ground, Via-Corp's headquarters weren't simply an office block; they sprawled into a small, bustling town made up of busy Via-Corp **devotees**[1]. Evans sought the **epicentre**[2], the **zenith**[3], where the most-**committed**[4] **personnel**[5] **proffered**[6] their lives to David Lewis.

Suddenly his fingers **glanced**[7] against **sleek**[8], **glacial**[9] steel. He let out a yelp. **Elated**[10], he knew he must be near. Metal and **ducting**[11] meant one thing: he had reached the compound. He fell to his knees with relief and exhaustion – he had feared his **demise**[12] was nigh. But thankfully, he had not forgotten how to navigate his own tunnels. Triumphant, he had arrived.

At least, he had thought so. For out of nowhere, rising **resplendently**[13] vertical, loomed a vast wall of ominous grey metal, an unexpected, towering, endless **monolith**[14]. The smug expression slowly slipped from his lips. Nothing but a solid barricade of **fortified**[15] **titanium**[16]-steel **alloy**[17] rose and spread, stretching **perpetually**[18] beyond his **scope**[19] of vision. A majestic **edifice**[20] built solely to keep the undesirables from the doors of Via-Corp's secret core. Dumbfounded, he inspected the stark metal's cold expanse for clues of an entrance. There were none.

---

1   **devotee** (*n*) someone who is enthusiastic and interested. (*s*) fan, fanatic, follower, disciple. (*ant*) critic.

2   **epicentre** (*n*) the central point. (*s*) birthplace, bullseye, centre, core, heart, hub, nucleus. (*ant*) surface, exterior.

3   **zenith** (*n*) the highest point or state. (*s*) top, apex, peak, summit, pinnacle, acme. (*ant*) nadir, bottom, pit.

4   **committed** (*adj*) pledged to a specific course or policy. (*s*) devoted, dedicated, loyal. (*ant*) uncommitted.

5   **personnel** (*n*) people employed in an organisation. (*s*) staff, workers, human resources, employees.

6   **proffer** (*v*) put forward or hold out to someone. (*s*) offer, extend, tender, volunteer, give. (*ant*) withdraw.

7   **glance** (*v*) briefly touch or deflect off something. (*s*) skim, graze, brush, bounce, clip, ricochet.

8   **sleek** (*adj*) smooth and shining. (*s*) glossy, glistening, polished, glassy. (*ant*) dull, rough, coarse.

9   **glacial** (*adj*) cold and icy like a glacier. (*s*) freezing, biting, polar, bitter, hostile, unfriendly. (*ant*) heated, warm.

10   **elated** (*adj*) incredibly happy. (*s*) exhilarated, thrilled, excited, exultant. (*ant*) depressed, disheartened.

11   **ducting** (*n*) a system of tubing or piping forming ducts (pipes). (*s*) pipework, conduit, channels.

12   **demise** (*n*) downfall or death. (*s*) ruin, end, failure, collapse, expiry, departure. (*ant*) ascent, birth.

13   **resplendently** (*adv*) in a resplendent (brilliant) manner. (*s*) splendidly, magnificently. (*ant*) unimpressively.

14   **monolith** (*n*) a large and characterless thing or building. (*s*) megalith, block, monument.

15   **fortified** (*adj*) strengthened against attack. (*s*) reinforced, braced, toughened, hardened. (*ant*) weakened.

16   **titanium** (*n*) a metal element used to make corrosion-resistant alloy (mixture).

17   **alloy** (*n*) a combination of two or more metallic elements. (*s*) mixture, compound.

18   **perpetually** (*adv*) in a perpetual (unending) manner. (*s*) endlessly, continuously, continually. (*ant*) intermittently.

19   **scope** (*n*) the extent (size) or range (scale) of something. (*s*) area, field, capacity, reach, bounds.

20   **edifice** (*n*) a big, imposing building. (*s*) structure, construction, creation, erection, monument.

Broken, he slumped back down as a **self-pitying**[1] tear **traced**[2] another dirty line down his hollow cheek. He closed his eyes, **reminiscing**[3] about his **lauded**[4] past as he capitulated to what felt like certain defeat.

Evans's **dedication**[5] to mapping this mesh of underground passages where he now lay had spanned many years. It enabled Instinctives to move unobserved using old underground **shafts**[6]. Without these, the knights would find it **ruinously**[7] difficult to outwit Mal-Instinctives. Ably Evans had kept most of these routes hidden for centuries. The earliest tunnels, the knights had **excavated**[8] themselves; later they used metal, slate and coal mines beneath the mountains and hills of Snowdonia. Thanks to Evans's **ingenuity**[9] and **expertise**[10], their **tentacles**[11] reached most **major**[12] towns and cities, even under some seas. A labyrinth of protection, movement and **escapology**[13] stretching to all corners of the earth, **rigorously**[14] and painstakingly developed over time and known by only the most **select**[15] honoured and trusted knights.

Aeons[16] ago, Robert Evans had been **appointed**[17] **chief**[18] **counsel**[19] **advocate**[20] and

---

1   **self-pitying** *(adj)* feeling sorry for oneself. *(s)* miserable, defeatist, depressed, self-indulgent. *(ant)* cheerful.

2   **trace** *(v)* take a specific path or route. *(s)* depict, mark, show, draw, outline, sketch.

3   **reminisce** *(v)* think about enjoyable events from the past. *(s)* recall, remember, recollect, evoke. *(ant)* forget.

4   **laud** *(v)* praise highly. *(s)* extol, applaud, acclaim, glorify, commend. *(ant)* criticise, abhor.

5   **dedication** *(n)* commitment to a task or purpose. *(s)* devotion, allegiance, loyalty. *(ant)* apathy.

6   **shaft** *(n)* a long, narrow hole that gives access to a mine. *(s)* bore, borehole, mineshaft, tunnel, passage.

7   **ruinously** *(adv)* in a ruinous (disastrous) way. *(s)* damagingly, destructively, catastrophically. *(ant)* favourably.

8   **excavate** *(v)* make a channel or hole by digging. *(s)* gouge, mine, quarry, exhume, shovel, scoop. *(ant)* fill, bury.

9   **ingenuity** *(n)* the quality of being creative and clever. *(s)* inventiveness, resourcefulness. *(ant)* ignorance.

10   **expertise** *(n)* expert knowledge or skill. *(s)* ability, prowess, capability, proficiency. *(ant)* inability.

11   **tentacle** *(n)* a long, thin part of an animal for grasping and feeling. *(s)* appendage, feeler.

12   **major** *(adj)* significant or important. *(s)* main, big, chief, foremost, dominant, leading, sizeable. *(ant)* minor.

13   **escapology** *(n)* the art of escape.

14   **rigorously** *(adv)* in a rigorous (careful) way. *(s)* thoroughly, meticulously, scrupulously. *(ant)* carelessly.

15   **select** *(adj)* the best of or most suitable. *(s)* superior, preferred, handpicked, first-rate, excellent. *(ant)* inferior.

16   **aeon** *(n)* an indefinite and long time. *(s)* age, yonks, eternity, forever. *(ant)* moment, jiffy, flash.

17   **appoint** *(v)* assign (give) a role, position or job. *(s)* employ as, nominate, engage as. *(ant)* reject, dismiss.

18   **chief** *(adj)* having the highest rank. *(s)* principal, main, leading, primary, highest. *(ant)* minor, subordinate.

19   **counsel** *(n)* legal adviser. *(s)* lawyer, advocate, guide, barrister, consultant, counsellor.

20   **advocate** *(n)* public supporter or lawyer. *(s)* backer, champion, defender, promotor, sponsor. *(ant)* opponent.

architectural[1] adviser[2] in the realm[3] of Prince Llywelyn. He had designed and calculated magnificent structures, built castles, negotiated[4] treaties[5] and drawn up complex legal[6] agreements for the prince. He had been a brilliant man held in high esteem[7] as a courtier and servant[8] of the Crown. Wherever Llywelyn had gone, Robert Evans had followed several unobtrusive steps behind. Prior to the pairing of the Gwalch Gem and the Welsh gold, Evans had occupied this position. When the full potency of the bracelet had been realised, Llywelyn's dependence[9] on Evans had increased further; his presence had become vital, almost indispensable[10].

However, jealousy can be virulent[11] and savagely[12] detrimental[13], clouding[14] the judgement of even the wisest, most scholarly[15] men. Llywelyn had suspected certain courtiers coveted the bracelet, so Evans had acted as his undercover[16] informant[17], his secret agent[18], there to serve the prince unfailingly[19]. Evans had planted a network of masterly spies, sleuthing[20] eyes and ears who informed him day and night, an army of moles[21] to scour the deepest, darkest corners of

---

1   **architectural** *(adj)* relating to the design and construction of buildings. *(s)* structural.

2   **adviser** *(n)* someone who gives advice in a specific field. *(s)* guru, consultant, mentor, guide.

3   **realm** *(n)* an area of responsibility or rule. *(s)* kingdom, domain, monarchy, empire, dominion, jurisdiction.

4   **negotiate** *(v)* attempt to reach agreement by discussion. *(s)* talk, confer, bargain, cooperate. *(ant)* disagree.

5   **treaty** *(n)* a formal agreement. *(s)* settlement, deal, accord, truce, pact, contract. *(ant)* disagreement.

6   **legal** *(adj)* relating to the law. *(s)* constitutional, judicial, statutory, contractual, lawful. *(ant)* illegal, unlawful.

7   **esteem** *(n)* admiration and respect. *(s)* acclaim, popularity, reverence, admiration, regard. *(ant)* contempt.

8   **servant** *(n)* a person who performs duties for others. *(s)* attendant, assistant, retainer. *(ant)* master.

9   **dependence** *(n)* the state of relying upon someone or something. *(s)* reliance. *(ant)* independence.

10 **indispensable** *(adj)* completely necessary. *(s)* crucial, essential, vital, requisite. *(ant)* dispensable.

11 **virulent** *(adj)* easily spread and vicious. *(s)* malignant, contagious, destructive, pernicious. *(ant)* harmless.

12 **savagely** *(adv)* in a savage (fierce and uncontrolled) way. *(s)* brutally, callously, ruthlessly. *(ant)* mildly.

13 **detrimental** *(adj)* causing harm. *(s)* damaging, injurious, unfavourable, negative, adverse. *(ant)* beneficial.

14 **cloud** *(v)* make uncertain or unclear. *(s)* impair, veil, distort, blur, confuse, obscure. *(ant)* clarify, enlighten.

15 **scholarly** *(adj)* relating to scholars (well-educated people). *(s)* erudite, intellectual. *(ant)* uneducated.

16 **undercover** *(adj)* involving espionage (spying) or secret work. *(s)* disguised, covert, clandestine. *(ant)* open.

17 **informant** *(n)* someone who gives information to another. *(s)* spy, informer, grass, sneak, snitch.

18 **agent** *(n)* a person who acts on behalf of (for) of another. *(s)* go-between, negotiator, proxy, envoy, trustee.

19 **unfailingly** *(adv)* in an unfailing (reliable) way. *(s)* dependably, steadily, consistently, abidingly. *(ant)* erratically.

20 **sleuth** *(v)* track, search or investigate in secret. *(s)* detect, expose, spy, snoop, stalk. *(ant)* overlook.

21 **mole** *(n)* someone who spies and betrays information. *(s)* informer, spy, sleuth, infiltrator, plant.

Llywelyn's realm, **relaying**[1] any covert hearsay or coded messages of **treason**[2].

Llywelyn had **bestowed**[3] the gift of Instinct and **longevity**[4] on only his **outstanding**[5] knights. This **prestige**[6] and **glory**[7] had remained Evans's greatest and most cherished honour, furthering his **ardent**[8] **compulsion**[9] to loyally serve the great prince and his memory, always.

But little had he, or indeed anyone, dreamed it would be those closest to the prince, the very people in whom Llywelyn and he, Evans, had placed their **implicit**[10] trust, who would falter and **conspire**[11] to steal the bracelet. The **conspirators**[12] had been the **innermost**[13] royal kin, the prince's wife and brother, Dewi. Both would cruelly betray and abandon Llywelyn in such a way as to scar him, indelibly, and make him **slay**[14] his **dutiful**[15] and innocent hound, Gelert.

Evans could never have foreseen the identity of the traitors. Not even the greatest **detective**[16] nor informant could have **chaperoned**[17] and monitored every move of the prince's wife and brother. Yet Evans felt that Llywelyn had somehow held him responsible for their deeds. From that moment on, he had fallen out of **favour**[18] with the prince. He had no longer ridden out with Llywelyn, nor had he been invited to dine at the prince's table. His counsel had no longer been called upon, and the prince had ceased to value his opinion.

---

1   **relay** *(v)* receive and pass on messages or information. *(s)* deliver, communicate, convey. *(ant)* withhold.

2   **treason** *(n)* the action of betraying one's country, a person or something. *(s)* treachery, disloyalty. *(ant)* allegiance.

3   **bestow** *(v)* offer or give an honour, gift or right. *(s)* confer, bequeath, grant, donate, present. *(ant)* withdraw.

4   **longevity** *(n)* long life. *(s)* permanence, durability, endurance, lastingness. *(ant)* impermanence, death.

5   **outstanding** *(adj)* exceptionally good. *(s)* eminent, distinguished, superlative, stupendous. *(ant)* abysmal, dire.

6   **prestige** *(n)* admiration and respect for quality or achievement. *(s)* status, reputation, esteem. *(ant)* notoriety.

7   **glory** *(n)* high honour won for noteworthy achievements. *(s)* admiration, credit, prestige, kudos. *(ant)* shame.

8   **ardent** *(adj)* passionate or enthusiastic. *(s)* avid, fervent, fierce, intense, keen. *(ant)* dispassionate.

9   **compulsion** *(n)* a strong or irresistible urge to do something. *(s)* need, impulse, craving. *(ant)* choice.

10   **implicit** *(adj)* without question. *(s)* absolute, unreserved, total, unconditional, complete, utter. *(ant)* limited.

11   **conspire** *(v)* make secret plans jointly to do harm. *(s)* plot, scheme, collude, connive, consort.

12   **conspirator** *(n)* someone who conspires and assists in a conspiracy. *(s)* collaborator, accomplice.

13   **innermost** *(adj)* closest to the centre. *(s)* central, interior, internal, furthest in. *(ant)* outermost, external.

14   **slay** *(v)* kill in a violent and brutal way. *(s)* murder, butcher, slaughter, assassinate, exterminate.

15   **dutiful** *(adj)* tending to fulfil one's duty. *(s)* obedient, attentive, faithful, loyal, devoted. *(ant)* irresponsible.

16   **detective** *(n)* someone employed (assigned) to investigate and solve crimes. *(s)* investigator.

17   **chaperone** *(v)* accompany (go with), look after or supervise (direct). *(s)* escort, monitor. *(ant)* abandon.

18   **favour** *(n)* the liking, approval or support of someone. *(s)* esteem, partiality, preference. *(ant)* disfavour.

From then on, in a turmoil of anger, **remorse**[1] and guilt, he had sweated and suffered, **strategically**[2] planning and plotting his network of tunnels. Toiling endlessly to create something Llywelyn would be proud of, he had scribbled, **sketched**[3], shaded and **refined**[4] multiple drawings and charts. He had then **diligently**[5] mapped them onto exquisite, **luxurious**[6] **parchments**[7] to prevent them from perishing over the years. **Tortuously**[8] he had **masterminded**[9] and **overseen**[10] the excavations, creating trails to confound all except the Knights Hawk. Only they would find their way through these endless **warrens**[11] of moist, earthy **underpasses**[12]. He, Evans, was the **maestro**[13] of this subterranean maze, and Llywelyn and Gwilym Cadwaladr should be grateful to him.

Now, in these fading moments slumped under the foundations of Via-Corp, he spent not one second reminiscing about his wife; he **mourned**[14] only his personal loss. Alas, he would not become **celebrated**[15] again, holding the position of esteemed **prominence**[16] and **gravitas**[17] he had once had. His family life, in truth, had become a well-rehearsed **pantomime**[18]. A

---

1   **remorse** *(n)* guilt or regret. *(s)* shame, repentance, sorrow, compunction, ruefulness. *(ant)* remorselessness.

2   **strategically** *(adv)* in a way relating to strategy (skill or long-term plan). *(s)* tactically. *(ant)* randomly.

3   **sketch** *(v)* roughly draw or outline. *(s)* depict, portray, represent, pencil, draft, blueprint, design.

4   **refine** *(v)* make minor (small) changes to improve or clarify. *(s)* perfect, revise, edit, enhance. *(ant)* coarsen.

5   **diligently** *(adv)* in a diligent (hard-working) way. *(s)* conscientiously, meticulously, attentively. *(ant)* carelessly.

6   **luxurious** *(adj)* extremely elegant and often expensive. *(s)* opulent, sumptuous, extravagant. *(ant)* meagre.

7   **parchment** *(n)* prepared animal skin with a papery appearance used in ancient writing. *(s)* vellum, scroll.

8   **tortuously** *(adv)* in a tortuous (complicated) way. *(s)* complexly, intricately, painfully. *(ant)* straightforwardly.

9   **mastermind** *(v)* plan and direct a complex scheme. *(s)* conceive, devise, conduct, organise. *(ant)* bungle.

10   **oversee** *(v)* supervise work, often in an official manner. *(s)* manage, direct, inspect, administer. *(ant)* neglect.

11   **warren** *(n)* tunnels or burrows like interconnecting rabbit holes (warren). *(s)* labyrinth, maze, lair, den.

12   **underpass** *(n)* an underground passageway. *(s)* subway, corridor, tunnel. *(ant)* flyover.

13   **maestro** *(n)* a distinguished (respected and well-known) figure. *(s)* master, prodigy, genius. *(ant)* amateur.

14   **mourn** *(v)* feel sadness or regret for. *(s)* grieve, miss, pine, bemoan, lament, rue, agonise. *(ant)* rejoice.

15   **celebrated** *(adj)* praised or honoured publicly. *(s)* extolled, glorified, acclaimed, applauded. *(ant)* criticised.

16   **prominence** *(n)* the state of being important, noticeable or famous. *(s)* eminence, distinction. *(ant)* obscurity.

17   **gravitas** *(n)* seriousness and dignity. *(s)* gravity, solemnity, grandeur, sobriety. *(ant)* frivolity.

18   **pantomime** *(n)* an absurd situation. *(s)* show, sham, farce, charade, mockery. *(ant)* reality.

carefully cultivated **facade**[1] **comprising**[2] a veneer of **pretence**[3], an outward **fiction**[4], a sham[5] so well practised – in truth, an **abysmal**[6] lie. He cared only for his **stately**[7] pride and how he ranked amongst others, their **sentiments**[8] and opinions all important. Sadly, his wife Marjorie's **complicit**[9] behaviour too often condoned and **sanctioned**[10] his deceitful selfishness. Rather than confronting his self-serving lies, she turned a cowardly eye to his bullying and obsessive **pursuit**[11] of glory and **reverence**[12]. His **compulsive**[13], **narcissistic**[14] **drive**[15] and **self-centred**[16] need for **applause**[17] from those in higher, privileged positions had **indisputably**[18] ruined his family, **tearing**[19] them **asunder**[20]. Still, they hid it very well.

As he slipped away into the beckoning white light that appeared before him, he **grieved**[21] only for his failure to **repeal**[22] his **relegation**[23], and the **inability**[24] to gain the **exoneration**[25] and

---

1 **facade** *(n)* a deceptive (false) outward appearance. *(s)* pretence, veneer, mask, front, charade. *(ant)* candour.

2 **comprise** *(v)* be made up or consist of. *(s)* include, contain, involve, compose, encompass. *(ant)* exclude.

3 **pretence** *(n)* a false display. *(s)* charade, sham, make-believe, act, deception, simulation. *(ant)* realism.

4 **fiction** *(n)* something untrue or invented. *(s)* falsehood, fabrication, lie, deceit, illusion. *(ant)* fact, truth.

5 **sham** *(n)* a thing that is not what it purports (claims) to be. *(s)* pretence, act, facade, charade. *(ant)* reality.

6 **abysmal** *(adj)* extremely bad. *(s)* appalling, woeful, atrocious, shameful, deplorable, lamentable. *(ant)* superb.

7 **stately** *(adj)* indicating high rank (position). *(s)* grand, courtly, imperial, majestic, pompous. *(ant)* modest.

8 **sentiment** *(n)* an opinion or view held or given by another. *(s)* feeling, response, reaction, attitude. *(ant)* apathy.

9 **complicit** *(adj)* involved in something viewed as wrong. *(s)* conspiratorial, guilty, collaborative. *(ant)* innocent.

10 **sanction** *(v)* approve or permit. *(s)* allow, authorise, endorse, empower, consent. *(ant)* veto, disapprove.

11 **pursuit** *(n)* the action of pursuing (searching, chasing, following). *(s)* quest, hunt, detection, pursual, stalking. *(ant)* retreat.

12 **reverence** *(n)* deep respect. *(s)* worship, admiration, awe, veneration, devotion, esteem. *(ant)* contempt.

13 **compulsive** *(adj)* acting because of an irresistible urge. *(s)* obsessive, fanatical, irrational. *(ant)* controllable.

14 **narcissistic** *(adj)* excessively (extremely) interested in oneself. *(s)* vain, self-absorbed, egotistical. *(ant)* selfless.

15 **drive** *(n)* an innate (inborn) determination to attain (achieve). *(s)* ambition, motivation, zeal. *(ant)* inertia.

16 **self-centred** *(adj)* overly interested in oneself. *(s)* selfish, egotistical, egocentric, narcissistic. *(ant)* altruistic.

17 **applause** *(n)* praise expressed by clapping. *(s)* acclaim, admiration, approval, ovation, accolade. *(ant)* criticism.

18 **indisputably** *(adv)* in a way that cannot be disputed (challenged). *(s)* undoubtedly. *(ant)* questionably.

19 **tear** *(v)* pull apart. *(s)* rip, split, slash, shred, destroy, divide, sever, separate, rive, wrest, sunder. *(ant)* join.

20 **asunder** *(adv)* apart. *(s)* in two, into pieces, to bits, to shreds. *(ant)* together.

21 **grieve** *(v)* feel intense sorrow. *(s)* mourn, lament, regret, ache, miss, rue, suffer, wail. *(ant)* rejoice, delight.

22 **repeal** *(v)* recall or withdraw. *(s)* cancel, reverse, revoke, rescind, abolish, annul, nullify. *(ant)* allow, keep.

23 **relegation** *(n)* the act of moving to an inferior position or rank. *(s)* demotion, downgrading. *(ant)* promotion.

24 **inability** *(n)* the state of being unable to do something. *(s)* incompetence, incapacity, incapability. *(ant)* ability.

25 **exoneration** *(n)* the act of officially freeing someone of blame. *(s)* pardon, acquittal. *(ant)* conviction.

recognition he felt he so greatly deserved. He mourned only the loss of title and prestige that failure to deliver the Cutter would leave. To him, this **legacy**[1] was worse than death itself.

Until this moment, he had **spurned**[2] all stories of a **heavenly**[3] brilliance appearing to beckon the dying into a painless, **unsullied**[4] **utopia**[5]. Yet this **ethereal**[6] light suggested such a welcome **clemency**[7], and called him so compassionately, that it **endowed**[8] his craven conscience with a tangible calm. As its luminescence increased, he exhaled deeply and awaited his perceived **harmony**[9]. Tangling time twice, he felt certain, had killed him.

But his departure from this world seemed to be taking longer than he had anticipated. As an **escalating**[10] heat warmed his face, he opened a **faltering**[11] eye and saw a ray of dazzling white light, momentarily blinding him. Certain of his imminent death, he felt the intense heat scorch his skin. However, the searing pain abruptly hurled him back from self-pitying **indulgence**[12], and he realised he was well and truly alive.

Almost disappointed, he scrabbled up onto his quivering knees. The ray of powerful light expanded into an overwhelmingly brilliant, spellbinding rectangle. Hiding his face behind his trembling fingers, he peeked through their gaps, squinting at the **ghostly**[13] human form that had **materialised**[14] from a misty **vapour**[15].

'Evans, do you have it?'

A measured yet intimidating voice sliced through the stillness.

---

1   **legacy** *(n)* a lasting effect of an event or process. *(s)* heritage, outcome, bequest, provision.

2   **spurn** *(v)* reject with disdain (scorn). *(s)* snub, rebuff, despise, refuse, repudiate, disapprove. *(ant)* accept.

3   **heavenly** *(adj)* of heaven. *(s)* divine, supernatural, holy, spiritual, saintly, blessed. *(ant)* hellish, unbearable.

4   **unsullied** *(adj)* not spoiled or made impure. *(s)* untainted, perfect, pure, clean, untarnished. *(ant)* tarnished.

5   **utopia** *(n)* an imagined place where all is perfect. *(s)* ideal, heaven, paradise, nirvana, dreamland. *(ant)* hell.

6   **ethereal** *(adj)* spiritual or heavenly. *(s)* celestial, airy, ghostly, wraithlike, eerie, unearthly. *(ant)* earthly.

7   **clemency** *(n)* mercy. *(s)* forgiveness, pity, leniency, pardon, compassion, moderation. *(ant)* heartlessness.

8   **endow** *(v)* provide with. *(s)* give, award, enable, empower, donate, grant, furnish, bestow. *(ant)* take.

9   **harmony** *(n)* a feeling of agreement or peaceableness (peace). *(s)* accord, togetherness, amity. *(ant)* discord.

10   **escalate** *(v)* increase quickly. *(s)* intensify, heighten, spiral, accelerate, soar, rocket, surge. *(ant)* drop.

11   **falter** *(v)* lose momentum or strength. *(s)* hesitate, waver, vacillate, pause. *(ant)* continue, rally.

12   **indulgence** *(n)* the act of indulging (satisfying). *(s)* comfort, pleasure, spoiling, excess. *(ant)* moderation.

13   **ghostly** *(adj)* like a ghost in appearance. *(s)* spooky, ethereal, spectral, eerie, wraithlike. *(ant)* normal.

14   **materialise** *(v)* appear. *(s)* emerge, arrive, arise, occur, manifest, develop, evolve. *(ant)* disappear, evaporate.

15   **vapour** *(n)* a misty substance suspended (floating) in the air. *(s)* haze, fog, cloud, suspension, miasma.

Jarred into reality, he straightened, awkwardly forcing his body upright. He stared speechlessly, **spellbound**[1] by the **apparition**[2] that lingered in the doorway. He parted his dry and shrivelled lips, but they refused to form words.

'Evans, do you have it?' repeated the feminine, husky voice in a low purr, a hint of **agitation**[3] and menace seeping into its **intonation**[4].

Awestruck[5], Evans blinked, trying to focus on the form **contoured**[6] by the beam.

'Evans, speak will you, man!' The threat was no longer veiled; the voice spat in a **demonic**[7] hiss. 'Did you obtain the Cutter?' it **interrogated**[8].

Evans's stomach lurched as he mustered enough air to articulate a **piteous**[9] and indistinct 'Yes.' Cowering lower and suppressing the urge to **vomit**[10], he repeated a **quavering**[11] 'Yes, I have it.'

'Ahhhh! Good man.' The **irate**[12] voice promptly returned to its even, constant pitch – a mixture of silk and stone.

The **lofty**[13] yet beautiful outline approached, moving towards a **quailing**[14] Evans. He squealed a **timorous**[15] squeak. Trembling, he lifted his clasped fist towards her and squeaked again.

'Open your hand, Evans,' ordered the **domineering**[16] voice.

---

1 **spellbind** *(v)* hold the attention of as if by magic. *(s)* beguile, mesmerise, compel, engross, rivet. *(ant)* bore.

2 **apparition** *(n)* a ghost or ghostlike image. *(s)* manifestation, appearance, phantasm, spectre, ghoul.

3 **agitation** *(n)* anxiety or nervous excitement. *(s)* perturbation, disquiet, tension, irritation. *(ant)* calm.

4 **intonation** *(n)* the rise and fall of a voice in speech. *(s)* pitch, inflection, tone, timbre, cadence.

5 **awestruck** *(adj)* filled with or revealing awe. *(s)* astonished, staggered, rapt, overwhelmed. *(ant)* unimpressed.

6 **contour** *(n)* an outline representing a shape. *(s)* form, silhouette, delineation, line, profile, figuration, curve.

7 **demonic** *(adj)* like a demon (devil). *(s)* crazed, wicked, fiendish, devilish, infernal, manic. *(ant)* sane, angelic.

8 **interrogate** *(v)* ask questions aggressively or formally. *(s)* examine, cross-examine, quiz, grill. *(ant)* answer.

9 **piteous** *(adj)* arousing or deserving pity. *(s)* pathetic, miserable, pitiable, wretched. *(ant)* enviable.

10 **vomit** *(v)* be sick. *(s)* regurgitate, disgorge, retch, gag, heave, spew, puke, barf. *(ant)* swallow.

11 **quaver** *(v)* shake or tremble. *(s)* quiver, warble, tremor, flinch, flutter. *(ant)* steady.

12 **irate** *(adj)* feeling great anger. *(s)* furious, incensed, mad, enraged, fuming, infuriated, livid. *(ant)* calm.

13 **lofty** *(adj)* haughty and aloof, or imposing in height. *(s)* tall, disdainful, superior, arrogant. *(ant)* humble, short.

14 **quail** *(v)* show or feel fear. *(s)* quake, quaver, blench, cower, cringe, flinch, recoil, wince. *(ant)* confront.

15 **timorous** *(adj)* nervous or lacking confidence. *(s)* faint-hearted, weak-kneed, timid, cowardly. *(ant)* brave.

16 **domineering** *(adj)* fond of controlling others. *(s)* bullying, oppressive, dictatorial. *(ant)* submissive.

Evans's hand trembled so **vigorously**[1] he feared its contents would fly **awry**[2]; he could not risk that calamity.

'Forgive me, ma'am; my ordeal overwhelms me somewhat,' said Evans, buying himself some time as he recovered his **dignity**[3]. 'It is here,' he said, uncurling his fist and offering it up **submissively**[4].

The tall figure's elegant hand reached out and grasped Evans's wrist, steadying the shake.

'Hold still, man, or we shall lose it. Give it to me now!' she demanded, her tone as **severe**[5] as before.

'Please take it, ma'am – I fear I cannot hold steady any longer,' he answered with righteous **supplication**[6]. **Embellishing**[7] for better effect, he **keeled over**[8] sideways, acting **light-headed**[9].

Not fooled for a second, she clamped his wrist harder and took the fine, slender object from his hand. Holding it between two impeccably manicured fingernails, she sighed.

'At last you are home,' she cooed at the **inanimate**[10] object she held, abruptly letting go of Evans's wrist.

As she admired the Cutter, an **egotistical**[11] rush of success oozed through her veins, invigorating her entire **devious**[12] being. She spun on her beige high heels, flicked her blonde hair over the shoulder of her tailored cream suit and marched swiftly away, back into the light. An exquisite aroma of **custom**[13]-blended fragrance following her.

As she stepped over the threshold back into the **cavernous**[14] Via-Corp headquarters,

---

1   **vigorously** *(adv)* with vigour (energy). *(s)* energetically, forcefully, strongly, boldly. *(ant)* sluggishly, feebly.

2   **awry** *(adv)* off course. *(s)* astray, badly, askance, afield, wrongly, amiss, askew, crookedly. *(ant)* straight.

3   **dignity** *(n)* a sense of pride in oneself. *(s)* self-respect, self-esteem, propriety, poise, worth. *(ant)* humiliation.

4   **submissively** *(adv)* in a submissive (obedient) manner. *(s)* compliantly, passively, meekly. *(ant)* assertively.

5   **severe** *(adj)* harsh and stern. *(s)* strict, hard, austere, unsympathetic, cruel, ruthless, hard-hearted. *(ant)* mild.

6   **supplication** *(n)* the action of appealing or pleading. *(s)* plea, prayer, request, appeal, petition. *(ant)* offer.

7   **embellish** *(v)* make more interesting for better effect. *(s)* elaborate, exaggerate, enhance. *(ant)* simplify.

8   **keel over** *(v)* fall over or collapse. *(s)* faint, drop, slump, swoon, topple, black out. *(ant)* stand, straighten.

9   **light-headed** *(adj)* dizzy and faint. *(s)* giddy, unsteady, woozy, wobbly, shaky, groggy, delirious. *(ant)* steady.

10   **inanimate** *(adj)* not alive or showing signs of life. *(s)* inactive, unresponsive, lifeless, inert, idle. *(ant)* animate.

11   **egotistical** *(adj)* overly interested in oneself. *(s)* selfish, smug, narcissistic, vain, arrogant, proud. *(ant)* selfless.

12   **devious** *(adj)* skilful at using underhand (deceitful) tactics. *(s)* conniving, dishonest. *(ant)* honest.

13   **custom** *(adj)* made to personal order. *(s)* personalised, bespoke, individualised, tailored. *(ant)* mass-produced.

14   **cavernous** *(adj)* like a cavern (large cave). *(s)* vast, spacious, capacious, roomy, yawning. *(ant)* small, cramped.

displaying no **contrition**[1], Jayne Lewis wasted not one single thought on the **subordinate**[2], **puny**[3] man she left on the floor.

'Bring the **prissy**[4] fool in after I have gone,' she instructed **tersely**[5] to the black-clad men guarding her. 'Be lenient; he may prove **superfluous**[6], but we might need the snivelling traitor again,' she said in a **humiliating**[7] tone. 'Ensure he **recuperates**[8] and remains onside,' she finished. Then she was gone.

Evans didn't hear the **disparaging**[9] **scorn**[10] and belligerence in her voice as he sobbed into his grubby waistcoat, just thankful to be alive now he had delivered the goods. He prayed she wouldn't leave him here, condemned to rot alone.

As he **mewled**[11] like an abandoned kitten, he didn't see the two **oval**[12]-shaped eyes observing the happenings patiently from an obscured **alcove**[13]. Deftly hidden, they peered from **amidst**[14] the cables that carried **unprecedented**[15] quantities of **data**[16] into the building.

As two uniformed men gathered up Evans's **forlorn**[17] body from the soil, the eyes' **astute**[18] gaze missed nothing. **Bolstering**[19] the slight man up under both arms, the muscled guards

---

1   **contrition** *(n)* a feeling of remorse and penitence (sorriness). *(s)* apology, regret, repentance. *(ant)* impenitence.

2   **subordinate** *(adj)* low-ranking and less important. *(s)* lesser, inferior, lowly, subservient. *(ant)* superior.

3   **puny** *(adj)* weak and small. *(s)* slight, minor, insignificant, inadequate, worthless, useless. *(ant)* mighty.

4   **prissy** *(adj)* fussily and excessively respectable. *(s)* prim, stuffy, strait-laced, fastidious, precious. *(ant)* unfussy.

5   **tersely** *(adv)* in a terse (short) manner. *(s)* snappily, abruptly, curtly, brusquely, concisely. *(ant)* long-windedly.

6   **superfluous** *(adj)* unnecessary or irrelevant. *(s)* redundant, unneeded, useless, dispensable. *(ant)* necessary, essential.

7   **humiliating** *(adj)* destructive to one's dignity or self-respect. *(s)* demeaning, disgracing. *(ant)* praising.

8   **recuperate** *(v)* recover from exertion (effort) or illness. *(s)* convalesce, improve, rally, mend. *(ant)* deteriorate.

9   **disparaging** *(adj)* regarding something as having little worth. *(s)* belittling, ridiculing, derisive. *(ant)* admiring.

10   **scorn** *(n)* open contempt (dislike). *(s)* disdain, derision, mockery, ridicule, sarcasm, sneering. *(ant)* admiration, respect.

11   **mewl** *(v)* cry feebly as a baby might. *(s)* weep, whimper, snivel, whine, grizzle, pule, moan. *(ant)* laugh.

12   **oval** *(adj)* possessing a rounded and slightly elongated outline, egg-shaped. *(s)* elliptical, ovoid.

13   **alcove** *(n)* a recess (hollow or indentation) in a wall. *(s)* niche, nook, corner, cubicle, bay. *(ant)* protrusion.

14   **amidst** *(prep)* surrounded by or in the middle of. *(s)* among, amongst, within, amid. *(ant)* outside.

15   **unprecedented** *(adj)* never known or done before. *(s)* unmatched, unparalleled, extraordinary. *(ant)* common.

16   **data** *(n)* information collected for use. *(s)* statistics, facts, figures, numbers, documents, records.

17   **forlorn** *(adj)* sad and abandoned or lonely. *(s)* pitiful, dejected, despondent, hopeless, pathetic. *(ant)* cheerful.

18   **astute** *(adj)* able to quickly assess and turn something to one's advantage. *(s)* sharp, shrewd, cunning. *(ant)* dim-witted.

19   **bolster** *(v)* support or strengthen. *(s)* boost, fortify, sustain, assist, prop, shore up. *(ant)* weaken, hinder.

escorted[1] the **whimpering**[2] Evans into Via-Corp's basement.

Watching the opening disappear in the same **stupendous**[3] way in which it had appeared, the **piercing**[4] oval eyes blinked, their pupils expanding like pools of spilled ink as they **acclimatised**[5] to their murkier surroundings. They stared **inquisitively**[6], trained on the vast steel wall. Informed and certain the **transaction**[7] was finalised, the green eyes conscientiously swept the immediate area once more. Satisfied at what it saw, and with a swish of its tail, the soot-black cat slinked away into the darkness, manoeuvring **attentively**[8] through the tunnels, heading for home.

---

1   **escort** *(v)* accompany (go with) someone somewhere. *(s)* shepherd, chaperone, lead, direct. *(ant)* abandon.

2   **whimper** *(v)* make low, feeble sounds expressing displeasure. *(s)* whine, mewl, snivel, bleat. *(ant)* rejoice.

3   **stupendous** *(adj)* incredibly impressive. *(s)* astounding, astonishing, remarkable. *(ant)* unremarkable.

4   **piercing** *(adj)* showing keen intelligence. *(s)* perceptive, insightful, sharp, shrewd, astute. *(ant)* dim.

5   **acclimatise** *(v)* become accustomed (used) to. *(s)* adapt, adjust, familiarise, habituate. *(ant)* misadjust.

6   **inquisitively** *(adv)* in an inquisitive (curious) way. *(s)* quizzically, curiously, enquiringly. *(ant)* indifferently.

7   **transaction** *(n)* an instance of conducting business or a deal. *(s)* exchange, agreement, arrangement.

8   **attentively** *(adv)* in an attentive (watchful) manner. *(s)* heedfully, vigilantly, alertly. *(ant)* carelessly.

SATURDAY

18. A Silent Witness

What Claire saw rocked her very core. Sickened, she watched from the shadows, paralysed by a piercing stab of anguish as her eyes tracked the scene with disbelief. Should she stay? Should she run? She was a lone witness to this unfolding crime; no one could help her.

She knew she should **intervene**[1] – scream, fight, stop her somehow – but this time, she knew she could not. Having to endure this **despicable**[2] act, this loathsome betrayal, was **unavoidable**[3] because, **undoubtedly**[4], Claire had neither the skill nor the might to **conquer**[5] this **perpetrator**[6].

How could this be happening? How had she misjudged her so badly? How could someone she had trusted so **implicitly**[7], so **explicitly**[8], deceive her so convincingly? Gwilym and Gladys had been wrong about her so-called *Instinct*. She didn't have any. If she did, surely she would have seen or at least suspected this **duplicity**[9]. Either way, the deceit unravelling before her eyes broke her heart.

Just yesterday, when she had achieved such incredible heights, she had felt invincible. Now, as she froze into **submission**[10], her limbs numb with delayed shock, everything she had believed,

---

1   **intervene** *(v)* take part to prevent or alter something. *(s)* interfere, intercede, interrupt, intrude. *(ant)* avoid.

2   **despicable** *(adj)* deserving contempt (scorn) and hatred. *(s)* appalling, loathsome, abhorrent. *(ant)* admirable.

3   **unavoidable** *(adj)* not able to be avoided, ignored or prevented. *(s)* inevitable, unescapable. *(ant)* avoidable.

4   **undoubtedly** *(adv)* without doubt. *(s)* certainly, undeniably, definitely, unquestionably. *(ant)* doubtfully.

5   **conquer** *(v)* successfully overcome. *(s)* defeat, overthrow, beat, vanquish, trounce, annihilate. *(ant)* lose to.

6   **perpetrator** *(n)* someone who does something wrong or illegal. *(s)* culprit, offender, criminal.

7   **implicitly** *(adv)* in an implicit (absolute) way. *(s)* completely, unquestioningly, unreservedly. *(ant)* restrictedly.

8   **explicitly** *(adv)* in an explicit (definite) way. *(s)* openly, clearly, obviously, unequivocally. *(ant)* ambiguously.

9   **duplicity** *(n)* deceitfulness. *(s)* deception, underhandedness, disloyalty, betrayal. *(ant)* honesty.

10   **submission** *(n)* the action of acceptance or yielding (surrender). *(s)* capitulation, resignation. *(ant)* rebellion.

all her hopes, dreams and **aspirations**[1], dwindled into nothing as **desolation**[2] seeped through her body.

Although the woman's long blonde hair lay **slicked**[3] back and knotted into an austere **chignon**[4], Claire would recognise her anywhere: the outline of her **willowy**[5] figure; the unmistakable shape of her long, lean limbs; the elegance of her stance as she **stalked**[6] like a hungry cat; her body **cloaked**[7] in a black all-in-one that hugged her **enviable**[8] figure as snugly as a surgeon's glove. Even in flat ballet shoes, Jayne Lewis stood almost six feet tall.

Rooted to the spot, Claire watched, obscured by the same towering bookshelves she had hidden behind only yesterday. Jayne, her dad's wonderfully kind girlfriend, who Claire had adored, who she had admired even more than her own mother, was standing over the glass case that held the Gwalch Gem bracelet. The bracelet of which Claire was supposedly a 'Keeper' and which, in the wrong hands, could cause devastation. As Claire observed, lost in shock, Jayne's bewildering perfection now seemed **obscene**[9]. Claire realised that hitherto every meeting, every conversation, every action had concealed a **depraved**[10] lie. Jayne Lewis was a Mal-Instinctive.

The familiar museum, the bracelet's safe place, was deserted. There was no sign of Mr or Mrs Evans, who were supposed to guard the **hallowed**[11] bracelet. Where were Gwilym and Owain? Claire willed them to appear, to land in the helicopter she had waved them off in just hours before from Gladys Jones's front door.

With a futile wish, she glanced at the basement door. In earnest she hoped Jack might appear to save the day, his teeth bared and hackles up, ready to outdo this immoral **charlatan**[12].

But as case 111 cracked and shattered before her eyes, its millions of sparkling crystals tinkling

---

1   **aspiration** *(n)* a hope or ambition of achieving. *(s)* desire, dream, wish, aim, purpose, goal. *(ant)* apathy.

2   **desolation** *(n)* great unhappiness or loneliness. *(s)* misery, heartbreak, despair, anguish, woe. *(ant)* gladness.

3   **slick** *(v)* make smooth and glossy. *(s)* sleek, flatten, plaster, gel. *(ant)* roughen, rumple, tousle.

4   **chignon** *(n)* a coil or knot of hair on the back of a woman's head. *(s)* bun, twist, updo.

5   **willowy** *(adj)* tall, slim and lithe. *(s)* slender, graceful, elegant, svelte. *(ant)* stocky, squat.

6   **stalk** *(v)* pursue (follow, chase) or approach stealthily (unseen). *(s)* hunt, trail, shadow, haunt, prowl.

7   **cloak** *(v)* cover, hide or disguise. *(s)* conceal, veil, shroud, wrap, envelop, swathe, camouflage. *(ant)* reveal.

8   **enviable** *(adj)* causing envy (jealousy). *(s)* attractive, admirable, desirable. *(ant)* unenviable.

9   **obscene** *(adj)* offensive against morality (decency). *(s)* vile, atrocious, outrageous, sickening. *(ant)* innocuous.

10   **depraved** *(adj)* morally (ethically) corrupt. *(s)* wicked, immoral, evil, vicious, deviant, warped. *(ant)* pure.

11   **hallowed** *(adj)* greatly honoured and revered (respected). *(s)* prized, beloved, esteemed. *(ant)* disgraceful.

12   **charlatan** *(n)* someone falsely claiming to have a certain skill or knowledge. *(s)* impostor, cheat. *(ant)* expert.

and scattering onto the floor amid plumes of noxious smoke and the incongruous smell of lilies, no one came. No knight in shining armour materialised, no rufty-tufty Jack Russell or smiling octogenarian appeared. A huge wave of disappointment, almost **grief**[1], washed over Claire, and any **semblance**[2] of hope was swept clean away.

Jayne was in the process of stealing the Gwalch Gem bracelet from the glass case. This meant only one thing: she must have both halves of the Cutter, the only tool capable of fracturing the magical glass.

Claire's mind raced. How had this traitorous **impostor**[3] managed to do this? Claire knew the Master had escaped with one half of the Cutter, and Gladys had said the knight Evans had taken the other half away to safety. Claire had never trusted Robert Evans.

Her heart was beating in her throat as she saw several things simultaneously: her once-beloved Jayne plucking the Gwalch Gem bracelet from the case and slipping it **ceremoniously**[4] onto her wrist as a crumpled Marjorie Evans appeared from the shadows behind, handing something to Jayne. Claire squinted to make out the object and realised the birdlike Mrs Evans was handing her school bag to Jayne. Claire had left it at the museum earlier. Then, without a word, Jayne took the bag and pirouetted in her ballet shoes, leaving the building, making no more noise than a shadow.

Claire felt like she'd swallowed a bag of snakes. Stricken by the **injustice**[5] of Jayne's deceit, she knew if she tried to move, she would sob out loud and give herself away.

Powerless, Claire lay on her side as hot, silent tears sploshed down her face, trickling off the end of her nose onto the floor. A blanket of despair smothered her. Unable to collect herself, she pulled up her hood and snuggled hopelessly into the fur trim that surrounded her wet face.

*

Transient[6] shadows scattered **hither and thither**[7], ducking back and forth, hiding amidst a thick murk of fog. Unsure of how long she had lain there, minutes or hours, Claire blinked furiously,

---

1   **grief** *(n)* intense sorrow because of a loss or death. *(s)* heartbreak, anguish, desolation, distress. *(ant)* comfort.

2   **semblance** *(n)* the outward appearance of something. *(s)* approximation, show, pretence. *(ant)* reality.

3   **impostor** *(n)* someone pretending to be someone else to deceive others. *(s)* phoney, charlatan.

4   **ceremoniously** *(adv)* done with an air (look) of ceremony. *(s)* grandly, grandiosely. *(ant)* informally.

5   **injustice** *(n)* lack of justice (fairness). *(s)* unjustness, unfairness, wrongdoing, abuse, crime. *(ant)* justice.

6   **transient** *(adj)* lasting for only a short while. *(s)* fleeting, passing, temporary, momentary. *(ant)* permanent.

7   **hither and thither** *(adv)* in various directions. *(s)* all around, round about.

urging her eyes to focus. A shard of stark, bright light shone in a horizontal strip to her right whilst a soft orange haze glowed down to her left. Then she remembered. The horror of Jayne's vile betrayal surfaced like a waking monster. She had lain so still, in such comatose desolation, she must have dozed off.

Sitting up slowly as her eyes adjusted to the light, she was struck by something oddly familiar. The outlines and **silhouettes**[1] in the room now comprised shapes she recognised well. Instinctively fumbling to her right, she found the switch and turned on the lamp. She lay in bed, her own bed, in her room, at home.

Reeling, she snatched at her **duvet**[2] and threw it off. She was wearing her pyjamas; they had stuck to her skin, soaked and cooling rapidly to a chilly sog. She shivered. She'd experienced this feeling before but never so strong as now. Waking from a dream so vivid, so palpably real, for several confused seconds, she had almost believed it was happening. The immense relief hit her so hard she laughed out loud.

'I knew it!' she said. 'I knew it! Jayne would never do that to me,' she laughed.

When her heart had slowed and some semblance of calm had worked its way through her, she hopped out of bed and quickly changed her pyjamas. On her chest of drawers, Wallace's head lay next to Gromit, but now the clock was ticking again. She picked it up and put it to her ear, listening to the rhythmic tick-tock. The clock said 3.30 a.m.

Having no idea whether it showed the right time, she crawled back into bed. As she was wide awake now, she leaned across and grabbed her book from her bedside table and read a few pages. But the words refused to **register**[3], and after repeatedly reading the same sentence over and over, she gave up and returned to where she had started, re-creasing the triangle at the top corner of the page.

Putting down her book, leaving her lamp on, she closed her eyes, but her mind tormented her, insisting on revisiting the nightmare she had just woken from. It had been so **graphic**[4], so detailed, the feelings it evoked so realistic, that she fought to discern between the imaginary and

---

1   **silhouette** *(n)* a visible, dark shape and outline. *(s)* contour, form, shadow, profile, line, figure.

2   **duvet** *(n)* a quilt filled with feathers, down or synthetic fibre. *(s)* eiderdown, comforter, coverlet, bedding.

3   **register** *(v)* make an impression (mark) on one's mind. *(s)* enter, penetrate, sink in. *(ant)* erase.

4   **graphic** *(adj)* showing clear and vivid (realistic) details. *(s)* lifelike, explicit, lucid, detailed. *(ant)* sketchy.

the real. Tossing and turning, counting sheep and forcing pleasant thoughts, she **fended off**[1] intruding images until finally, as dawn broke, she drifted off into a **fitful**[2] and restless sleep.

---

1   **fend off** *(v)* defend oneself from something. *(s)* stop, block, repel, resist, parry, discourage. *(ant)* encourage.
2   **fitful** *(adj)* not regular or steady. *(s)* disturbed, broken, restless, erratic, sporadic. *(ant)* unbroken, peaceful.

19. The Flying Sponge

Claire woke weighed down with a **portentous**[1] sense of doom. Although she realised it was probably the lingering effects of the worst nightmare she had ever had, she struggled to quell the bubbling niggle of apprehension in the pit of her stomach.

Wallace and Gromit reckoned it was 7.30 a.m., but what did they know? They had let her oversleep yesterday morning. Was that due to the broken clock or, as Gladys had said, the Knights Hawk having tangled time for her? In the cold light of a Saturday morning, after barely any sleep, yesterday's extraordinary happenings seemed utterly preposterous.

What does 'tangling time' mean, anyway? Claire asked herself.

Maybe that was all a dream too, she thought as she headed downstairs to face her family.

'Hey, Choccy Eclair, how's Chorlton's resident heroine feeling this morning, then?' joked Pete. He lay sprawled **lethargically**[2] in his usual place on the sofa, controller in hand. 'You, my sis, are the talk of the town,' he continued to tease.

Claire ignored him and headed for the kitchen. She was surprised to find that Dee wasn't parked in the Throne, getting ready for work. Saturday was a hairdresser's busiest day.

'Where's Mum?' she asked Pete as he crashed through the kitchen door in search of food.

'She's in bed; she's taking the day off to keep an eye on daft Becs,' he answered.

'Oh,' said Claire, thinking about how appalling and vulnerable her sister had looked last night.

'I don't reckon Mum slept much last night; she had Becs in with her,' Pete continued.

'Right,' said Claire.

---

1 **portentous** *(adj)* of or like a portent (sign of something bad). *(s)* ominous, threatening, fateful. *(ant)* trivial.

2 **lethargically** *(adv)* in a lethargic (lazy) manner. *(s)* indolently, leisurely, idly, lifelessly. *(ant)* energetically.

'Come on, spit it out,' Pete said. 'What really went on yesterday with you and Drane at that museum? I know you're not telling all,' Pete asked, squinting at her.

'I am; I have,' she answered in too **shrill**[1] a voice. 'Honestly, I just got lucky. I saw red and shoved Drane as hard as I could. He must have hit his head when he landed or something, and he let go of Becs. Honestly, Pete, it's nothing more than that. How could it be? I'm hardly tiny though, am I? Let's face it, I **bowled**[2] him over with a fair bit of **heft**[3] and a lot of luck,' she finished, avoiding all eye contact with her brother.

Claire hurried her breakfast – Ben would be calling for her at nine-ish. She quickly finished her cereal and rinsed out her bowl and spoon.

'One day, I'm buying Mum a dishwasher,' she said to Pete.

'No room,' drawled Pete, his mouth full. 'And anyway, no need, Eclair – we've got you,' he added, ducking the wet sponge she threw at him. It narrowly missed Pete but hit Dee, who had just walked through the kitchen door.

'Oh, Mum, I'm so sorry,' Claire gasped, her hand over her mouth. The square yellow sponge, like a Post-it note, had stuck to the front of Dee's fluffy dressing gown before plopping to the floor.

A silence fell as Claire and Pete exchanged glances; Dee had not had her coffee yet – this did not **bode**[4] well.

Dee's face was unreadable; then, uncharacteristically, she burst out laughing. Both her kids exhaled in relieved sighs.

'Phew, you were lucky!' Pete whispered out of the corner of his mouth as he squashed past Claire to leave.

'Hey, where are you going, laddie?' asked Dee, back to her normal self in a flash. 'Bowl!' she said, pointing to his **detritus**[5] on the table. 'Sink!' she ordered. 'And don't expect Claire to clear up after you – she's not Cinderella,' added Dee, much to Claire's amusement.

'Nah, but she's got an ugly sister,' retorted Pete in Claire's ear.

---

1   **shrill** *(adj)* high-pitched. *(s)* sharp, piercing, jarring, strident, thin, blatant. *(ant)* moderate, low, calm, soft.

2   **bowl** *(v)* strike (hit). *(s)* knock, collapse, fling, toss, roll, chuck, lob, propel, butt, impel.

3   **heft** *(n)* weight or heaviness. *(s)* bulk, size, clout, mass, immensity. *(ant)* lightness.

4   **bode** *(v)* be a portent (sign) of a certain outcome. *(s)* promise, forecast, portend, indicate.

5   **detritus** *(n)* debris or waste. *(s)* leftovers, scraps, rubbish, refuse, litter, garbage, trash, bits.

Claire laughed out loud, hoping her mum hadn't heard, especially given the state Rebecca had come home in last night.

'How are *you* this morning, Claire, love?' asked Dee.

'I'm fine, Mum. Is Becs OK?'

'She seems to be,' replied Dee. 'She slept well, but then she would do, wouldn't she, drugged up to the eyeballs by that boy?' she finished.

'I'm so glad she's OK, Mum. I really am. I need to rush now though, if you still don't mind,' replied Claire, swiftly closing down the **oncoming**[1] **debriefing**[2].

'Rush?' asked Dee.

'I've got Ben's competition,' answered Claire **breezily**[3], but holding her breath again, silently praying her mum would still let her go.

'Oh yes,' replied Dee. 'But make sure the **snobby**[4] Brady Bunch let me know EXACTLY what time you'll be home, won't you?' sniped Dee, true to form.

'Course, Mum,' laughed Claire. 'They're hardly **snobs**[5] though, Mum. They wouldn't bother with me if they were snobbish, would they?' she said as she left the kitchen and closed the door behind her, hoping her **quip**[6] wasn't a step too far.

Halfway up the stairs, she shouted, 'Oh, Mum, don't forget I'm out with Dad and Jayne tomorrow too,' and with that, she ran up the rest of them before Dee could answer.

---

1 **oncoming** *(adj)* approaching or about to happen. *(s)* looming, nearing, advancing, imminent. *(ant)* receding.

2 **debriefing** *(n)* an interview about a completed mission or undertaking. *(s)* probe, interrogation. *(ant)* brief.

3 **breezily** *(adv)* in a breezy (light) manner. *(s)* briskly, brightly, cheerily, merrily, flippantly. *(ant)* seriously.

4 **snobby** *(adj)* like a snob (one who feels or acts superior). *(s)* snooty, conceited, pretentious. *(ant)* humble.

5 **snob** *(n)* someone who overly respects position and wealth, and looks down on other people. *(s)* snoot.

6 **quip** *(n)* a witty (humorous) remark. *(s)* witticism, joke, wisecrack, retort, banter, jest, jibe.

20. An Unexpected Change of Plan

Claire waited for a few seconds, her ear to her bedroom door, fully expecting her mum to thunder up the stairs at the mention of Jayne. Relieved at the lack of impending footsteps, she threw on some clothes and headed to the bathroom to clean her teeth. Surprised, she bumped into a bleary-eyed Rebecca emerging from her mum's bedroom.

'Becs, you're up early,' said Claire, noticing her sister's raw, puffy eyes. 'How are you feeling? You OK?'

Rebecca didn't look OK, but she nodded, pulling her dressing-gown cord tighter around her hunched[1] body. 'Yeah, I suppose so,' she whispered.

Claire knew how difficult Rebecca would find admitting her gullibility and vulnerability to her little sister.

'Claire, I'm … I'm so grateful for what you did yesterday,' Rebecca stuttered, her voice cracking, but Claire interrupted her.

'It's OK, Becs, really. There's no need to say anything more. Honestly, it's cool,' Claire finished. The look on her sister's face was thanks enough.

'Do you mind if I go in first? Ben's picking me up soon, and I need to hurry,' Claire asked, nodding towards the bathroom.

'No, course not. You go in,' answered Rebecca, all fight in her gone. Normally, she'd have physically barged her little sister out of the way and locked the door behind her.

'Thanks,' said Claire, with not a single smug bone in her body.

How the heck am I supposed to keep this from Ben? she thought, when her mother's rapping

---

1   **hunched** *(adj)* bent over with shoulders raised. *(s)* curled, bowed, stooped, arched, curved. *(ant)* straightened.

on the door shocked her into dropping her toothbrush. It hit the sink, flicking white **speckles**[1] across the front of her dark hoody.

'Claire, open this door now,' Dee hissed in a low, insistent voice.

'What is it? What's wrong, Mum? Becca's OK, isn't she?' asked Claire, opening the door, worried her sister might have been taken ill.

'Yes, yes, *she's* fine. It's me that's not! Your father has just knocked on the door unexpectedly, and I opened it to him dressed like this!' Dee groaned, pointing to her dressing gown.

'Mum, is that it? I thought something was *really* wrong. You're fine. Pink fluffy suits you,' she joked as she headed past Dee down the stairs.

Vince stood in their lounge, talking gaming **strategy**[2] with Pete.

'Hiya, Dad. What is it?' Claire asked, that earlier niggle returning **with a vengeance**[3].

'Hi, darling. How are you today?' asked Vince, **pecking**[4] her on the cheek before hugging her.

'I'm fine, Dad,' said Claire. 'Why are you here *today*? Is everything OK?'

'Yes, love, everything's fine. Did you sleep OK last night?' he asked.

Claire knew full well her dad didn't have good news.

'Dad, what is it?' she insisted.

'I'm so sorry, love,' he said, grimacing. 'Jayne had a work emergency after she dropped you home yesterday evening; she's been there all night.'

'Oh no,' said Claire, clearly disappointed.

'I hate to let you down, love, but we're going to have to **postpone**[5] our theatre visit tomorrow. Some sort of **catastrophic**[6] security **breach**[7] has attacked the Via-Corp headquarters' systems, and I doubt she'll be able to get away this weekend. It's pretty serious stuff, I think,' he finished.

'Oh, that's a real shame, Dad. Could we go next weekend instead?' asked Claire hopefully.

'Maybe. I hope so, love. I'm sure Jayne will rebook the tickets as soon as she can,' he added.

---

1   **speckle** *(n)* a small speck (spot) or patch of colour. *(s)* mark, spatter, dot, fleck, dapple, mottle. *(ant)* mass.

2   **strategy** *(n)* a plan to achieve an overall or long-term aim. *(s)* tactic, action, approach, method. *(ant)* disorder.

3   **with a vengeance** *(adv)* with intensity (force, strength). *(s)* vigorously, powerfully, fiercely. *(ant)* mildly.

4   **peck** *(v)* kiss lightly or perfunctorily (quickly).

5   **postpone** *(v)* arrange to take place later than planned. *(s)* delay, defer, rearrange, reschedule. *(ant)* advance.

6   **catastrophic** *(adj)* extremely unfortunate and damaging. *(s)* disastrous, calamitous, ruinous. *(ant)* beneficial.

7   **breach** *(n)* a break or gap in something, often made by an attacking enemy. *(s)* violation. *(ant)* repair.

'What's up?' asked Dee, clattering down the stairs into the lounge. She had changed out of her dressing gown into jeans and a shirt. Claire didn't miss the quick **application**[1] of make-up; she suspected Dee would **reunite**[2] with Vince in a heartbeat, given half a chance.

Poor Mum, she thought.

'What is it?' Dee asked again, staring at Vince.

'Er … Jayne's needed at work this weekend, so we need to **reschedule**[3] tomorrow,' said Vince, looking down as he spoke.

'Really? After her ordeal yesterday, you're letting Claire down?' said Dee, wagging her finger at him.

'Mum, it's fine,' said Claire, realising her mum's attempt at **capitalising**[4] on the opportunity to **berate**[5] Jayne. 'I'm going out with Ben today, anyway, and we're bound to be back late. It might be a good thing it's postponed. I'm a bit tired; it'll give me a chance to catch up,' said Claire, placating her mother.

'I'm sorry, Claire,' said Vince again.

'It's fine, Dad. Will you just ask Jayne to rebook as soon as she can?' said Claire, giving him a goodbye hug.

'Is Becs up yet?' he asked.

'She's in the shower,' replied Dee.

'Oh, OK,' said Vince. 'I'm really sorry, Dee,' he continued, nodding towards her. 'See you, Pete,' he added, reaching over to his sofa-**splayed**[6] son and lifting one of the earpieces from the side of his head. 'See you, son,' he said again, letting go of it with a playful **twang**[7].

'See ya, Dad,' Pete replied, not taking his eyes off the screen.

'Would you ask Becs to give me a call later today, please?' Vince asked.

Dee didn't speak.

---

1   **application** *(n)* the action of applying something to a surface. *(s)* dab, administering. *(ant)* removal.

2   **reunite** *(v)* come or get back together. *(s)* reconcile, reunify. *(ant)* split, separate, estrange.

3   **reschedule** *(v)* replan or change the time of. *(s)* postpone, defer, rearrange, reorganise.

4   **capitalise** *(v)* take the chance to gain advantage from. *(s)* maximise, exploit, profit. *(ant)* lose.

5   **berate** *(v)* criticise or scold (tell off). *(s)* rebuke, slate, censure, chide, revile, lambaste. *(ant)* praise.

6   **splay** *(v)* spread or thrust apart. *(s)* spread out, expand, extend, drape, stretch, strew, span. *(ant)* huddle.

7   **twang** *(n)* a pinging or ringing sound or movement caused by pulling or plucking. *(s)* boing.

'I will, Dad,' responded Claire quickly.

Vince walked past the sofa, heading for the front door.

'Oh, yikes, I nearly forgot,' said Vince, bending down and reaching for something on the floor by the front door. 'Claire, Jayne asked me to give you this.'

Vince straightened up, Claire's school bag in his hand. 'Here you go, love.'

Speechless, her mind racing, her bag dangling from her hand, Claire stuttered, 'Dad … Dad, when did Jayne get this from the museum? Did she tell you? Did you go with her?' she asked, her dream vivid now.

'I'm not sure, love,' Vince answered. 'When she called to say she had to work, I went home. It was outside my flat this morning with a note on the top of it. She must have dropped it off at some point.'

'Oh, OK,' said Claire, forcing a normal voice.

'I didn't see her again last night, after dropping Becs here. She could be away all weekend, love,' he added, none the wiser, heading for the door.

Dee slammed it closed behind him.

21. Another Unexpected Change of Plan

Claire shot upstairs, bag in hand, traumatised. She'd had a rotten nightmare, hadn't she? It was sheer **coincidence**[1] Jayne had collected her bag from the museum, wasn't it? And been called to an emergency at work.

'Of course it is,' she said out loud, flopping down onto her bed. She wished Gladys had a phone. She didn't have time to run around there – Ben was due any moment.

I'm being daft, she thought, emptying her bag and stuffing in miscellaneous supplies for the day ahead. But she couldn't banish the **pervasive**[2] images of her dream. Could it possibly have meant something?

She would have to make an excuse to Ben and his parents and try to get around to Gladys's house.

Rushing from her bedroom, Claire bumped into a **chastened**[3]-looking Rebecca heading away from the bathroom.

Exchanging uncomfortable smiles, Claire spoke first. 'Dad asked if you'd give him a call today.'

'Yeah, course,' replied Rebecca. 'You out somewhere?'

'Yeah, with Ben.'

'See you later, maybe?'

Claire nodded. This level of **civility**[4] from her sister was both unusual and quite **novel**[5]. 'Yeah,

---

1   **coincidence** *(n)* something that seems to happen by chance. *(s)* accident, fluke, luck, quirk, fate.

2   **pervasive** *(adj)* spreading throughout. *(s)* prevalent, inescapable, persistent. *(ant)* scarce, limited.

3   **chasten** *(v)* correct, restrain or moderate behaviour. *(s)* humiliate, subdue, humble. *(ant)* encourage.

4   **civility** *(n)* courtesy in behaviour or speech. *(s)* politeness, consideration, courteousness. *(ant)* rudeness.

5   **novel** *(adj)* unusual or new. *(s)* different, unfamiliar, peculiar, unprecedented, curious. *(ant)* normal, familiar.

see you later,' replied Claire, heading down the stairs into the lounge, agonising over what to say to Ben.

Preoccupied, Claire hovered around the lounge, constantly glancing out of the window.

'You'll get a sore neck if you keep craning it,' said Dee. 'Don't forget, when the Brady Bunch arrive, make sure you ask them what time you'll be home tonight. I don't want another day like yesterday,' she instructed Claire.

'Course, Mum,' she replied, checking out of the window. 'You shouldn't call them that, Mum,' **admonished**[1] Claire light-heartedly.

'Why? They were a nice American TV family, the Brady Bunch, just like that lot,' responded Dee with her customary sarcastic ring.

'They're here!' shouted Claire, picking up her bag and coat.

'Give us a kiss, then,' said Dee, handing her a five-pound note.

Claire's eyes widened – Dee was not normally the kissy, huggy, generous type.

'Thanks so much, Mum! Byeeee,' said Claire, hugging her just as Ben knocked.

Claire broke free and made for the door. Snatching it open, she smiled and said, 'Hiya, Ben.'

'Hi. What happened to you yesterday? How come you missed school?' he asked.

'Long story. I'll tell you later, not in front of my mum,' she whispered, rolling her eyes, as Dee approached from behind.

'Hello, Benjamin,' said Dee in her posh voice. 'Could you kindly ask your dad what time you'll be back, please?' she said, waving **regally**[2] at John Brady sitting in his car.

Before Ben could move, Mr Brady's window descended. 'Hi, Dee. How are you?' he asked in his deep American **lilt**[3].

'I'm great, thanks, John,' she **trilled**[4]. 'No Jennifer with you today?' she asked, sounding like the Queen. 'What time might you be back?'

As Claire jumped into the back of the Brady's Tesla, she was sure her mum's cheeks had blushed – Mr Brady was handsome.

---

1   **admonish** *(v)* reprimand (tell off) firmly. *(s)* warn, advise, reproach, chide, caution, rebuke. *(ant)* allow, praise.

2   **regally** *(adv)* in a regal (royal) manner. *(s)* nobly, majestically, grandly, ceremoniously. *(ant)* commonly.

3   **lilt** *(n)* a characteristic rise and fall of the voice. *(s)* cadence, intonation, accent, tone, rhythm. *(ant)* monotone.

4   **trill** *(v)* make a warbling or quavering sound like a bird. *(s)* sing, chirp, twitter, shrill, tweet.

'Yeah, Jenny's sitting this one out today. She's marking **mock**[1] exams for school. We'll be back quite late,' replied Mr Brady. 'Is that a problem? I'll call you as we set off,' he added.

'That's fine,' said Dee. 'Her dad's cancelled her day out tomorrow, so no rush at all,' she finished with a disapproving frown.

'OK, great. We'll keep you posted, then,' said Mr Brady. 'Bye for now, Dee.'

'Bye, Claire,' said Dee to her daughter through the window.

'Bye, Mum.' Claire waved as they pulled away, the electric car making not a sound.

Claire knew she must say something before Ben quizzed her about her school absence; she hoped it would come out right.

'Excuse me, Mr Brady,' she said, without giving anyone a chance to speak. 'Could we quickly pop round to Gladys's house, please? Only, she wasn't well last night when I saw her,' she blurted in one breath.

She had done it – she had lied to her best friend and his dad. She didn't feel good about it.

'Really?' asked Ben, surprised. 'Is she OK?'

'Yes,' replied Claire, her voice strained. 'She said so, but she didn't look or seem right, and as she hasn't got a phone, I'm worried about her,' she fibbed, fingers crossed down at her side.

'Can we, Dad?' asked Ben.

'Of course,' replied his dad. 'We can take a five-minute **detour**[2].'

'You know where she lives, right?' asked Ben. 'It's on the Green, number twenty-two.'

'Yes, thanks, son. I know where she lives.'

They turned onto Beech Road, towards the Green.

'What happened yesterday?' whispered Ben. 'There are rumours of police and stuff.'

Claire didn't answer; they'd pulled up outside Gladys's terrace.

'Thanks, Mr Brady,' she said, jumping out of the car so quickly it had barely stopped.

She slammed the door before Ben could follow. Mortified at her rudeness, she ran up the short path and rapped on Gladys's door. To her relief, Jack's warning bark rang out. She knocked again as he flung his little body at the back of the door, springing up and yapping at the letterbox.

'Quiet, Jack! Quiet, boy.'

---

1   **mock** *(adj)* not real, but not intended to deceive (trick). *(s)* pretend, simulated, imitation. *(ant)* genuine.

2   **detour** *(n)* an alternative route (course). *(s)* diversion, digression, deviation.

Claire was so relieved to hear Gladys's voice.

'Hello, Claire,' said Gladys, opening the door. 'Is everything all right?' she asked.

Jack whirled in excited circles, his tail wagging.

'Hi, Jacky,' said Claire, giving him only a cursory pat. 'Gladys, I had a dream, an awful nightmare, and I'm scared it might be true,' Claire gushed.

'Cariad, cariad, slow down,' said Gladys. 'What is it?'

Claire glanced over her shoulder, checking Ben was still in the car.

'Can we go in for a second, please, Gladys? Ben's waiting; I pretended you're ill.'

'Of course, come in,' said Gladys, shooing Jack through the door.

'It was horrible, Gladys. Jayne, my dad's girlfriend, smashed the glass case and took the Gwalch Gem bracelet. The case shattered to **smithereens**[1]; she must have both halves of the Cutter. It was a dream, wasn't it?' asked Claire, expecting Gladys to quash her fears immediately, but Gladys didn't answer.

Claire's words continued to pour out. 'What scared me most was that Mrs Evans gave my school bag to Jayne. What do you think, Gladys?'

'Cariad, what about this dream unnerves you so?'

'It's the bit I've not told you about yet,' said Claire. 'My dad called in earlier. He cancelled our trip out tomorrow, saying Jayne had to work, but what freaked me out was he gave me my school bag, which I'd left at the museum yesterday.'

'Ah,' answered Gladys. 'I see.'

'Oh, I'm so confused,' said Claire. 'Am I being silly, Gladys?' Claire didn't wait for an answer. 'But when did Jayne go back to the museum? Wouldn't it have been closed? How did Jayne get my bag, Gladys? How?' Claire pressed on, her eyes searching Gladys's face for answers. 'Something isn't right, Gladys; I know it,' said Claire. 'I know it.'

'You must go now; Ben is waiting. Go about your day as normal. Remain **vigilant**[2] and strong, as you did yesterday. Trust your Instinct, and Cadwaladr *will* watch over you,' said Gladys, her expression suddenly grave.

'What's happening, Gladys? What is it? Tell me,' Claire pleaded.

---

1   **smithereens** *(n)* small pieces. *(s)* bits, fragments, shards, particles, smithers. *(ant)* whole, completeness.

2   **vigilant** *(adj)* watching carefully for problems or danger. *(s)* watchful, observant, attentive. *(ant)* inattentive.

'I'm not entirely certain, but rest assured, as soon as I am, I will let you know.'

'How will you let me know, Gladys? You don't even have a phone,' asked Claire.

'Trust, Claire,' she replied. 'Trust. We will find a way to be with you if need be,' said Gladys.

Claire gave Gladys a brief hug, rubbed Jack's head and left, trying to appear as normal as she possibly could.

Horribly isolated, unable to share her knowledge, Claire climbed back into the Bradys' car.

'Is Gladys OK?' asked Ben. 'She looked fine from here,' he added, waving through the window to her as they pulled away.

'Yeah, she says so; best take her word for it,' replied Claire, a sense of overwhelming **foreboding**[1] shadowing her again, and she *still* hadn't mentioned to Gladys the **grisly**[2] vision she'd seen in the gem.

'Is Gladys ill?' asked Mr Brady from the front.

'She seems fine today, thanks, Mr Brady,' said Claire.

'Come on, you,' whispered Ben. 'I know you're hiding something. Tell me about yesterday. What happened?'

Claire hesitated, choosing her words prudently. 'I was really stupid,' she answered. 'I was envious of Becca's trip, so I skipped school and got the bus into town.' She looked out of the window the entire time she spoke.

'You truanted to go to a *museum*?' exclaimed Ben, chuckling. 'Only you could do that, Claire!' he giggled.

'Yeah. I know, I know. I'm so embarrassed,' she said. 'It's totally dumb. Can we leave it now?' she asked, looking at him for the first time.

'You really OK?' asked Ben, frowning at her.

'Yeah, I'm fine. Sorry for being **ratty**[3],' she apologised. 'I feel a right idiot.' She gave a half smile.

'OK, cool. Forgotten.' He smiled back.

'Where's the competition today?' she asked, changing the subject.

'In some weird-sounding place,' said Ben. 'Can't remember the name of it. Dad, where's

---

1 **foreboding** *(n)* a bad feeling about something. *(s)* apprehension, dread, misgiving. *(ant)* confidence.

2 **grisly** *(adj)* causing disgust or horror. *(s)* abominable, appalling, ghastly, frightful, hideous. *(ant)* delightful.

3 **ratty** *(adj)* irritable and bad-tempered. *(s)* moody, tetchy, irascible, grumpy, mean. *(ant)* good-humoured.

the **venue**[1] today?' he asked, calling towards his dad.

'It's quite a drive today, son. The **organiser**[2] has changed it at the last minute,' he replied. 'It's in North Wales now.'

North Wales! thought Claire, jolted into high alert.

'Wow, North Wales,' she remarked, trying to sound breezy. 'Where in North Wales, Mr Brady?'

'Bangor,' he replied.

Claire gulped, briefly catching his eye in his rear-view mirror. She quickly looked away.

'You OK, Claire?' asked Ben. 'You seem different. Is something bothering you?' he persisted.

'Nah. I'm cool. Just tired after yesterday,' she said, looking out of the window again. 'My mum flipped, and I couldn't get to sleep.'

She was desperate to share her story with him, but instead, she just stared at the same countryside she had passed through on the train to Bangor yesterday.

'Dad, any chance you could turn Radio Bore off and put Radio One on, please?' Ben asked, laughing.

'Sure, son,' replied Mr Brady just as the phone rang through the car's speakers, interrupting the music. The name 'William C' flashed up onto the Tesla's screen.

'You gonna kill that call, Dad?' moaned Ben as the ringing persisted, blocking out the music.

'It's work,' replied his dad after a few seconds. 'I fancy a coffee, so I'll stop at the services, give the car a charge and call them back then.'

'It's Saturday, Dad; ignore it,' said Ben, laughing.

'That's why I *won't* ignore it, Ben,' replied his dad. 'They wouldn't call me if it wasn't important.'

*

'Don't even ask,' said Mr Brady to Ben and Claire, who stood drooling over a glass cabinet containing American-style doughnuts. He clutched a large coffee in one hand, and his phone in the other. 'Come on, you two,' he said, nodding towards the exit of the services' bustling main **thoroughfare**[3].

'Change of plan,' said Mr Brady, unplugging the Tesla. 'Jump in and I'll fill you in,' he finished.

---

1   **venue** *(n)* a place where something (an event) happens. *(s)* site, location, setting, spot, ground.

2   **organiser** *(n)* someone who arranges something. *(s)* coordinator, manager, director, controller.

3   **thoroughfare** *(n)* a path, route or road between two places. *(s)* access, passage, way.

Claire's stomach clenched. She climbed into the back of the car, trembling so much she could barely fasten her seat belt.

Mr Brady turned to face them in the back. 'I'm really sorry, guys, but the competition is off.'

'Oh no! Why?' asked a disappointed Ben.

Claire dreaded what Mr Brady might say next.

'I'm sorry, but I have to go into work, son,' he began. 'There's been a huge security breach overnight, and they're calling everyone in. It's **all hands on deck**[1],' he finished.

Security breach, thought Claire. She had heard those words already today, from her dad. Hadn't that been why Jayne had gone into work too?

'All's not lost though,' Mr Brady continued. 'Our headquarters are in the Welsh mountains, so I don't have to go back to the Manchester office. I'll get you two a work phone for the day, and you can go **sightseeing**[2] in the village whilst I go in and help. If you're *really* lucky, you might see some low-flying fighter jets circling the **Mach Loop**[3], where the pilots train. It's all in the company's grounds, so you'll be safe,' he finished.

'Hey, that would be soooo cool, Dad,' said Ben, beaming at Claire.

'Yeah, great,' added Claire. 'Sounds fun,' she said, trying to sound enthusiastic. 'Where do you work, Mr Brady?' she asked, her voice hollow.

'I work for a company called Via-Corp,' he answered, glancing at her in the mirror.

'Oh,' she replied, her heart banging in her chest.

It was the same company Jayne worked for and the same reason she, too, had been called in. Claire swallowed hard, trying to steady her voice. 'Where are we heading now, then, Mr Brady? Where are the headquarters?'

'Oh, they're on the outskirts of a quaint little place, quite a famous place though – in Wales, that is,' he added. 'It's called Beddgelert.'

Claire felt the blood drain from her face. She stared out of the window so Ben couldn't see her **pallid**[4], sickly appearance. **Beads**[5] of sweat glistened above her top lip as the true

---

1   **all hands on deck** *(idiom)* a saying used to indicate that all team members are required to help.

2   **sightseeing** *(n)* the activity of visiting places of interest. *(s)* touring, exploring, trekking, jaunting, scouting.

3   **Mach Loop** *(n)* (the Machynlleth Loop) valleys in Wales, notable for their use as low-level training areas for fast jet aircraft.

4   **pallid** *(adj)* pale-faced. *(s)* wan, pasty, white, ashen, sallow, anaemic, blanched. *(ant)* rosy, healthy.

5   **bead** *(n)* a drop of liquid on a surface. *(s)* dot, droplet, drip, globule, blob.

realisation[1] hit her. Jayne Lewis must be a Mal-Instinctive, and her dream was no dream. She yearned for Jack to be by her side.

'Ben,' she whispered, turning towards him, 'there's something I need to tell you.'

TO BE CONTINUED

---

1   **realisation** *(n)* the act of becoming aware that something is a fact. *(s)* understanding, comprehension. *(ant)* ignorance.

A Sneak Peek!

Thank you for reading *The Cadwaladr Quests: Tangled Time*.
I hope you enjoyed reading it as much as I did writing it!

If you did, here's a sneak peek at the first chapter of the next book in
The Cadwaladr Quests Trilogy: Race For The Gold

S.L. Ager

SATURDAY

1. Mountain Rescue

Is Jayne Lewis a Mal-Instinctive? Is Jayne Lewis a Mal-Instinctive?

Like an **irksome**[1] pop song, the **intrusive**[2] **earworm**[3] **burrowed**[4] deeper into Claire's brain, **chanting**[5] its **stark**[6], repetitive tune. Her head throbbed. She rested it awkwardly against the Tesla's **rear**[7] window, tempted to bang her skull against the glass to **expel**[8] and **expunge**[9] the **invasive**[10] worm, but its **monotone**[11] **droned**[12] on. *Is Jayne Lewis a Mal-Instinctive?* The smell of the Tesla's **opulent**[13] leather **interior**[14] reminded her of Jayne's **luxurious**[15] four-by-four. Could her dad's girlfriend really be a **hideous**[16] traitor?

Claire had chickened out, **disclosing**[17] nothing of yesterday to Ben. He still thought she'd

---

1   **irksome** *(adj)* irritating. *(s)* annoying, vexing, galling, exasperating. *(ant)* agreeable, pleasant.

2   **intrusive** *(adj)* disturbing and impossible to ignore. *(s)* inescapable, invasive, obtrusive. *(ant)* inconspicuous.

3   **earworm** *(n)* a song or tune that repeats continually in a person's mind.

4   **burrow** *(v)* dig. *(s)* excavate, penetrate, tunnel, probe, bore. *(ant)* withdraw.

5   **chant** *(v)* say or shout repeatedly in a sing-song tone. *(s)* chorus, repeat, carol.

6   **stark** *(adj)* sharply clear. *(s)* crisp, distinct, obvious, sheer, blatant, glaring. *(ant)* indistinct, ambiguous.

7   **rear** *(adj)* placed at the back part of something. *(s)* posterior, hind, aft. *(ant)* front, fore, anterior.

8   **expel** *(v)* force something out. *(s)* exclude, eject, oust, evict, banish. *(ant)* admit.

9   **expunge** *(v)* erase or remove entirely. *(s)* delete, efface, eliminate. *(ant)* preserve.

10   **invasive** *(adj)* intruding undesirably (difficult to ignore). *(s)* intrusive, persistent. *(ant)* non-invasive, restrained.

11   **monotone** *(n)* a continuing, unchanging sound. *(s)* monotony, drone, flatness. *(ant)* variation.

12   **drone** *(v)* speak in a dull or monotonous way. *(s)* murmur, intone, mumble. *(ant)* lilt.

13   **opulent** *(adj)* extremely luxurious or lavish. *(s)* splendid, sumptuous, extravagant. *(ant)* austere.

14   **interior** *(n)* the inner part of something. *(s)* inside. *(ant)* exterior, outside.

15   **luxurious** *(adj)* extremely elegant and often expensive. *(s)* opulent, sumptuous, extravagant. *(ant)* meagre.

16   **hideous** *(adj)* extremely unpleasant. *(s)* ugly, revolting, repugnant, appalling, monstrous. *(ant)* attractive.

17   **disclose** *(v)* make known. *(s)* show, reveal, uncover, unveil, divulge, impart, tell. *(ant)* hide, conceal, secrete.

truanted[1] from school to visit a museum, and besides, the Tesla was so quiet John Brady would hear everything. She stared at the various shades of countryside colours, which **gradated**[2] from **rustic**[3] browns to **lush**[4] greens as they headed to Mr Brady's headquarters in Beddgelert.

'How much further, Dad?' asked Ben. 'It's hilly now,' he added, poking his **index finger**[5] into his ear and wiggling it around. 'Your ears popped yet?' he asked Claire, nudging her from her **unsettling**[6] **reverie**[7].

She cracked a weak half smile and stuck a **forefinger**[8] into each ear. Wiggling them hard, she nodded, **feigning**[9] interest. 'Yeah,' she replied, then held her nose, blowing out her cheeks to help pop her ears.

'These roads are narrow, hey, kids?' Mr Brady interrupted, eyeing them both through the rear-view mirror.

Not compared to yesterday's, thought Claire, casting her mind back to the **perilous**[10] journey in the **rickety**[11] trap with Anwen, Gwilym and Jack the dog.

Yesterday, she **mused**[12] in disbelief, **mulling**[13] over Gladys's explanation of 'time-tangling'. It was a complete **cliché**[14], but yesterday felt like a **parallel**[15] life. *Perhaps this is another universe, or maybe it's not happened yet at all.* She almost laughed out loud at the **preposterous**[16] **notion**[17].

---

1   **truant** *(v)* stay away from school without leave or explanation. *(s)* wag, skive, bunk off. *(ant)* attend.

2   **gradate** *(v)* change by gradations or degrees. *(s)* blend, adjust.

3   **rustic** *(adj)* of or relating to the countryside. *(s)* rural, bucolic, pastoral. *(ant)* urban, cosmopolitan.

4   **lush** *(adj)* rich and pleasing to the eye. *(s)* fresh, abundant, profuse, healthy. *(ant)* dull.

5   **index finger** *(n)* the first finger (the one next to the thumb). *(s)* pointer, forefinger, indicator.

6   **unsettle** *(v)* cause to feel anxious. *(s)* bother, upset, disturb, worry, perturb, unnerve. *(ant)* appease, soothe.

7   **reverie** *(n)* a state of being lost in thought. *(s)* daydream, musing, contemplation, fantasy. *(ant)* concentration.

8   **forefinger** *(n)* the first finger (the one next to the thumb). *(s)* pointer, index finger, indicator.

9   **feign** *(v)* simulate or pretend. *(s)* affect, fake, bluff, sham.

10   **perilous** *(adj)* full of extreme risk or danger. *(s)* unsafe, hazardous, treacherous, precarious, chancy. *(ant)* safe.

11   **rickety** *(adj)* likely to collapse, poorly manufactured. *(s)* wobbly, unstable, unsound. *(ant)* reliable, sound.

12   **muse** *(v)* ask oneself in a thoughtful manner. *(s)* think, wonder, ponder, consider, contemplate. (ant) disregard.

13   **mull** *(v)* think about. *(s)* ponder, consider, contemplate, deliberate, muse, reflect, ruminate. *(ant)* disregard.

14   **cliché** *(n)* an expression used by many people. *(s)* banality, saying, stereotype. *(ant)* originality, novelty.

15   **parallel** *(adj)* existing at the same time. *(s)* coexisting, concurrent, simultaneous. *(ant)* divergent.

16   **preposterous** *(adj)* utterly nonsensical. *(s)* stupid, ridiculous, absurd, ludicrous. *(ant)* sensible, reasonable.

17   **notion** *(n)* an idea or something imagined. *(s)* thought, concept, conception.

'OK, guys, nearly there. We're approaching Beddgelert village,' said Mr Brady in his **distinctive**[1] American **accent**[2]. 'It's real **quaint**[3]. Shame it's so chilly; otherwise, you guys could have braved a dip,' he added as they drove alongside a fast-flowing river. 'It's as **shallow**[4] as a **brook**[5] in parts, but you'd freeze today.'

I'd rather not, thank you very much, thought Claire, eyeing the **ominous**[6] sky and angry-looking clouds gathering above the snow-capped mountains. She'd never been keen on getting wet.

Beddgelert. Claire tried to remember how Anwen, Gladys's sister, had **pronounced**[7] it yesterday.

As if reading her thoughts, Mr Brady asked, 'Are you guys familiar with Beddgelert's legend? That's Gelert's **supposed**[8] grave way over there. You can come down later. It's not too far.'

Before Ben could answer, Claire **blurted**[9] a clumsy, 'Yeah, I read it somewhere. It's dead boring. Summat about a Welsh prince who accidentally killed his dog. Are we nearly there yet, Mr Brady?'

'Yes, Claire, not much further,' he answered.

The Tesla glided through the **picturesque**[10] village and joined a tarmac road that **tapered**[11] to a single lane, leaving behind empty cafes, **lonesome**[12]-looking gift shops and a **plethora**[13] of grey stone cottages.

---

1   **distinctive** *(adj)* standing out because of a specific characteristic. *(s)* distinguishing, peculiar. *(ant)* indistinct.

2   **accent** *(n)* pronouncing of language in a way that is distinctive. *(s)* pronunciation, intonation.

3   **quaint** *(adj)* attractive or pleasingly old-fashioned. *(s)* picturesque, appealing, charming. *(ant)* ordinary, modern.

4   **shallow** *(adj)* having little depth. *(s)* depthless. *(ant)* deep.

5   **brook** *(n)* a small stream. *(s)* streamlet, rill, rivulet, runnel, beck.

6   **ominous** *(adj)* indicating imminent misfortune. *(s)* threatening, warning. *(ant)* unthreatening, auspicious.

7   **pronounce** *(v)* sound out. *(s)* say, speak, utter, enunciate, articulate. *(ant)* mispronounce.

8   **supposed** *(adj)* assumed to be true. *(s)* presumed, claimed, apparent, alleged. *(ant)* real.

9   **blurt** *(v)* say something suddenly and without consideration. *(s)* announce, exclaim, cry, utter.

10   **picturesque** *(adj)* visually attractive. *(s)* quaint, charming, delightful, scenic, pleasing. *(ant)* unattractive.

11   **taper** *(v)* narrow, diminish or reduce in thickness towards one end. *(s)* contract, decrease. *(ant)* thicken, expand.

12   **lonesome** *(adj)* remote and unfrequented. *(s)* solitary, forlorn, desolate. *(ant)* frequented, crowded.

13   **plethora** *(n)* a large or excessive amount of something. *(s)* abundance. *(ant)* lack, dearth, deficiency.

Ubiquitous[1] countryside stretched out before them, but its **terrain**[2] became **steeper**[3], **barren**[4] and **bleak**[5], **akin**[6] to **moorland**[7] in parts. Claire spotted a **lone**[8] **chestnut**[9] horse nibbling for grass in a bare, muddy field. She pictured the Welsh mountain pony Lady, who had pulled them along in the trap with such **courage**[10] yesterday.

Me, possibly becoming a Knight Hawk, she thought. It sounded **ludicrous**[11]. *How the heck will I explain this to Ben? He'll think I'm* **insane**[12].

The horrific dream that had **roused**[13] Claire this morning still haunted her. She refused to believe Jayne, her dad's amazing girlfriend, was a traitor, a Mal-Instinctive. Jayne would never hurt her or her dad, Vince, in that way, would she? Claire couldn't believe Mr Evans, the museum curator, was a Knight Hawk, and she struggled to shake the **unease**[14] that had **niggled**[15] her from the moment she'd clapped eyes on him when she'd caught the train to Bangor with Jack yesterday.

'Hey, Dad, is my skateboard in the **boot**[16]?' Ben asked in his Mancunian-American **twang**[17].

'Yeah, son. I threw in a couple of your decks and the snowboarding gear for tomorrow's lesson. Save me packing it tonight.'

'Claire, you sure you don't want to come boarding with us tomorrow? Oh no, sorry, I forgot. You're at the theatre with your dad, right?' said Ben, shaking his head.

---

1   **ubiquitous** *(adj)* present everywhere. *(s)* abundant, omnipresent, pervasive. *(ant)* absent, limited, rare, scarce.

2   **terrain** *(n)* a stretch of ground or its features. *(s)* area, land, environment, territory, setting, shape.

3   **steep** *(adj)* sharply rising or falling. *(s)* sheer, bluff, precipitous, vertical, vertiginous. *(ant)* gentle, gradual.

4   **barren** *(adj)* (of land) producing little or no vegetation. *(s)* arid, austere, bare, bleak, deserted. *(ant)* productive.

5   **bleak** *(adj)* stark and not encouraging or favourable. *(s)* unwelcoming, austere, desolate. *(ant)* appealing.

6   **akin** *(adj)* similar in character. *(s)* related, close, comparable. *(ant)* unlike, dissimilar.

7   **moorland** *(n)* a large area consisting of moors (uncultivated, open upland).

8   **lone** *(adj)* having no companions (company). *(s)* individual, solitary, single, alone, solo. *(ant)* accompanied.

9   **chestnut** *(adj)* deep reddish brown like the colour of a chestnut. *(s)* rusty, coppery.

10   **courage** *(n)* the ability to do something frightening. *(s)* bravery, pluck, valour, audacity. *(ant)* cowardice.

11   **ludicrous** *(adj)* so foolish, stupid or unreasonable as to be amusing. *(s)* absurd, farcical, comical. *(ant)* sensible.

12   **insane** *(adj)* foolish, mad and irrational. *(s)* crazy, idiotic, irresponsible, senseless. *(ant)* sensible, rational.

13   **rouse** *(v)* cause to stop sleeping. *(s)* wake, waken, awaken. *(ant)* lull, calm.

14   **unease** *(n)* want or lack of ease. *(s)* anxiety, angst, apprehension, dread, foreboding, jitters. *(ant)* calmness, ease.

15   **niggle** *(v)* slightly irritate. *(s)* bother, trouble, worry, annoy. *(ant)* ease, alleviate, appease.

16   **boot** *(n)* storage space in an automobile (often at the rear). *(s)* trunk.

17   **twang** *(n)* a distinctive manner of pronunciation. *(s)* sound, accent, diction, articulation.

She nodded and said, 'Yeah,' her answer too **upbeat**[1]. She hated herself for lying to her best friend. Anyway, she didn't want to snowboard again. She'd hurt her backside so much last time, she'd **waddled**[2] like a duck for a week.

Claire stared at the bag lying by her feet.

Why, and how, did Jayne return to the museum last night to collect it?

No matter how much Claire tried to forget the **grim**[3] scene she had **witnessed**[4] yesterday, it still sickened her. The image of Gwilym in the cracked glass case, turning into emerald and shattering into smithereens. *What did that **grisly**[5] vision mean? Will something dreadful happen to the Knights Hawk if the Gwalch Gem is separated from the magical gold bracelet, just like the image in the scene?* Claire was sure the man **depicted**[6] in that terrifying **portrayal**[7] of death had been Gwilym, the leader of the Knights Hawk.

'You OK, Claire?' Ben's eyes **scrutinised**[8] hers.

'Yeah, just tired after yesterday.' At least that wasn't a fib; Ben knew her too well to **dupe**[9] him for long.

Preoccupied[10], she muttered something about how peaceful the landscape looked. In truth, she was **rehearsing**[11] the explanations of yesterday she would give Ben the minute his dad was out of **earshot**[12]. The **nausea**[13] surfacing in her **gut**[14] was not a **consequence**[15] of travel sickness.

---

1   **upbeat** *(adj)* cheerful. *(s)* optimistic, positive, confident, hopeful. *(ant)* negative, pessimistic, cynical.

2   **waddle** *(v)* walk with a clumsy swaying motion. *(s)* toddle, wobble, totter, sway. *(ant)* stride, glide.

3   **grim** *(adj)* worrying or unpleasant. *(s)* frightful, sinister, terrible. *(ant)* pleasant.

4   **witness** *(v)* see something happen. *(s)* observe, view, watch, perceive, eyeball, notice. *(ant)* ignore, overlook.

5   **grisly** *(adj)* causing disgust or horror. *(s)* abominable, appalling, ghastly, frightful, hideous. *(ant)* delightful.

6   **depict** *(v)* represent in some form. *(s)* portray, show, describe, paint, picture, illustrate. *(ant)* misrepresent.

7   **portrayal** *(n)* a vivid depiction of something or someone. *(s)* representation, picture, rendering, sketch.

8   **scrutinise** *(v)* look, inspect or examine closely and thoroughly. *(s)* study, search, survey, analyse. *(ant)* glance.

9   **dupe** *(v)* deceive and trick. *(s)* fool, hoodwink, mislead, cheat, delude, beguile, bamboozle, con.

10   **preoccupied** *(adj)* engrossed in thought or mentally distracted. *(s)* absorbed, concerned. *(ant)* unconcerned.

11   **rehearse** *(v)* practise or prepare (sometimes mentally). *(s)* recite, list, review, repeat, iterate. *(ant)* improvise.

12   **earshot** *(n)* the distance within which one can hear or be heard. *(s)* close range, hearing range.

13   **nausea** *(n)* a feeling of sickness. *(s)* queasiness, biliousness, revulsion. *(ant)* wellness.

14   **gut** *(n)* the belly or stomach. *(s)* tummy, tum, insides, abdomen, intestines.

15   **consequence** *(n)* a result or effect. *(s)* outcome, upshot, repercussion, product. *(ant)* cause.

After Beddgelert village disappeared behind them, the **stealthy**[1] Tesla powered up through the **meandering**[2] lane, managing its steep **incline**[3] with ease. As if **conjured**[4] by the magic of ancient[5] **rituals**[6], **mighty**[7] stacks of **monolithic**[8] **slate**[9]-coloured rock **jutted**[10] **incongruously**[11] from the sides of sloping hills. Gushing streams slashed through open moorland. Gone were the **patchwork**[12] fields **hemmed**[13] in by yellow **gorse**[14] hedges and grey **drystone**[15] walls.

'Hey, Dad, where are your headquarters? How do they build stuff up here?' Ben laughed, **peering**[16] upwards out of the window.

'Oh, it's tucked away in an **ingenious**[17] spot,' his dad replied. 'David Lewis, our **founder**[18], is a **stickler**[19] for security and **privacy**[20], but then he has to be in his line of work – **artificial intelligence**[21] and **data**[22] storage.'

Claire's ears pricked up as her stomach **clenched**[23], not because of excitement but because of shock and dread. The name he'd just mentioned, Lewis, was the same surname as Jayne's.

---

1   **stealthy** *(adj)* done so as not to be seen or heard. *(s)* quiet, cautious, covert, surreptitious. *(ant)* blatant, overt.

2   **meandering** *(adj)* following a winding, twisting course. *(s)* zigzagging, bendy, curvy, twisty, snaky. *(ant)* straight.

3   **incline** *(n)* a slope. *(s)* gradient, pitch, ascent, rise, cant. *(ant)* decline.

4   **conjure** *(v)* make something appear unexpectedly or from nowhere. *(s)* summon, raise, rouse. *(ant)* dispel.

5   **ancient** *(adj)* in existence for a long time. *(s)* early, antique, olden, obsolete, archaic. *(ant)* contemporary, new.

6   **ritual** *(n)* relating to or done as a religious or solemn rite. *(s)* ceremony, observance, sacrament, practice.

7   **mighty** *(adj)* strong and powerful, especially due to size. *(s)* forceful, huge, almighty. *(ant)* weak, insignificant.

8   **monolithic** *(adj)* formed of a single very large block of stone.

9   **slate** *(n)* grey, green or bluish-purple rock that can be split easily into thin layers.

10   **jut** *(v)* protrude (stick out from). *(s)* poke out, project, extend, overhang. *(ant)* indent, depress, recede.

11   **incongruously** *(adv)* in a way that is out of keeping. *(s)* oddly, inappropriately. *(ant)* appropriately.

12   **patchwork** *(n)* a thing composed of many different parts or sections. *(s)* assortment, jumble, medley.

13   **hem** *(v)* surround and restrict. *(s)* enclose, border, edge.

14   **gorse** *(n)* spiky, yellow-flowered shrub.

15   **drystone** *(adj)* (of a stone wall) built without using mortar.

16   **peer** *(v)* look with concentration. *(s)* stare, scrutinise, gaze, scan, focus, examine, study, rake. *(ant)* glance.

17   **ingenious** *(adj)* clever, inventive and original. *(s)* innovative, smart, enterprising, creative. *(ant)* ignorant.

18   **founder** *(n)* a person who sets up something. *(s)* originator, creator, initiator.

19   **stickler** *(n)* someone who believes something should be done properly. *(s)* perfectionist, fusspot. *(ant)* neglecter.

20   **privacy** *(n)* the state of being free from observation and disturbance. *(s)* privateness, seclusion, isolation. *(ant)* publicity.

21   **artificial intelligence** *(n)* computer technology that simulates intelligent behaviour.

22   **data** *(n)* information collected for use. *(s)* statistics, facts, figures, numbers, documents, records.

23   **clench** *(v)* contract or tighten. *(s)* constrict, tense, cramp. *(ant)* relax.

*Surely that's a **coincidence**[1], Claire thought. It must be.*

The same **debilitating**[2] fear she had suffered yesterday **paralysed**[3] her again. Claire **yearned**[4] to have Jack by her side. She missed his doggy smell and **wiry**[5] coat, but **moreover**[6], his unfailing **loyalty**[7]. He was clearly a dog with Instinct, perhaps a Knight Hawk even.

'Not long now,' said Mr Brady as the **responsive**[8] Tesla picked up speed on a straighter, wider stretch. 'You guys hungry yet? There's a superb twenty-four-hour, **subsidised**[9] restaurant at work. David Lewis is **renowned**[10] for his **philanthropy**[11] and staff relations, although people rarely get to meet him – he's a **reclusive**[12] kinda guy.'

Most days, Claire would have perked up at the sound of **gourmet**[13] food, but today, even promises of **culinary**[14] delights didn't tempt her. Her usual **voracious**[15] **appetite**[16] had vanished.

'That sounds ace. I'm starved.' Ben looked straight at Claire, an **expectant**[17] **expression**[18] on his face.

'Er, yeah, me too,' she answered, her tone **unconvincing**[19].

Ben's eyes narrowed. 'You sure you're OK?' he whispered.

---

1   **coincidence** *(n)* something that seems to happen by chance. *(s)* accident, fluke, luck, quirk, fate.

2   **debilitating** *(adj)* tending to weaken or hinder. *(s)* incapacitating, draining, enervating. *(ant)* invigorating.

3   **paralyse** *(v)* cause to become unable to act or function properly. *(s)* disable, incapacitate. *(ant)* mobilise.

4   **yearn** *(v)* really want something. *(s)* long, ache, pine, crave, desire, hanker, thirst. *(ant)* reject, abjure.

5   **wiry** *(adj)* resembling wire in texture or form. *(s)* coarse, rough, bristly, scratchy. *(ant)* soft, sleek, smooth.

6   **moreover** *(adv)* even more so, as a further matter. *(s)* in addition, furthermore, also.

7   **loyalty** *(n)* the quality of giving constant support. *(s)* faithfulness, allegiance, reliability, devotion. *(ant)* disloyalty, treachery.

8   **responsive** *(adj)* reacting speedily. *(s)* active, reactive, receptive. *(ant)* sluggish, unresponsive.

9   **subsidise** *(v)* pay some of the cost to keep prices low for customers. *(s)* sponsor, fund, finance, back, assist. *(ant)* defund.

10   **renowned** *(adj)* known or talked about widely. *(s)* famous, eminent, esteemed. *(ant)* obscure, unknown.

11   **philanthropy** *(n)* the act of helping others, especially by donating money. *(s)* benevolence, charity. *(ant)* miserliness.

12   **reclusive** *(adj)* avoiding the company of others. *(s)* solitary, isolated, withdrawn, asocial. *(ant)* sociable.

13   **gourmet** *(adj)* of high quality and prepared by an expert. *(s)* luxurious, opulent, decadent. *(ant)* poor.

14   **culinary** *(adj)* relating to cooking. *(s)* gastronomic, dietary.

15   **voracious** *(adj)* having a large appetite. *(s)* gluttonous, greedy, ravenous. *(ant)* full, sated, satiated.

16   **appetite** *(n)* an impulse to eat. *(s)* hunger, desire.

17   **expectant** *(adj)* eagerly waiting for something. *(s)* anticipative, awaiting. *(ant)* unexpectant, uninterested.

18   **expression** *(n)* look that conveys (shows) a certain emotion. *(s)* face, appearance, air.

19   **unconvincing** *(adj)* unable to persuade someone that something is true. *(s)* unbelievable. *(ant)* convincing, believable.

'Yeah. I'm a bit carsick. Don't tell your dad. It's **embarrassing**[1],' she lied, again.

Suddenly the car swung in a sharp **veer**[2] to the right, **careering**[3] across the narrow road. Mr Brady stiffened, **grappling**[4] with the Tesla's steering wheel while **simultaneously**[5] hitting the brakes. Claire froze. A weakness **pervaded**[6] her muscles, **sapping**[7] their strength.

'What's happening, Dad?' asked Ben in an **anxious**[8] tone.

'I suspect a tyre's blown,' Mr Brady answered, **wrestling**[9] back control of the Tesla. 'Hear that flapping sound? My guess is it's shredded.'

While guiding the Tesla to an **undignified**[10] stop in a tiny lay-by, Mr Brady's voice remained calm, his **demeanour**[11] **unflustered**[12].

As the car **halted**[13], Claire breathed again. She glanced through the window to her right, then to her left, and back through the rear screen, battling to **conceal**[14] her **anxiety**[15].

'That was close!' she said, her **senses**[16] **heightened**[17].

'They build these cars to **withstand**[18] more than a blown tyre,' Mr Brady **reassured**[19] her. 'Although I wouldn't want to test it at super-high speeds,' he added with a light laugh as he opened his door and stepped outside to inspect the damage.

---

1   **embarrassing** *(adj)* causing awkwardness or shame. *(s)* humiliating, mortifying, degrading. *(ant)* dignifying.

2   **veer** *(v)* suddenly change direction. *(s)* turn, depart, deviate, diverge, divert, swerve.

3   **career** *(v)* move in a quick, uncontrolled manner. *(s)* hurtle along, race, tear, gallop, dash, rush. *(ant)* dawdle.

4   **grapple** *(v)* engage in a struggle. *(s)* wrestle, fight, battle, tussle, scuffle. *(ant)* surrender.

5   **simultaneously** *(adv)* at the same time, all together. *(s)* concurrently, instantaneously. *(ant)* separately.

6   **pervade** *(v)* spread throughout, be present and apparent. *(s)* permeate, infiltrate, encompass. *(ant)* evacuate.

7   **sap** *(v)* gradually weaken, erode, destroy or deplete power. *(s)* drain, debilitate, reduce. *(ant)* bolster.

8   **anxious** *(adj)* feeling uneasy about uncertainty. *(s)* worried, apprehensive, edgy, fretful. *(ant)* calm, carefree.

9   **wrestle** *(v)* force or fight by grappling (tussling). *(s)* struggle, brawl, battle, scuffle, scramble.

10   **undignified** *(adj)* lacking a composed manner or style (dignity). *(s)* unseemly, shameful, unbecoming. *(ant)* dignified.

11   **demeanour** *(n)* outward bearing or behaviour. *(s)* appearance, attitude, disposition, air, character, conduct.

12   **unflustered** *(adj)* self-controlled. *(s)* unruffled, composed, unperturbed, cool. *(ant)* flustered.

13   **halt** *(v)* stop abruptly. *(s)* still, pull up, hold up, stall. *(ant)* go, start.

14   **conceal** *(v)* hide or disguise. *(s)* screen, shroud, cloak, cover, camouflage, obscure, veil. *(ant)* reveal, uncover.

15   **anxiety** *(n)* worried and nervous feeling. *(s)* apprehension, unease, disquiet. *(ant)* calmness, reassurance.

16   **sense** *(n)* a faculty of the body that perceives the external environment. *(s)* awareness, ability, perception.

17   **heighten** *(v)* increase. *(s)* intensify, strengthen, amplify, enhance. *(ant)* lessen, reduce.

18   **withstand** *(v)* stay unaffected by. *(s)* resist, combat, fight, repel, defy. *(ant)* succumb to, yield to, capitulate to.

19   **reassure** *(v)* remove doubt and fear. *(s)* assure, comfort, soothe, cheer. *(ant)* discourage, unnerve, alarm.

'You sure you're OK?' Ben asked Claire again. 'Still carsick?'

'Yeah, but I'll be fine once we get there.'

To Claire, nothing felt fine. Everything felt wrong: the last-minute change of **venue**[1] for Ben's **martial**[2] arts **tournament**[3], its **subsequent**[4] cancellation, Jayne's theatre trip **postponement**[5], John Brady and Jayne Lewis both being called into Via-Corp's headquarters at Beddgelert, and even worse, David Lewis, the founder of Via-Corp, having the same surname as Jayne. The sum of all these parts left Claire with a **portentous**[6] sense of doom. Her stomach **squirmed**[7] like a snake pit.

'Kids, I'm afraid we're going nowhere fast. Both front tyres have blown.' Mr Brady sat back in the driver's seat. 'I'll call Tesla, but I doubt they'll **deploy**[8] their recovery vehicles out here. We'll need a local place. I'll call Via-Corp too; they can send a car to collect us.'

'OK, Dad,' said Ben. 'Can we get out for a minute, please? Claire needs fresh air,' he added, glancing at Claire's **ashen**[9] face.

'Sure, but stay close. My guess is Via-Corp will show up soon.'

'Cool,' said Ben. 'Come on, Claire, let's get out.'

Claire pressed the button to unbuckle her seat belt, but nothing happened.

'What's up?' asked Ben, getting out of the car and heading around to her.

'My seat belt's stuck,' she answered, **jabbing**[10] repeatedly at the release **mechanism**[11].

'Hey, your hands are trembling,' **observed**[12] Ben. 'What's up?'

'It's 'cause I feel sick,' she answered too quickly, avoiding Ben's eyes. 'Maybe something broke

---

1   **venue** *(n)* a place where something (an event) happens. *(s)* site, location, setting, spot, ground.

2   **martial** *(adj)* relating to fighting (or war). *(s)* military, warlike, combative, belligerent. *(ant)* civilian, peaceable.

3   **tournament** *(n)* a series of contests with multiple contestants. *(s)* competition, series, event.

4   **subsequent** *(adj)* occurring after something in time. *(s)* ensuing, following, later. *(ant)* antecedent, prior, former.

5   **postponement** *(n)* the action of delaying something. *(s)* deferral, suspension.

6   **portentous** *(adj)* of or like a portent (sign of something bad). *(s)* ominous, threatening, fateful. *(ant)* trivial.

7   **squirm** *(v)* wriggle or twist nervously. *(s)* writhe, turn, jiggle, fidget, flail. *(ant)* relax.

8   **deploy** *(v)* use for a purpose. *(s)* employ, utilise, call on, exploit.

9   **ashen** *(adj)* pale because of shock, fear or illness. *(s)* wan, pasty, pallid, sallow, ghostly, ashy, grey. *(ant)* rosy.

10   **jab** *(v)* poke roughly or quickly. *(s)* prod, dig, stab, push, nudge.

11   **mechanism** *(n)* a system of parts working together in a machine, tool or apparatus. *(s)* device, contraption.

12   **observe** *(v)* remark perceptively. *(s)* note, comment, mention, state, announce. *(ant)* ignore, overlook.

when the tyres blew,' she grumbled, still struggling with the **jammed**[1] **restraint**[2].

'Dad, we can't release Claire's seat belt.'

Mr Brady was a few metres away, making calls.

'Dad, she's stuck fast.'

Mr Brady **gesticulated**[3], signalling he'd be there soon.

The seat belt was jammed so tight Claire fought to move. 'So much for this **posh**[4], **expensive**[5] car,' she said. 'Exploding tyres, and now I'm trapped in the daft thing!'

Claire's laugh was light-hearted, but beneath her **veneer**[6], her heart hammered so hard she feared it might stop. She sat **ensnared**[7] in the back of a top-of-the-range Tesla on a mountainside in North Wales, convinced this was something to do with the Mal-Instinctives and Dewi – the one they called 'the Master'. After playing that name over and over in her mind, it now sounded **absurd**[8]. *I'm sure* Doctor Who *has a baddy called the Master*, she thought, trying to **quash**[9] her racing thoughts. Her mouth felt as **coarse**[10] as **sandpaper**[11]; it was so dry she struggled to speak.

'Is your dad coming? Can he hurry?' she snapped, her words a command. 'I hate this! I'm **claustrophobic**[12]!' **Evidently**[13], crawling through **numerous**[14] tiny, dark tunnels yesterday had failed to cure her **irrational**[15] fear of **confined**[16] spaces.

Still tugging at the **taut**[17] belt, she thought of yesterday when she'd turned that rusty old key

---

1   **jammed** *(adj)* stuck. *(s)* frozen, lodged, wedged, fast, fixed, glued, trapped. *(ant)* free, loose.

2   **restraint** *(n)* a device that limits movement. *(s)* harness, seat belt.

3   **gesticulate** *(v)* use gestures (movements) to communicate. *(s)* wave, signal, motion, indicate.

4   **posh** *(adj)* elegant or luxurious and stylish. *(s)* superior, snobbish, grand, upmarket. *(ant)* downmarket, common.

5   **expensive** *(adj)* costing a lot of money. *(s)* dear, costly, pricey, steep. *(ant)* inexpensive, cheap.

6   **veneer** *(n)* the outside layer or appearance of. *(s)* front, facade, mask, guise, show. *(ant)* inside, interior.

7   **ensnare** *(v)* catch or seize as though in a trap. *(s)* capture, entangle, snare, trap, enmesh. *(ant)* release.

8   **absurd** *(adj)* something ridiculous or very unreasonable. *(s)* ludicrous, preposterous, farcical. *(ant)* sensible, reasonable.

9   **quash** *(v)* put an end to. *(s)* suppress, quell, repress, crush, curb, overwhelm, defeat, conquer. *(ant)* allow.

10 **coarse** *(adj)* rough or hard, bristly. *(s)* wiry, scratchy, prickly, hairy, shaggy, abrasive. *(ant)* smooth, sleek, silky.

11 **sandpaper** *(n)* paper with a rough surface, used for smoothing other surfaces.

12 **claustrophobic** *(adj)* fearful of enclosed spaces.

13 **evidently** *(adv)* it would seem that. *(s)* apparently, seemingly. *(ant)* implausibly.

14 **numerous** *(adj)* many. *(s)* frequent, plentiful, abundant, various, copious, several, diverse. *(ant)* few, one.

15 **irrational** *(adj)* without logic or reason. *(s)* unfounded, unreasonable, illogical. *(ant)* rational, logical, reasonable.

16 **confined** *(adj)* very small or restricted. *(s)* cramped, constricted, limiting. *(ant)* open, roomy.

17 **taut** *(adj)* tight, with no slack. *(s)* stretched, strained, rigid, stressed. *(ant)* slack, loose.

in the lock beneath the police station. *Why can't I open this now?* she asked herself, **yanking**[1] at the belt with **frustration**[2]. *I don't have any Instinct*, she **admonished**[3] herself **bitterly**[4]. *It's nonsense!*

'Calm down. My dad's coming now,' said Ben.

'Oh, thank goodness!' replied Claire.

'Hey, Dad, it is stuck,' **reiterated**[5] Ben. 'Look,' he said, tugging harder at the **immobile**[6] seat belt.

'Ben, watch out! You're gonna choke me!' spluttered Claire.

'Sorry, buddy,' said Ben.

'Let me look closer, Claire,' suggested Mr Brady, his voice **soothing**[7]. 'I'm sure we can fix this,' he added, **furrowing**[8] his **brow**[9] as he inspected the seat belt. Ben stood behind him, **craning**[10] his neck to see.

'Push your shoulders and back into the seat as hard as you can,' Mr Brady instructed.

Claire pushed her **torso**[11] into the Tesla's leather.

'Bit further. I need you to create some **slack**[12],' he added.

'That won't be easy with my **barrel**[13] belly,' joked Claire, though she meant it. 'They don't call me "Choccy **Eclair**[14]" at home for nothing.' She **self-consciously**[15] sucked in her stomach and pushed back harder into the seat, holding her breath.

---

1 **yank** *(v)* pull with a sudden, hard movement. *(s)* tug, jerk, wrench, heave, haul. *(ant)* push, shove.

2 **frustration** *(n)* an upset or annoyance. *(s)* aggravation, irritation, exasperation. *(ant)* success, satisfaction.

3 **admonish** *(v)* reprimand (tell off) firmly. *(s)* warn, advise, reproach, chide, caution, rebuke. *(ant)* allow, praise.

4 **bitterly** *(adv)* in a bitter (harsh or resentful) way. *(s)* cruelly, sullenly, ruefully, sourly. *(ant)* gently, sweetly, pleasantly.

5 **reiterate** *(v)* say again for emphasis or clarity. *(s)* repeat, restate, recap, retell.

6 **immobile** *(adj)* not moving. *(s)* motionless, static, unmoving, still. *(ant)* mobile, moving.

7 **soothing** *(adj)* gently calming or quietening. *(s)* relaxing, reassuring, comforting, consoling. *(ant)* aggravating, exacerbating.

8 **furrow** *(v)* line with grooves or wrinkles. *(s)* crinkle, crease, pucker, crumple. *(ant)* smooth.

9 **brow** *(n)* the area on the head comprising (consisting of) the forehead and temples.

10 **crane** *(v)* stretch one's body or neck to see something. *(s)* outstretch, extend, stick out. *(ant)* retract, shrink.

11 **torso** *(n)* the trunk (body without head or limbs) of a human. *(s)* upper body.

12 **slack** *(n)* part of a rope or line that is held loosely. *(s)* play, give, looseness.

13 **barrel** *(n)* a cylindrical container usually wider around the middle. *(s)* cask, butt, keg, vat, tub, drum.

14 **eclair** *(n)* an oblong choux dough pastry filled with cream and topped with icing. *(s)* cake, bun.

15 **self-consciously** *(adv)* done with excessive awareness of oneself. *(s)* shyly, insecurely. *(ant)* confidently, assuredly.

As Claire's face reddened, Mr Brady angled the seat belt a fraction outwards and upwards, as if weighing up the **pivot**[1] point where it might **relent**[2] and yield its grip.

Just as Claire felt she might explode, the belt's pressure **eased**[3]. With a huge **exhalation**[4] of relief, she began to wriggle out of it. The belt remained stuck in its **clasp**[5], but Mr Brady had somehow created enough room for her to escape its clutches.

'Phew! Thanks, Mr Brady.'

'Now that was a close shave,' joked Mr Brady with an **ambiguous**[6] laugh. 'I thought we might have to leave you here.'

'Huh, that's funny,' **retorted**[7] Claire, **confused**[8] at the unsettling tone in Mr Brady's voice, and not finding any of it **remotely**[9] funny.

'What's happening, Dad? Are Via-Corp sending a car?'

'Yes, son, they'll arrive soon. A local recovery company will fit new front tyres, but they'll have to take the car away. We can't leave it **stranded**[10] here. They're heading up from the village now.'

'OK, cool. How long will they take to fix them? Don't forget my gear is in the back.'

'Depends if they have the right tyres, I guess. Let's hope they source them soon. Don't bet on it though, not after Lady Luck's unfavourable treatment of us today,' his dad said with a **wry**[11] smile.

I doubt any of this is bad luck, thought Claire **cynically**[12]. She stretched out her legs and rubbed her shoulder where the seat belt had **chafed**[13] it.

'Hey, Dad, can you get my decks from the boot, please? We might get a chance to use them today.'

---

1   **pivot** *(n)* the point that something balances on or turns around.

2   **relent** *(v)* give in to something. *(s)* capitulate, acquiesce, surrender, yield, concede, weaken. *(ant)* stand firm.

3   **ease** *(v)* become less severe or slacken. *(s)* lessen, reduce, diminish. *(ant)* increase, tighten.

4   **exhalation** *(n)* a release of air from the lungs (a breath out). *(s)* sigh. *(ant)* inhalation.

5   **clasp** *(n)* a device that fastens things together. *(s)* catch, clip, fastener, buckle.

6   **ambiguous** *(adj)* open to misinterpretation. *(s)* unclear, vague, equivocal. *(ant)* clear, definite, unambiguous.

7   **retort** *(v)* say something in answer to a remark. *(s)* reply, snap, counter, retaliate, riposte, bite back.

8   **confused** *(adj)* bewildered or perplexed. *(s)* puzzled, baffled, mystified, bamboozled. *(ant)* enlightened, clear.

9   **remotely** *(adv)* in the smallest degree. *(s)* in the least bit, at all, one bit. *(ant)* completely, entirely.

10   **stranded** *(adj)* left without the means (capability) to leave. *(s)* trapped, stuck, marooned. *(ant)* rescued.

11   **wry** *(adj)* (of the face) twisted to express disappointment or annoyance. *(s)* unimpressed, vexed. *(ant)* pleased, impressed.

12   **cynically** *(adv)* in a cynical (distrustful or disbelieving) way. *(s)* suspiciously, sceptically. *(ant)* trustfully, naively.

13   **chafe** *(v)* make sore by rubbing. *(s)* abrade, irritate, scour.

Before Claire could say, 'No, thanks; I don't need one,' Mr Brady had reached into the boot and handed her a skateboard.

'Here are the helmets too,' he added, passing one to each of the kids.

'Really? Do I have to wear one? They're **unsightly**[1],' Ben **whined**[2].

'Yes, you do!' answered his dad. 'Especially if you have Claire skating with you. What on earth would Dee say if Claire **sustained**[3] a **concussion**[4], or worse?' he added.

If only you had any idea what I went through yesterday, thought Claire. She tucked the sticker-**adorned**[5] skateboard under one arm and plonked the helmet onto her head. *I bet I look ridiculous*, she thought as it wobbled.

'Ben, you know I'm hopeless at anything with the word *boarding* in it,' she hissed under her breath. 'Don't expect me to carry this thing around all day and wear your stupid pink helmet just 'cause you reckon it's a cool colour,' she grumbled.

'Why not? It matches your cheeks now,' Ben joked, flashing his broadest white smile at her. 'Come on, dude!' he chuckled, **mustering**[6] his strongest American accent. 'I'll teach you how to do an **ollie**[7].'

'An ollie?' she replied. 'Are you kidding? I can't even stand up on the daft **contraption**[8]!' she **scoffed**[9].

'Oi, you two, Laurel and Hardy!' joked Mr Brady **affectionately**[10]. 'Looks like the recovery truck is here to rescue the Tesla.'

'No prizes for guessing which one of the comedy **duo**[11] I am,' laughed Claire, forcing her cheer. 'Being compared to Oliver Hardy is the closest I'll get to doing an ollie today.' She patted

---

1   **unsightly** *(adj)* not pleasing to look at. *(s)* unattractive, ugly, disagreeable. *(ant)* pleasant, attractive.

2   **whine** *(v)* complain in a petulant way. *(s)* moan, whinge, grouch, gripe. *(ant)* compliment.

3   **sustain** *(v)* suffer or undergo (an injury or other discomfort). *(s)* experience, endure.

4   **concussion** *(n)* a brain injury resulting in confusion and sometimes loss of consciousness.

5   **adorn** *(v)* make more attractive or beautiful. *(s)* decorate, embellish, ornament, enhance. *(ant)* strip.

6   **muster** *(v)* summon up (a response, attitude or feeling). *(s)* gather, collect, rally, raise, call on. *(ant)* disperse.

7   **ollie** *(n)* (in skateboarding and snowboarding) a jump performed by pushing the foot down on the tail of the board.

8   **contraption** *(n)* an unnecessarily complicated, badly made or unsafe thing. *(s)* gadget, device, gubbins.

9   **scoff** *(v)* speak in a mocking or derisive way. *(s)* ridicule, deride, sneer at. *(ant)* praise, respect.

10   **affectionately** *(adv)* in an affectionate (kind or fond) way. *(s)* warmly, amicably. *(ant)* coldly.

11   **duo** *(n)* two people, especially in a performance. *(s)* couple, pair, duet.

her **rotund**[1] stomach. She and Ben often watched old black-and-white movies with Mr Brady –
he loved **slapstick**[2] comedy.

A **gnarled**[3] pickup truck rumbled towards them, **spewing**[4] out **plumes**[5] of dark smoke
amid[6] clouds of **toxic**[7] diesel **fumes**[8]. Claire coughed, waving away the smoke as it pulled up
behind the **stricken**[9] Tesla. A round-faced man, built like a barrel and wearing greasy **overalls**[10],
heaved[11] himself from the driver's seat and **stomped**[12] over to the waiting threesome, an oil-
stained hand **thrust**[13] out before him.

'Geraint the Garage at your service!' the man announced, in such a strong **accent**, Claire only
just caught what he said. Even though she'd **encountered**[14] Welsh accents all day yesterday, it still
sounded **alien**[15] to her ears.

As they shook hands, Geraint appeared capable of **wresting**[16] Mr Brady's arm from its
socket[17]. Claire couldn't help noticing Geraint's oil-stained **meat hook**[18] of a hand and Mr Brady's
manicured[19] fingers, the **latter**[20] never having seen the sun or done a day's **manual**[21] labour.

---

1   **rotund** *(adj)* plump. *(s)* chubby, dumpy, portly, round, stout. *(ant)* thin, slender, skinny.

2   **slapstick** *(n)* comedy based on clumsiness and humiliation.

3   **gnarled** *(adj)* battered and misshapen, usually with age. *(s)* contorted, deformed. *(ant)* straight, smooth.

4   **spew** *(v)* expel or pour out rapidly. *(s)* eject, emit, spout, spurt, gush, flow, stream, spill. *(ant)* dribble, trickle.

5   **plume** *(n)* a long puff of smoke. *(s)* trail, cloud, curl, spiral, column.

6   **amid** *(prep)* surrounded by, in the middle of. *(s)* among, within, amidst, between, during. *(ant)* outside.

7   **toxic** *(adj)* poisonous. *(s)* noxious, dangerous, harmful, unsafe, injurious. *(ant)* non-toxic, harmless, safe.

8   **fume** *(n)* a gas or vapour that is harmful to breathe in. *(s)* exhaust, smoke.

9   **stricken** *(adj)* gravely affected by a disagreeable feeling or unwanted condition. *(s)* afflicted, troubled. *(ant)* unaffected.

10   **overalls** *(n)* a one-piece garment (clothing) worn over ordinary clothes. *(s)* coveralls, all-in-one.

11   **heave** *(v)* lift or drag with great effort. *(s)* haul, lug, hoist, heft.

12   **stomp** *(v)* tread heavily. *(s)* stamp, clump, plod, clomp, trudge. *(ant)* tiptoe.

13   **thrust** *(v)* move or extend forcefully. *(s)* shove, propel, drive.

14   **encounter** *(v)* meet unexpectedly. *(s)* face, confront, run into, come across. *(ant)* avoid.

15   **alien** *(adj)* unfamiliar. *(s)* unusual, foreign, incongruous, strange. *(ant)* familiar, usual.

16   **wrest** *(v)* forcefully pull something from someone's grasp. *(s)* snatch, seize, wrench, grab. *(ant)* give.

17   **socket** *(n)* a hollow that something fits into or revolves within. *(s)* opening, niche.

18   **meat hook** *(n)* a pejorative (unpleasant) term for a person's hand. *(s)* fist.

19   **manicured** *(adj)* trimmed and neatly maintained. *(s)* cut, shaped. *(ant)* overgrown, unkempt.

20   **latter** *(n)* the second mentioned of two people or things. *(s)* last. *(ant)* former.

21   **manual** *(adj)* involving or relating to the hands. *(s)* physical, hand-operated. *(ant)* automatic, mechanical.

Strangely, it left her with an odd **sensation**[1], one she failed to **fathom**[2]: the same **queasy**[3] sort of unease she'd experienced too often yesterday. However, what **perturbed**[4] her most was the fact that this uneasy feeling was directed towards Mr Brady, her best friend's dad. Dismissing the thought, she plonked the skateboard onto the ground and followed the men over to inspect the Tesla's tyres.

'Blimey O'Reilly!' **exclaimed**[5] Geraint in his **barely**[6] **decipherable**[7] accent. ''Ave you **savaged**[8] these tyres? What the 'eck did you drive across? Two running chainsaws and a smashed-up greenhouse?' He glanced around the **vicinity**[9] as if looking for **incriminating**[10] **evidence**[11]. 'You ain't gonna be driving this car anywhere today.'

'That's the mystery,' replied Mr Brady. 'I didn't see anything sharp on the road. Perhaps the tyres are **defective**[12]. The car's not a year old yet,' he added. 'It's a Via-Corp company vehicle, so I'll report this.'

Claire and Ben searched, hunting for clues as to what might have **annihilated**[13] the Tesla's front tyres, but they, too, found no evidence.

'Well, if you can't find anything, it's gotta be a fault,' said Geraint. 'I'd get onto this fancy-schmancy Tesla firm right away and tell 'em Geraint the Garage is fixing it for 'em,' he added **emphatically**[14]. 'I don't trust these **newfangled**[15], battery-operated cars. Gimme a good old dirty diesel any day, something you can get your 'ands **grimy**[16] on and fix with tools, not with a ruddy

---

1 **sensation** *(n)* a physical feeling or perception. *(s)* sense, impression, awareness.

2 **fathom** *(v)* comprehend after much thought. *(s)* understand, grasp, perceive. *(ant)* misunderstand.

3 **queasy** *(adj)* feeling slightly sick (nauseous) or uneasy. *(s)* odd, unsettled, troubled. *(ant)* well, untroubled.

4 **perturb** *(v)* make uneasy or anxious. *(s)* worry, concern, upset. *(ant)* reassure, calm.

5 **exclaim** *(v)* cry out suddenly. *(s)* blurt, proclaim, declare, shout, call, yell. *(ant)* whisper, mutter.

6 **barely** *(adv)* only just, almost not. *(s)* hardly, narrowly, scarcely. *(ant)* easily, amply, fully, profusely.

7 **decipherable** *(adj)* able to be understood or identified. *(s)* fathomable, discernible. *(ant)* unclear, unintelligible.

8 **savage** *(v)* attack. *(s)* maul, bite, mutilate, lacerate, mangle. *(ant)* nurture, tend, care for.

9 **vicinity** *(n)* surrounding or nearby areas. *(s)* proximity, propinquity, locale. *(ant)* distance.

10 **incriminate** *(v)* make someone seem guilty of a crime. *(s)* implicate, blame, accuse. *(ant)* acquit, vindicate, exonerate.

11 **evidence** *(n)* facts or information presented to support the truth. *(s)* proof, confirmation, corroboration.

12 **defective** *(adj)* faulty or flawed. *(s)* broken, inoperative, malfunctioning. *(ant)* working, perfect.

13 **annihilate** *(v)* destroy completely. *(s)* obliterate, eliminate, exterminate, kill. *(ant)* create, build.

14 **emphatically** *(adv)* in an emphatic (clear and forceful) way. *(s)* vehemently, ardently, vigorously. *(ant)* tentatively.

15 **newfangled** *(adj)* recently created or overly modern. *(s)* novel, advanced. *(ant)* old-fashioned, dated.

16 **grimy** *(adj)* covered with grime. *(s)* dirty, grubby, filthy, stained, soiled. *(ant)* clean.

computer! And self-driving, what's that nonsense all about, eh? What's the point of 'avin' a car if you can't drive the ruddy thing yourself?'

'I hear you, Mr … er, Geraint,' replied Mr Brady, shooting a glance over at Claire and Ben, who were **stifling**[1] chuckles. 'You have a **valid**[2] point,' he agreed in a **faux**[3] **grave**[4] tone.

'Right, then! I'll 'oist this useless 'eap onto my truck and get it sorted for you.' Geraint handed an oil-**soiled**[5] business card over to Mr Brady. 'Stick your number on there, an' I'll call you when it's ready. Don't be bothering with them texts or social **medium**[6], or whatever it's called, apps or something. I don't use 'em. It's good old-fashioned conversation for me,' he said as he readied the **winch**[7] on the back of his truck.

'Come on, Lily, you lazy lump!' Geraint commanded out of the blue. 'Stop **shirking**[8]! Get your backside out of the truck, and give me a hand with this 'eap o' metal.'

To Claire's surprise, a youngish girl, **hitherto**[9] concealed in the truck's cab, stepped out, pulled a baseball cap low over her brow and joined Geraint at the rear of the recovery vehicle. The girl was anything but a 'lump'. Claire observed she was **petite**[10], **nimble**[11] and, from what Claire **glimpsed**[12] of her under the baseball cap, pretty.

'My **idle**[13] daughter, Lily,' mumbled Geraint in a **dismissive**[14], **gruff**[15] voice as he continued his work.

---

1   **stifle** *(v)* restrain a reaction or stop oneself acting on an emotion. *(s)* suppress, repress, curb. *(ant)* encourage.

2   **valid** *(adj)* grounded in fact or reason. *(s)* logical, sound, rational, justifiable. *(ant)* invalid.

3   **faux** *(adj)* not genuine. *(s)* false, fake, pretend, imitation, unreal. *(ant)* authentic, genuine.

4   **grave** *(adj)* serious or solemn. *(s)* sombre, sober, thoughtful, unsmiling, stony, gloomy. *(ant)* cheerful, upbeat.

5   **soil** *(v)* make dirty. *(s)* foul, sully, muddy, stain, spot. *(ant)* cleanse.

6   **medium** *(n)* a means of communication. *(s)* channel, method, way, forum, avenue.

7   **winch** *(n)* a device for hauling or lifting using rope or cable wrapped around a rotating drum, powered by a motor or crank.

8   **shirk** *(v)* neglect or avoid work or responsibility. *(s)* dodge, evade, skive, duck. *(ant)* embrace, pursue.

9   **hitherto** *(adv)* until this point. *(s)* previously, formerly, beforehand, yet, before, thus far. *(ant)* henceforth.

10   **petite** *(adj)* attractively small and dainty. *(s)* slight, elfin, delicate, diminutive, little, tiny. *(ant)* large, bulky.

11   **nimble** *(adj)* light and quick in movement. *(s)* agile, sprightly, lithe, deft, lissom. *(ant)* awkward, clumsy.

12   **glimpse** *(v)* view something quickly or partially. *(s)* peep, peek, glance. *(ant)* stare.

13   **idle** *(adj)* not inclined to work. *(s)* lazy, indolent, slothful, work-shy. *(ant)* industrious, hard-working, diligent.

14   **dismissive** *(adj)* showing something is unworthy of consideration. *(s)* indifferent, unconcerned. *(ant)* interested.

15   **gruff** *(adj)* rough and deep (voice), or abrupt in manner. *(s)* brusque, curt, surly, stern, blunt. *(ant)* friendly.

'Hello, Lily.' Mr Brady flashed a **charming**[1] smile in the girl's direction.

Lily didn't speak but dipped a slight nod at Mr Brady.

Daughter? thought Claire. *She's his daughter? He's the lump, not her!*

'Hey, was that thunder just then?' asked Ben, picking up the skateboard Claire had dumped near the Tesla in the **vain**[2] hope of leaving it there.

'I dunno. The sky's getting darker though,' Claire said, looking upwards, causing the pink helmet to fall off her head.

'That ain't thunder,' answered Lily as Claire bent to pick up the helmet.

She sounds like her dad, thought Claire, straightening up to face Lily and wondering how old she might be.

'See, did you hear it?' Ben pointed to the sky. 'Thunder, in the distance.'

'It ain't thunder,' Lily reiterated in the same bored tone she'd used the first time.

'What is it, then?' asked Ben.

'It's the fighters,' mumbled Lily as she inspected a shiny **spanner**[3].

'Fighters?' **remarked**[4] Ben.

'Yeah, more junk flying around and **polluting**[5] our skies with noise and fumes,' Geraint the Garage **chimed**[6] in, **contradicting**[7] his earlier comments about preferring dirty diesel. 'Damn filthy 'eaps of winged metal! **Scandalous**[8]!'

'Really?' replied Claire, taken immediately back to yesterday, in Anglesey, when the RAF Hawk had zoomed into view, its noise deafening, frightening the **pursuing**[9] Mal-Instinctives away from Gwilym's pony and trap.

'Yep, they practise low-level flying up here in the mountains. Makes 'em better pilots,

---

1   **charming** *(adj)* very pleasant or attractive. *(s)* appealing, charismatic, delightful, pleasing. *(ant)* unattractive.

2   **vain** *(adj)* producing no result. *(s)* useless, pointless, futile, worthless. *(ant)* productive, successful.

3   **spanner** *(n)* a tool for turning nuts and bolts.

4   **remark** *(v)* notice, say, or regard (look at) with attention. *(s)* comment, observe, state, utter.

5   **pollute** *(v)* contaminate with hazardous substances. *(s)* poison, taint, foul, dirty. *(ant)* purify, clean.

6   **chime** *(v)* join in a conversation. *(s)* say, interrupt, comment, contribute, add.

7   **contradict** *(v)* deny the truth, assert the opposite. *(s)* oppose, counter, dispute, refute. *(ant)* agree, confirm.

8   **scandalous** *(adj)* unacceptably bad. *(s)* shocking, monstrous, outrageous. *(ant)* praiseworthy, acceptable.

9   **pursue** *(v)* chase or follow. *(s)* hunt, trail, track, tail, shadow, hound, seek, trace, stalk. *(ant)* guide, lead.

apparently[1], Lily said, her tone still disinterested.

'Wow!' **enthused**[2] Ben. 'I hope we get to see one up close. How cool would that be?' He turned to Claire with his huge **pearly**[3] grin.

'So cool,' replied Claire **glibly**[4], meaning the complete opposite.

'Hey, guys, that was a Via-Corp **colleague**[5] on the phone,' interrupted Mr Brady. 'A car will be here in five, so grab your stuff from the Tesla before Geraint **hoists**[6] it onto his truck.' He swiped his finger across his phone.

Drawn again to his long, **slender**[7], almost-**feminine**[8] fingers, Claire was reminded, creepily, of Jayne's perfectly manicured hands. Perturbed, she went to grab her school bag from the car's **footwell**[9] and slung it onto her shoulder.

Why did Jayne return for my bag last night? she thought. *How could she have even entered the closed museum?* It **flummoxed**[10] her. Although Claire had found nothing **awry**[11] when she'd repacked her bag this morning, everything still felt wrong.

Suddenly, from nowhere, a **fleeting**[12] black shadow darted across the ground beneath them, followed by an **ear-splitting**[13] boom. Claire, Ben and even Mr Brady jumped so much they practically **collided**[14].

'Yikes! What in the heavens was that?' exclaimed Mr Brady, patting his chest above his heart.

---

1   **apparently** *(adv)* as far as one knows or can see. *(s)* supposedly, seemingly, evidently. *(ant)* implausibly.

2   **enthuse** *(v)* express with delight, interest or approval. *(s)* rave, gush, effuse, acclaim. *(ant)* lament, denounce.

3   **pearly** *(adj)* like a pearl in lustre or colour. *(s)* shimmery, milky, shiny. *(ant)* dull, lustreless.

4   **glibly** *(adv)* in a glib (easy) manner. *(s)* urbanely, neatly, smoothly, slickly, casually. *(ant)* inarticulately.

5   **colleague** *(n)* a person who one works with. *(s)* associate, workmate, co-worker.

6   **hoist** *(v)* lift with effort (often with pulleys or ropes). *(s)* heave up, raise, elevate. *(ant)* lower.

7   **slender** *(adj)* slim and graceful. *(s)* lean, willowy, trim, lithe, svelte. *(ant)* big, chubby, firm, heavy, plump, fat.

8   **feminine** *(adj)* having qualities associated with a woman. *(s)* womanly, womanlike, ladylike. *(ant)* masculine.

9   **footwell** *(n)* a space in front of a seat to place one's feet in.

10   **flummox** *(v)* perplex or bewilder. *(s)* baffle, confound, puzzle, mystify, bemuse. *(ant)* clarify, demystify.

11   **awry** *(adj)* out of the ordinary. *(s)* amiss, wrong, untoward. *(ant)* right, in order.

12   **fleeting** *(adj)* lasting for a very short time. *(s)* brief, momentary, sudden, transitory. *(ant)* lasting, permanent.

13   **ear-splitting** *(adj)* very loud. *(s)* deafening, piercing, booming. *(ant)* quiet, soft, low.

14   **collide** *(v)* come into contact with (usually forcefully). *(s)* bump, impact, crash, hit, ram, knock. *(ant)* miss.

Ben looked **utterly**[1] **bewildered**[2], but Claire knew what it was.

'See? See what I mean? Scared you lot 'alf to death, didn't it?' shouted an **overzealous**[3] Geraint the Garage. 'Those ruddy nuisances, noisy, filthy flying pests,' he **declaimed**[4], pausing his work to gesticulate **furiously**[5] at the now-empty sky. 'I'd shoot the damn things down if I could!' he **ranted**[6].

'Ahhh, yes. How could I forget the **Mach Loop**[7]?' Mr Brady rubbed his ears **ruefully**[8].

'What did you say, Dad?' asked Ben.

'Yeah, they're flyin' the Mach Loop all right.' It was **laid-back**[9] Lily who replied. 'Mmm, that was a bit of an odd one though,' she puzzled, removing her baseball cap, staring skywards and **ruffling**[10] her short copper-coloured hair.

'What do you mean?' asked Claire. 'Why was it odd?' She shuddered as if something **elusive**[11] had crawled over her skin, leaving goosebumps in its **wake**[12].

Lily replaced her cap and pulled it down over her eyes. 'It's odd,' she **drawled**[13], ''cause that was an RAF Tornado.'

Claire waited, her **apprehensive**[14] gaze attempting to **locate**[15] Lily's **evasive**[16] eyes, shielded

---

1   **utterly** *(adv)* to an extreme degree. *(s)* absolutely, completely, totally, entirely. *(ant)* somewhat, partly.

2   **bewildered** *(adj)* perplexed or confused. *(s)* baffled, bemused, mystified, confounded, discombobulated. *(ant)* enlightened.

3   **overzealous** *(adj)* too zealous (keen). *(s)* enthusiastic, eager, spirited, intense. *(ant)* apathetic, uninterested.

4   **declaim** *(v)* speak as if giving a speech. *(s)* pronounce, preach, lecture, spout.

5   **furiously** *(adv)* in a furious (energetic) manner. *(s)* energetically, feverishly, frantically. *(ant)* slowly, calmly.

6   **rant** *(v)* speak or shout in a lengthy and passionate way. *(s)* bluster, yell, bellow, rage, go on. *(ant)* sweet-talk.

7   **Mach Loop** (the Machynlleth Loop) valleys in Wales, notable for their use as low-level training areas for fast jet aircraft.

8   **ruefully** *(adv)* in a rueful (regretful or sorrowful) way. *(s)* sheepishly, agonisingly, dolefully. (ant) blissfully, joyfully.

9   **laid-back** *(adj)* easy-going and relaxed. *(s)* casual, informal, nonchalant. *(ant)* edgy, uptight, tense.

10   **ruffle** *(v)* mess up something or someone's hair. *(s)* tousle, disarrange, dishevel, mess. *(ant)* smooth, straighten.

11   **elusive** *(adj)* hard to catch or find. *(s)* evasive, slippery, shifty, intangible. *(ant)* accessible.

12   **wake** *(n)* disturbed air or water following behind something. *(s)* aftermath, trail, path, track, furrow, wash, train.

13   **drawl** *(v)* speak in a slow, idle way. *(s)* drone, draw out. *(ant)* gabble, gush.

14   **apprehensive** *(adj)* worried that something bad will happen. *(s)* alarmed, anxious, concerned. *(ant)* confident, calm.

15   **locate** *(v)* find the exact position or place of. *(s)* track down, detect, establish, discover, pinpoint. *(ant)* lose.

16   **evasive** *(adj)* tending to avoid, hard to catch. *(s)* elusive, avoiding, dodging. *(ant)* direct, frank.

by the cap. Trying her best to sound **nonchalant**[1], **summoning**[2] her **breeziest**[3] tone, Claire asked, 'Odd? Why?'

Lily didn't answer. She continued to help her father setting up the winch, seeming to mull over Claire's question **interminably**[4].

Patience not being one of Claire's **fortes**[5], she blurted again, 'What do you mean, odd?' Her tone was so **abrupt**[6] Mr Brady's eyebrows shot upwards.

With a **languid**[7] movement, Lily put down her spanner, turned to face Claire and drawled, 'It's odd 'cause that stunning machine was a Tornado GR4, and I'm gonna miss 'em now they're **put out to grass**[8].' Her blue eyes **bored**[9] into Claire's.

What? thought Claire as the first stabs of **panic**[10] **inflicted**[11] their pain.

'Spit it out, then, **lass**[12]! What is it you're wanting to say?' snapped Geraint the Garage. 'Now you know why we **dubbed**[13] 'er "Lazy Lily",' he **mocked**[14], looking over at the onlooking, expectant threesome.

For such a **lithe**[15]-looking girl, Lily reacted at the speed of a **sloth**[16]. 'The reason it's odd,' she responded finally, 'is those little beauties ain't supposed to be **frequenting**[17] our Welsh skies any more.'

---

1   **nonchalant** *(adj)* casual and relaxed. *(s)* cool, calm, untroubled, unruffled, blasé. *(ant)* nervous, concerned.

2   **summon** *(v)* try to produce from within oneself. *(s)* call, muster, rouse, find, mobilise, rally. *(ant)* suppress.

3   **breezy** *(adj)* relaxed and cheerily brisk. *(s)* carefree, airy, jaunty. *(ant)* uptight.

4   **interminably** *(adv)* in an interminable (endless) way. *(s)* ceaselessly, continuously, eternally, forever.

5   **forte** *(n)* a great strength, something one excels at. *(s)* strong suit, speciality, thing. *(ant)* weakness, failing.

6   **abrupt** *(adj)* brief, almost rude. *(s)* brusque, curt, sharp, terse. *(ant)* polite, unhurried.

7   **languid** *(adj)* lacking quickness of movement. *(s)* unhurried, relaxed, unenergetic. *(ant)* energetic.

8   **put out to grass** (v) force someone or something to retire.

9   **bore** *(v)* drill a hole into (often used figuratively). *(s)* stare, pierce, penetrate, burrow, mine.

10   **panic** *(n)* uncontrollable anxiety or fear. *(s)* fright, dread, alarm, consternation, horror. *(ant)* calm, self-control.

11   **inflict** *(v)* cause or impose pain or suffering. *(s)* enforce, wreak, exact, perpetrate, force. *(ant)* relieve, remit.

12   **lass** *(n)* a girl or young woman. *(s)* miss, lassie, young lady. *(ant)* lad.

13   **dub** *(v)* give a nickname to. *(s)* designate, entitle, call, label, name, term, tag, style, knight.

14   **mock** *(v)* tease or make fun of. *(s)* ridicule, deride, scorn, insult, taunt. *(ant)* praise, compliment, flatter.

15   **lithe** *(adj)* (especially of the body) thin, supple and graceful. *(s)* agile, fit, nimble. *(ant)* dumpy, chubby, stiff.

16   **sloth** *(n)* a slow-moving mammal from Central and South America that hangs from the branches of trees using its claws.

17   **frequent** *(v)* visit often. *(s)* attend regularly, revisit.

'Oh my word! Stop being so **cryptic**[1] and just tell us,' snapped Claire, so **aggressively**[2] even Ben's eyebrows now shot skywards.

'Yeah, sure, hold your horses, missus,' Lily drawled. 'It's odd 'cause in February the Tornado GR4s took their final ride. The RAF **decommissioned**[3] them in favour of the Typhoon,' she finished, turning back to her spanner.

The blood drained from Claire's face. She rubbed at her right eye, trying to conceal its nervous twitching as, in a **quavering**[4] voice, she muttered, 'Ben, give me that daft thing. I'll carry it.'

Snatching the skateboard from Ben, Claire fought to regain some **semblance**[5] of calm. She dropped the deck onto the road, prodding at it with her foot, feigning interest to buy herself time.

Lily had said the Tornado had been 'decommissioned'. Claire knew *exactly* what that meant, because Gladys had told her yesterday – 'no longer in service'. The RAF Hawk and the yellow Sea King helicopter that had saved their bacon were both retired from service. Gladys had **explicitly**[6] told her, the only pilots left flying this class of aircraft were Knights Hawk. So *who* was commanding this retired Tornado just minutes ago, and more importantly, *why*? It had to have been a Knight Hawk.

'Right, come on, you guys.' Mr Brady nodded at Ben and Claire. 'Go wait over there. Let these **seasoned**[7] **mechanics**[8] do their work. I can hear a car approaching; it's probably for us.'

Claire **clocked**[9] the throaty growl of the powerful car before it came into view, rounding the snaking bend. She immediately recognised the **sleek**[10] black Bentley with its **iconic**[11] 'B'

---

1   **cryptic** *(adj)* having a mysterious or obscure (unclear) meaning. *(s)* enigmatic, puzzling. *(ant)* straightforward.

2   **aggressively** *(adv)* done in an aggressive (forceful) way. *(s)* violently, belligerently, vigorously. *(ant)* gently.

3   **decommission** *(v)* withdraw (remove) from service. *(s)* mothball, retire, discharge. *(ant)* introduce, activate.

4   **quaver** *(v)* shake or tremble. *(s)* quiver, warble, tremor, flinch, flutter. *(ant)* steady.

5   **semblance** *(n)* the outward appearance of something. *(s)* approximation, show, pretence. *(ant)* reality.

6   **explicitly** *(adv)* in an explicit (definite) way. *(s)* openly, clearly, obviously, unequivocally. *(ant)* ambiguously.

7   **seasoned** *(adj)* experienced and accustomed to certain conditions. *(s)* veteran, expert. *(ant)* inexperienced.

8   **mechanic** *(n)* a worker who repairs and maintains vehicles, machinery and engines.

9   **clock** *(v)* notice or watch. *(s)* see, note, perceive, discern, detect. *(ant)* overlook, ignore.

10   **sleek** *(adj)* smooth and shining. *(s)* glossy, glistening, polished, glassy. *(ant)* dull, rough, coarse.

11   **iconic** *(adj)* of or relating to an icon (something or someone worthy of admiration). *(s)* emblematic. *(ant)* obscure.

nestled[1] between the silver wings above the criss-crossed front **grille**[2]. The **emblem**[3] was unmistakable, as was the stunning car that cruised towards them, commanding the **entire**[4] carriageway of the narrow mountain pass. Claire had always **harboured**[5] a secret **penchant**[6] for **prestige**[7] cars.

'Wow!' Ben let out a long, low whistle. 'I hope *that's* our ride,' he cried, beaming as the supercar approached.

'I wish!' laughed Mr Brady.

With **longing**[8] looks, Claire and Ben stared at the car as it slowed to pass the **marooned**[9] onlookers, its growl **diminishing**[10] to a purr as it glided past them. Although they craned their necks to see inside, the Bentley's blacked-out windows prevented them.

'Blimey, how can the driver see the road?' asked Ben. 'Even the windscreen is tinted,' he remarked as the car picked up speed and disappeared around the mountain bend.

'D-L-one,' Claire mouthed to herself. DL1. Why did that **exorbitantly**[11] priced and rare number plate **rankle**[12] her so much?

'That was the boss's car.' Mr Brady chuckled at the kids. '*That* was *not* our ride, but I am wondering where ours is.'

Geraint finished securing the Tesla onto his truck and waddled over to the waiting party, nodding his **bulbous**[13] head, which **aptly**[14] accompanied the **smug**[15] smile on his face. 'See, now

---

1   **nestle** *(v)* be situated. *(s)* lie, hide, shelter, settle, huddle, burrow.

2   **grille** *(n)* wire mesh or metal bars placed in front of something for protection or ventilation.

3   **emblem** *(n)* a distinctive symbol of an organisation. *(s)* badge, representation, mark, sign, image.

4   **entire** *(adj)* whole or complete. *(s)* total, full. *(ant)* fractional, partial.

5   **harbour** *(v)* hold a thought or feeling in the mind. *(s)* nurture, foster, entertain.

6   **penchant** *(n)* a liking for something. *(s)* fondness, preference, affection, weakness. *(ant)* aversion, dislike.

7   **prestige** *(n)* something that inspires extensive admiration and respect.

8   **long** *(v)* have a strong wish or desire. *(s)* crave, yearn, hunger, pine, ache, wish, hanker.

9   **maroon** *(v)* trap in an inaccessible place. *(s)* strand, leave, abandon, desert, forsake. *(ant)* reclaim.

10   **diminish** *(v)* become or make less. *(s)* reduce, decrease, lessen, wane. *(ant)* increase.

11   **exorbitantly** *(adv)* of or in an exorbitant (excessively high) manner. *(s)* overly, unduly, remarkably. *(ant)* moderately.

12   **rankle** *(v)* cause ongoing irritation. *(s)* bother, annoy, upset, nark. *(ant)* please, gratify.

13   **bulbous** *(adj)* round, fat or bulging. *(s)* rotund, spherical, swollen, bloated.

14   **aptly** *(adv)* in an apt (suitable) manner. *(s)* appropriately, fittingly, pertinently. *(ant)* inappropriately.

15   **smug** *(adj)* having an overly high opinion of oneself. *(s)* self-satisfied, superior, complacent. *(ant)* humble, modest.

that was a *real* car. A **classy**[1] piece of **engineering**[2] sits under 'er **bonnet**[3], not like the useless stack of rechargeable batteries under yours!' Geraint waved at the Tesla. ''E's a flash so-and-so though, that one,' he ranted, barely pausing for breath. ''E doesn't send it to me for **servicing**[4]. Must reckon I ain't good enough for the likes of 'im,' he added, ending his **diatribe**[5] with a **disgruntled**[6] grunt.

'I'm sure that's not the case,' replied Mr Brady, his tone **diplomatic**[7] and **conciliatory**[8]. 'Your service **thus far**[9] is excellent.'

Geraint puffed out his **portly**[10] chest, stuck his nose in the air and said, 'Right, then. Me an' Lazy-Lump Lily 'ere'll be off now. 'Ope your lift comes soon, else you'll catch a nasty chill up 'ere,' he finished, turning on his heel and **trundling**[11] off to his truck with not a hint of concern for the stranded party.

'Dad, Claire and I are starving. When's our ride getting here?' whined Ben, spluttering as Geraint's truck left amid plumes of **noxious**[12] fumes.

Most **uncharacteristically**[13], hunger was the furthest thing from Claire's mind.

'Benjamin, you are NOT starving,' replied his dad. 'I *will* call again though,' he added. 'I guess everyone's busy trying to **patch**[14] this security breach.'

There's that security breach *phrase again*, thought Claire.

Just as Mr Brady went to press dial on his phone, the distant sound of a car's engine cut through the silent mountain air.

---

1   **classy** *(adj)* having sophistication and style. *(s)* superior, high-class, elegant. *(ant)* inferior, cheap.

2   **engineering** *(n)* a branch of technology for the design, building and use of engines, machines and structures.

3   **bonnet** *(n)* a liftable canopy covering the engine of a vehicle.

4   **servicing** *(n)* routine maintenance or repair work on a vehicle. *(s)* repairs, aftercare, upkeep.

5   **diatribe** *(n)* a bitter and strong verbal attack. *(s)* harangue, tirade, criticism. *(ant)* compliment.

6   **disgruntled** *(adj)* displeased or angry. *(s)* aggrieved, discontented, dissatisfied. *(ant)* pleased, contented.

7   **diplomatic** *(adj)* showing tact (diplomacy) and sensitivity (feeling). *(s)* tactful, politic, discreet. *(ant)* tactless.

8   **conciliatory** *(adj)* likely or intended to calm. *(s)* peacemaking, appeasing, pacifying. *(ant)* antagonistic.

9   **thus far** *(adv)* up to now. *(s)* hitherto, to this point, so far.

10   **portly** *(adj)* large, fat or overweight. *(s)* round, corpulent, chubby, tubby, heavy. *(ant)* slim, slender, skinny.

11   **trundle** *(v)* move slowly and heavily. *(s)* trudge, plod, slog, traipse, wander. *(ant)* sprint.

12   **noxious** *(adj)* harmful, poisonous or unpleasant. *(s)* toxic, deadly, lethal, foul. *(ant)* harmless, pleasant.

13   **uncharacteristically** *(adv)* in an uncharacteristic (unusual) way. *(s)* strangely, unexpectedly. *(ant)* typically.

14   **patch** *(v)* fix or strengthen something. *(s)* mend, repair, cover. *(ant)* damage, weaken.

'Ah, this might be for us.' Mr Brady popped his phone back into his pocket and tilted his head towards the approaching sound.

'Hope so,' said Ben. 'I'm getting cold now too.'

Claire rolled her eyes at him. 'Check you've got your stuff,' she said, 'and quit whining.'

A surprised and now-**biddable**[1] Ben **duly**[2] followed her.

Thankfully, the oncoming car slowed and pulled into the lay-by where they waited.

'Hey, John. How are you? I'm sorry I kept you guys waiting so long,' said a young woman jumping out of the car and holding out her hand to Mr Brady. 'It's been **manic**[3] panic at work!' she added. She had an American accent. 'I came as soon as possible. You must be Ben and Claire. John told me you were with him when he called.' She shook their hands. 'I'm Cristy Grant. So pleased to meet you. I'll pop the **trunk**[4], and you can throw your gear in there,' she said, pressing a button on the key **fob**[5] in her hand.

Claire noticed Cristy's hair was the same colour and style as Jayne's. She was tall and slim too.

Why do Americans call the boot a trunk? Claire asked herself **rhetorically**[6] as she placed her belongings into the boot of the car, Ben following suit.

Mr Brady placed his jacket on top and slammed the boot shut.

'Hop in,' Cristy **chirped**[7] with a cheery **lilt**[8]. 'Let's get you up to Via-Corp.'

Claire and Ben were climbing into the car when something stopped Claire in her tracks.

'What's up?' asked Ben.

'Can you hear that?' Claire replied.

'No. What?' Ben's face creased with confusion.

'That sound. Shush and listen.' Claire put her finger to her lips.

In the near distance, but gradually getting louder, was the clip-clop of metal on the tarmac, a sound Claire recognised from yesterday.

---

1 **biddable** *(adj)* ready to accept and carry out instructions. *(s)* obedient, amenable, pliant. *(ant)* disobedient.

2 **duly** *(adv)* as is required. *(s)* fittingly, correctly, aptly. *(ant)* improperly.

3 **manic** *(adj)* incredibly busy. *(s)* frenzied, feverish, hectic, intense. *(ant)* calm.

4 **trunk** *(n)* (US English) storage space in an automobile (often at the rear). *(s)* boot.

5 **fob** *(n)* an object on a key ring.

6 **rhetorically** *(adv)* in a rhetorical (not seeking information) way.

7 **chirp** *(v)* speak cheerfully. *(s)* cheep, squeak, twitter, pipe, sound, tweet. *(ant)* lament, groan.

8 **lilt** *(n)* a characteristic rise and fall of the voice. *(s)* cadence, intonation, accent, tone, rhythm. *(ant)* monotone.

'What is it?' repeated Ben, but Claire didn't answer.

'Come on, kids, get in! We need to go right now!' Mr Brady's tone sounded **irate**[1], but Claire didn't move. Coming up from the bend where the Bentley had disappeared, and heading towards them at a fast trot, was a pony and trap.

'Dad! You gotta see this before we go,' exclaimed Ben. 'Look, it's a real horse and cart,' he said, pointing at the pony as it approached in the distance.

In the half-light of the **murky**[2] grey day, Claire couldn't make out the pony's colour at first, but as it neared, its unmistakable rich chestnut tone shone, its cream-coloured mane **billowing**[3] in the wind.

'You gotta snap a picture of this, Dad. We don't have many horses in Manchester,' **pleaded**[4] Ben as Mr Brady turned to see.

Claire's eyes remained fixed on the rapidly approaching trap.

'It is charming,' said Mr Brady. 'But get in now. We're leaving.' His tone was suddenly **acerbic**[5] and out of character.

As the trap **clattered**[6] past them, the **ruddy**[7]-faced driver, with hands the size of shovels, **doffed**[8] his worn **tweed**[9] cap. He swiftly replaced it, growled 'Yarrhhh' to the pony and sped away without a backward glance. All the while, a small, scruffy white dog with black and tan patches remained **steadfastly**[10] perched by his side, his proud, upright head **surveilling**[11] all from his position at the **helm**[12] of the rickety old trap.

It was Gwilym and Jack, being pulled along by Lady.

---

1   **irate** *(adj)* very angry. *(s)* furious, incensed, mad, enraged, fuming, infuriated, livid. *(ant)* calm.

2   **murky** *(adj)* gloomy and dark. *(s)* dim, shadowy, sombre, dreary, dingy, obscured. *(ant)* bright, light, clear.

3   **billow** *(v)* inflate and move outwards. *(s)* undulate, wave.

4   **plead** *(v)* make an emotional appeal. *(s)* beg, beseech, implore, supplicate, request. *(ant)* offer.

5   **acerbic** *(adj)* (of speech) direct and sharp. *(s)* cutting, caustic, biting, harsh. *(ant)* mild, kind.

6   **clatter** *(v)* make a continuous rattling sound. *(s)* clack, clank, jangle, clash, bump, hurtle, clang.

7   **ruddy** *(adj)* having a reddish colour to the face. *(s)* blooming, florid, flush, rosy, bronzed. *(ant)* pale.

8   **doff** *(v)* remove (clothing). *(s)* raise, lift, shed, take off. *(ant)* don.

9   **tweed** *(n)* a rough cloth (originating from Scotland) flecked with colours.

10   **steadfastly** *(adv)* in a steadfast (firm) way. *(s)* unwaveringly, persistently, staunchly. *(ant)* weakly, irresolutely.

11   **surveil** *(v)* keep under surveillance (watch closely). *(s)* observe, monitor, inspect.

12   **helm** *(n)* a position of leadership (the front). *(s)* command, reins, controls.

Learn With *The Cadwaladr Quests* Series

The Cadwaladr Quests: Book 1 – Tangled Time forms part of *The Cadwaladr Quests* integrated education series.

Read the first book in the series – the vocabulary novel *Tangled Time* – then consolidate your comprehension, creative writing and vocabulary skills with the *Tangled Time Workbook*.

Finally, further test your knowledge with the *Vocabulary Revision Notebook*.

Find all the available *The Cadwaladr Quests Series* books online via your local Amazon store.

The Cadwaladr Quests - Book 1: Tangled Time

The Cadwaladr Quests - Book 1: Tangled Time Workbook

The Cadwaladr Quests - Book 1: Tangled Time Vocabulary Revision Notebook

PS: Need *The Cadwaladr Quests* in US English? Please visit your local Amazon site for the US version!

Get A Free Comprehension Exercise

Some *Cadwaladr Quests* novels have accompanying workbooks.

To receive your free, 45-question comprehension (with answers) based on *Tangled Time* (this comprehension does not appear in the workbooks), please leave a review for *Tangled Time* on Amazon and email a screenshot to: **freebies@slager.co.uk**

I will add you to my mailing list[1] and send you the comprehension by return.

---

1   You can unsubscribe from the mailing list at any time. Further details will be emailed to you, as soon as you are added.

Reviews, please!

If you've enjoyed *The Cadwaladr Quests: Book 1 – Tangled Time*, please feel free to leave a review online at the book's Amazon or Goodreads page.

Errata and Information

To report any **errata**[1], please email: **errata@slager.co.uk.**
If you would like information about new books in *The Cadwaladr Quests* series, please visit:

SLAGER.CO.UK

You can stay up to date with S. L. Ager, author of *The Cadwaladr Quests* series, on social media:

facebook.com/SLAgerAuthor
instagram.com/SLAgerAuthor
linkedin.com/in/SLAgerAuthor
pinterest.com/SLAgerAuthor
twitter.com/SLAgerAuthor

---

1   **erratum** *(n)* an error in writing or publishing (plural: *errata*).

Printed in Great Britain
by Amazon